Royal Doulton Figures

Produced at Burslem *c*1890-1978

Desmond Eyles &
Richard Dennis

Royal Doulton Tableware Limited
Stoke-on-Trent 1978

Edited by Paul Atterbury, Historical Adviser to Royal Doulton Tableware Limited

Additional research by Jocelyn Lukins

Editorial assistance by Avril Atterbury

Photography by Prudence Cuming Associates, Malcolm Jennings (Etruria Studios) and Morland Braithwaite Photography. The authors and publishers would also like to thank the many other photographers in Great Britain and North America who have contributed to the book. The photographs on pages 13, 14 and 15 are reproduced by permission of the City Museum and Art Gallery, Stoke-on-Trent.

Designed by Paul Sharp

Printed and bound in Great Britain by W. S. Cowell Limited, Ipswich, Suffolk

Published and distributed in Great Britain and Europe by Royal Doulton Tableware Limited, PO Box 100, London Road, Stoke-on-Trent ST4 7QD

Distributed in the United States of America by Doulton & Co Inc, 400 Paterson Plank Road, Carlstadt, New Jersey 07072, USA

Distributed in Canada by Doulton China of Canada Limited, 10 Carnforth Road, Toronto, Ontario M4A 2K8, Canada

Distributed in Australia by Doulton Tableware Pty Limited, PO Box 47, 17–23 Merriwa Street, Gordon, New South Wales 2072, Australia

ISBN 0 906262 00 3

The Potter, modelled in terracotta by John Broad at the Doulton Lambeth factory, 1883

Contents

Acknowledgements

We are very grateful to the many collectors and antique dealers all over the world who have supplied information about, or made available photographs of Doulton figures in their private collections. By their efforts, we have been able to fill many of the gaps in the story of figure-making at Burslem.

Many individuals and organisations have contributed to the making of this book, and we should particularly like to thank Richard Bailey, Managing Director of Royal Doulton Tableware Limited, and the many Royal Doulton employees, past and present, the staffs of the Victoria & Albert Museum, London, the City Museum & Art Gallery, Stoke-on-Trent and the Hanley Central Library, Stoke-on-Trent, and of W. S. Cowell Limited.

Special thanks are also due to Mr R. Bentley, Mrs M. Bentley, Miss Josie Cole, Mrs L. Curnock, Mr F. S. Dearden Jnr., Mrs H. E. Elsmore, Mrs O. Eyles, Mr A. Foden, Mr & Mrs R. Fortune, Captain W. F. Fortune, Mrs A. Foster, Mrs M. Harradine, Mrs B. J. Heirs, Mr J. Pierpoint, Mrs P. Ransley, Mr H. Sandon, Mr & Mrs A. Schirris, Mrs E. Staton, Mr J. Shorter, Mr R. Wright, and Mr & Mrs J. Vitkovics.

DESMOND EYLES
RICHARD DENNIS

Advertisement for Royal Doulton figures from the *Pottery Gazette*, 1935

Foreword

There has long been a need for an authentic record of the HN series of Royal Doulton figures, from HN 1 onwards up to the present day, to give collectors the details and background information they have so often requested. This book is the result of a long and detailed study of figures, pattern books, old catalogues, price lists, trade and other journals and other records, supplemented by discussions with designers, artists and craftsmen past and present and correspondence and meetings with collectors in many lands.

The aim throughout has been to try to answer those questions most asked by collectors concerning the origins, historical development, styles of design and decoration, dating, and later development of the Royal Doulton figure. Up till now, these collectors have had at their disposal only incomplete and often misleading lists, lacking illustrations, and published without the authority of Royal Doulton. A feature of this book is the unusually large number of illustrations of figures, nearly all in full colour. Here, for the first time since the Royal Doulton figures were introduced over 65 years ago, will be found a complete record of all known discontinued models, as well as those in current production.

Royal Doulton figures form a unique chapter in the history of ceramic sculpture for many reasons. First, the range of figures produced is probably more extensive than any made by other European potteries. Second, the range is remarkable for its variety, for the inventiveness of its designers and modellers and for the skills of the craftsmen and artists; the skills and the inventiveness are as apparent today as in 1913 when the range was launched. Third, the range continues the tradition of figure-making established in the 18th century by Meissen, Nymphenburg, Sèvres, Chelsea, Bow, Derby, Whieldon and the Woods, and expanded in the 19th century by Minton, Copeland, Worcester and the many Staffordshire figure makers. Royal Doulton figures not only reflect this experience of the past, but have also succeeded in bringing about a revival of figure making in England by their ability to combine tradition with a rare facility of expressing the immediacy of any particular period. Royal Doulton figures manage to combine timelessness with an accurate reflection of the age that created them.

In showing these qualities in full, this book should therefore be more than a simple catalogue. Rather, it should help in broadening the appreciation of Royal Doulton figures, to give them their rightful place alongside the great names in the history of figure making in Europe.

RICHARD BAILEY
Managing Director, Royal Doulton Tableware Limited

HN 2856 St George (third version)

CHAPTER I

‘Heirlooms of Tomorrow’

Beautiful in form and feature,
Lovely as the day,
Can there be so fair a creature
Formed of common clay?

LONGFELLOW

Most Royal Doulton products are destined sooner or later to become ‘collectables’. Of none is this more manifestly true than of the famous china figures. In their case, indeed, each piece is *intended*, from the very dawn of its conception in the designer’s mind, to become a collector’s item, one that may fully justifiably be described as ‘an heirloom of tomorrow’.

The Royal Doulton figures have established in our time a reputation comparable with that of their Chelsea, Derby and Staffordshire predecessors of two centuries ago. As gifts they have always had a special attraction; one can always be found appropriate for every occasion. And such is their innate appeal that anyone who is fortunate enough to become the possessor of one or two examples—whether by purchase, gift or inheritance—is almost inevitably fired with the urge to make these the nucleus of a collection. And this urge grows into a passionate enthusiasm.

In creating a Royal Doulton figure, the designer, the sculptor, the potter and the painter fuse their talents. The result of their collaboration is an impeccably finished example of ceramic art. Collectors find a special incentive in the knowledge that as new models are added to the range a number of older ones are withdrawn. Since 1913, indeed, when the series beginning with HN-1 was introduced, more than 2,000 different figures have been created but of these fewer than 200 are in current production.

One of the first to realise the merits and potentialities of the Doulton figure was J. F. Blacker, the well-known authority on English ceramics, author of *The ABC of Collecting Old English China* and many other books for collectors. Soon after seeing the first examples of the new range of figures in 1911 (this was before they were given numbers) he wrote in the *Connoisseur Magazine:*

> You may be certain that in the gems of art eagerly bought and treasured by the collector, even among the finest productions of this age none will take higher rank than the masterly and magnificent creations of the Royal Doulton Potteries, Burslem. . . . As we have seen the ceramic art of the nineteenth century merge into that of the eighteenth, so, in due course, when the twentieth century too has become historical, the Doulton ware of today will find its home in the cabinets of the museum and the collector.

The Doulton figures, like so many other products emanating from the historic Nile Street Pottery in Burslem, have not in fact had to wait for this century to fade into history to see Blacker’s prophecy fulfilled.

Of all the manifold products of the potter’s artistry, ingenuity and craftsmanship, probably none has had a more universal and continuous appeal right down the ages from prehistoric times than the statuette or figure. No decorative china item of the present day is more sought after and admired. And none enjoys greater world wide fame and popularity than the Royal Doulton figure. Here, in one endlessly varied yet unmistakably distinctive range—which imitators have tried in vain to emulate—is to be found a galaxy of modern ceramic art, a veritable panorama of human life and activities past and present.

Many of the enchanting studies evoke nostalgic thoughts and images of bygone days which, in this frantic era of stresses and strains, of increasing hurry and bustle, probably accounts in part for their never dwindling popularity. Such, for instance, is the bevy of dainty, shimmering ladies in crinolines and other period or fancy dress; the perennially popular characters from Dickens; the heart-warming portrayals of children—among them the quite recently introduced *Kate Greenaway* series; and the *Figures of Williamsburg*, a notable tribute to American history and culture. Then there are the evocative studies of picturesque and rapidly vanishing, (if not already vanished) street sellers of flowers, fruit, balloons, silks and ribbons, masks, toys and the like; the subtle character studies such as *Nanny*, *Eventide*, *A Stitch in Time* and the *The Lobster Man*. The exquisite figures inspired by drama, opera, ballet and literature have a different but equally strong appeal for many, as have the historical characters and the legendary personages—*Bluebeard*, *The Pied Piper*, *The Old King*, *Omar Khayyam* and many others redolent of mystery, myth and magic.

These are but a few examples drawn at random from a vast array of what one ardent admirer has described as 'poems in pottery'. A study of the hundreds of illustrations in this book will disclose, far more adequately and directly than any mere description can hope to do, the extraordinary flair of the Royal Doulton designers, artists and sculptors—past and present—for creating subjects which will appeal to a wide variety of tastes, whether these be for the nostalgic, the legendary, the make-believe, the historical, the realistic, the unashamedly sentimental—or any of the other categories into which may fall the associations aroused by this or that particular figure.

It has sometimes been said that the Royal Doulton figures have revived the eighteenth and early nineteenth century traditions of figure making. It would be more accurate to say that, while reviving the art and fame of earlier wares, the Doulton figures have created a refreshingly new tradition *all their own*. One of the most extraordinary things about them—and one that is quite impossible to put into words—is that, despite the astonishing variety of subjects, there is something—a kind of aura or atmosphere—about each one, whether it be a tiny miniature or a large 'prestige piece' that stamps it just as effectively as any applied backstamp or trade mark.

The essence of any living art tradition is that it develops and progresses within the basic idiom. And so, over the years, the range has grown as Royal Doulton designers have found new subjects which fit into the tradition, and new techniques for presenting these subjects. Among significant developments of this kind during recent years are the arresting *Haute Ensemble* range of ladies with their tall slender elegance, the limited edition series of *Lady Musicians* and *Dancers of the World* and the vividly authentic studies of *The Soldiers of the Revolution* produced in association with The Colonial Williamsburg Foundation.

There are in existence today in many different parts of the world many collections of Doulton figures ranging from a modest score or so to several hundred different models. Most of these collections have begun in a very small way. A spontaneous purchase, the Christmas, birthday or wedding gift of a single figure, a discovery in a disused attic—these and similar happenings have been known to kindle the collecting urge for many. The names themselves of many of the figures are fascinating and suggest all kinds of possibilities; one extensive collection, for instance, stemmed from a twenty-first birthday present of *The Parson's Daughter* to a young woman who was, *in fact*, a parson's daughter.

It is the avowed intention of at least one collector, for whom space, time and money are no problems, to own an example of every Royal Doulton figure ever produced! Most collectors have more limited ambitions. Some decide to specialise in a particular genre—the child studies, the street sellers, the male figures, the historical, literary or legendary characters. The miniature figures have a special fascination for some; others like to concentrate on assembling all the painted variations of those models, such as *A Victorian Lady*, *Madonna of the Square*, *The Welsh Girl*, *A Jester*, *One of the Forty*, *Polly Peachum* and *Sweet and Twenty*, which have appeared again and again in many different guises. Probably most people are quite happy, to begin with, to build up a miscellaneous collection; later, if and when the desire to specialise should develop, opportunities can be found through contacts with fellow collectors and friendly dealers to exchange figures with a view to re-organising one's collection along new lines.

The poet, John Keats, wrote of the youth and the maiden figured on a Greek vase: 'Forever wilt thou love and she be fair'. The painter had arrested a moment of beauty and fixed it for the enduring delight of all who, in time to come, would behold his work. So too, the Royal Doulton designers, artists and craftsmen body forth in form and colour works of art which, because of the thought, imagination, and unfailing attention to detail which go into their creation, will have an enduring appeal.

CHAPTER 2

The Master Potter at Fulham

'Fulham is a pretty village, about four miles from London, on the banks of the Thames'. This is how Fry's *London* described Fulham in 1885. The remark could just as well have been written in the 1670s when John Dwight was building up his pottery activities there.

There are at least *three* good reasons why Fulham should have a place in the story of the Royal Doulton figures and their predecessors. *First*, it was there that John Dwight—'the father of English pottery', as he has been called—established his famous manufactory in the last third of the seventeenth century. In Fulham, to quote Bernard Rackham, former Keeper of Ceramics at the Victoria & Albert Museum, Dwight 'succeeded in producing a white stoneware with something of the translucence of porcelain. *Thus the discovery was made without which Staffordshire figures as we know them would have been impossible* (my italics). Dwight found that he could produce a white 'Body' like that of Chinese porcelain by adding calcined flints to the grey- and buff-firing clays of ordinary stoneware . . .' *Secondly*, it was from Fulham that there emanated what Reginald Haggar, the well-known ceramic historian, has described as 'the first and unparalleled flowering of ceramic sculpture in England'. *Thirdly*, it was at Fulham, as an apprentice under one of Dwight's descendants, that John Doulton acquired the reputation of being the best potter in London, and by his mastery there of the fundamentals of the craft laid a good foundation for what were to become the Royal Doulton Potteries.

Dwight's Patents

Dwight obtained from King Charles II two patents, the first in April 1671 and the second in June 1684. In the first he claimed to have discovered 'The Mistery of Transparent Earthenware, commonly known by the names of Porcelaine or China, and Persian Ware, as also the Mistery of the Stone Ware, vulgarly called Cologne Ware'. In the second he stated, among other claims, that he had 'invented and set up at Fulham . . . several new manufactures . . . and also discovered the Mistery of transparent Porcellane and Opacous Redd, and dark-coloured Porcellane or China, and Persian Wares, and the Mistery of the Cologne or Stone Wares'.

The words 'porcelain' and 'china' were used somewhat vaguely in earlier times. (The unqualified Chinese word *tz'u*, often translated as porcelain, seems to have meant any high-fired vitrified ceramic body which gave a resonant ring; it did not in itself imply either whiteness or translucence. The general opinion today is that Dwight (because the essential china clay and china stone had not yet been exploited in Cornwall) never actually succeeded in making a translucent, white china. What he did was to produce not only an excellent brown salt-glaze stoneware but also an evenly potted, finely finished, semi-translucent, white stoneware, and a refined red stoneware similar to that used for the much-admired Chinese tea-pots from Yi-Hsing. These achievements in London were soon to have important repercussions in Staffordshire.

Saltglaze stoneware figures modelled at Fulham by John Dwight
Far left A sportsman, *Centre* Lydia, his daughter, *Left* Bust of Prince Rupert

Fulham Figures

It is with his ceramic sculptures that Dwight's name is particularly associated—the classical and allegorical figures of Minerva, Jupiter, Neptune, Mars, Meleager, Adonis and Flora; the statuettes of Lydia, his daughter, of a sportsman and his dog, and of a young girl, holding a flowering branch and with two sheep at her feet; the busts of Charles II, James II and Prince Rupert, the last-mentioned generally regarded as his masterpiece. Some are of off-white stoneware, translucent in the folds of the drapery and other thin parts of the modelling; some in brown salt-glaze; others with a thin wash of brown-burning clay, giving the effect almost of bronze. Several of these works may be seen in the British Museum and the Victoria and Albert Museum, London.

John Doulton, through his friendship with Charles White, a descendant of Dwight and proprietor of the Fulham Pottery, was familiar with several of the stoneware sculptures, which were still in the family's possession until the early 1860s. He knew too the old family tradition that Dwight had buried all the models and tools connected with his artistic activities and researches in some secret place on the premises at Fulham, so that his successors would not be tempted to carry on this expensive and unrewarding side of the business but concentrate on the 'bread and butter lines', such as the brown salt-glaze bottles, jars, pitchers and pipkins for which there would always be a good demand. It was no doubt because of his having heard so much of the disappointments, frustrations and expenses which had beset Dwight, that John Doulton viewed with a certain suspicion any signs of his brilliant son, Henry, becoming involved with what was known as 'art pottery' as distinct from the undecorated domestic and chemical stoneware, and the pipes and conduits which were the basis of the Doulton establishment's prosperity during the first four decades of its existence. This essentially practical and 'common-sense' viewpoint undoubtedly influenced Henry in the early stages of his career but, as we shall see, he was able to rise above it and thereby bring about a veritable renaissance in decorated ceramics.

CHAPTER 3

The Rise of Staffordshire

Staffordshire stoneware 'crinoline' figure, *c*1725

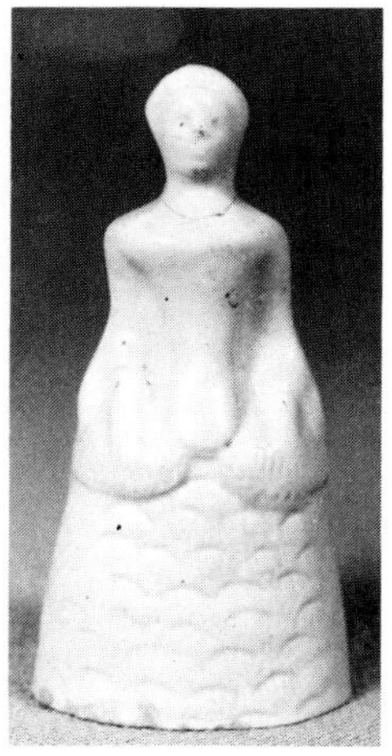

Dr Plot, in *The Natural History of Staffordshire*, published in 1686, remarked that 'The greatest pottery they have in the county is carried on at Burslem, near Newcastle-under-Lyme, where for making their several sorts of pots they have as many different sorts of clay, which they dig round about the towns, all within half a mile distance, the best being found nearest the coals'.

There had been potters in Burslem long before the seventeenth century but probably no more—and possibly even fewer—than in Thames-side London and other areas. The eighteenth century, on the other hand, was to see the rise of Staffordshire to become the predominant centre of the British pottery industry, so that today the very designation 'The Potteries', without any further elucidation, denotes for users and collectors of china everywhere a concentrated area of North Staffordshire, embracing the six towns of Burslem (the mother-town), Fenton, Hanley, Longton, Stoke and Tunstall.

Before the Industrial Revolution there was no reason for potters to congregate in a special centre. Almost every town and large village had its resident potter or potters. In the countryside, many a farmer and his family, in the winter evenings and other times not devoted to agricultural pursuits, would make kitchen crocks for their own needs and naive image-toys for the children. Any surplus could be sold at the nearest market. It was from such simple beginnings as a purely peasant art that the Staffordshire pottery industry sprang.

John Astbury of Shelton

Few, if any, Staffordshire figures can be dated with confidence before the early eighteenth century. From about 1725 onwards, however, there appears a veritable host of them both in salt-glaze stoneware and in dark and light coloured earthenware. They include many small 'image-toys' as they have been called—bands of musicians playing bagpipes and various strange-looking instruments, whole troops of soldiers both on foot and on horseback, quaint negro drummers, gesticulating actors, and the early naive forerunners of what were to prove the perennially popular 'crinoline ladies'. Perhaps most intriguing of all are the unsophisticated 'arbour-groups', usually of lovers, seated in secluded alcoves or leafy-shaded bowers. In similar vein are the often droll 'pew-groups' of couples—and sometimes trios—seated, gazing into space, on high-backed benches or settles. Delightful to behold and handle, these figures express the vigorous flowering of a naive, dramatic and fanciful peasant art which made not the slightest attempt as yet to imitate the sophisticated airs and graces of either the German or the English china models.

It was at one time the practice to attribute most of these small figures, all of which were unmarked, to John Astbury (1686-1743) but it is now clear that he was only one of several potters who made them. They are now generally described more safely as 'Astbury-type'.

Earthenware musician figures of the Astbury/Whieldon type, *c*1745

Whieldon and the Woods

Thomas Whieldon (c 1719-1795), who had been apprenticed to Astbury, set up on his own account in 1740 in a small thatched pot-works in Fenton Low, near Stoke. Among his many invaluable contributions to the evolution of English pottery were the cream-coloured earthenware and his brilliant exploitation of translucent coloured lead glazes, stained with metallic oxides, as a decorative medium. Some figures were made from the same moulds in both salt-glaze stoneware and earthenware; they differ slightly in size because of differences in the shrinkage of these two materials during firing. The subject range included musicians, singers, dancers, soldiers, game keepers and other rural types, animals and birds. Whieldon retired in 1780, having acquired what in those days was regarded as a considerable fortune.

Another of Astbury's apprentices whose name will ever be associated with the popularisation of Staffordshire figures and Toby jugs was Ralph Wood the Elder (1715-1772), also known as Ralph Wood I to distinguish him from his son and grandson, Ralph Wood II and III. Ralph's equally famous brother, Aaron (1717-1785) became his chief modeller; during the forty years or so of his creative activity, he worked for Ralph Wood I and II, Whieldon and other potters, producing some of the most delightful groups, figures and figure jugs that Staffordshire had yet seen, including many country and sporting types, politicians and writers, as well as the usual allegorical and classical characters. His son, Enoch, who was to carry the family figure-making tradition into the next century, wrote of him that he was 'modeller to all the potters of Staffordshire at the latter end of the time that Whiteware or white stoneware was made'.

Ralph Wood the Younger (1748-1795), also known as Ralph Wood II, succeeded his father and continued to produce figures from many of the old moulds at the Burslem pottery. He also introduced new subjects, some in humorous or satirical vein, others of a somewhat sentimental nature.

Yet another member of the 'Wood dynasty' was Ralph Wood III, son of Ralph the Younger. He died, however, at the early age of twenty, within a few years of his father and so had little influence on the tradition. It is quite a different story with Enoch, son of Aaron, the famous modeller, and cousin of Ralph Wood II. In 1784 he set up his own pottery at Fountain Place, Burslem; this enterprise was carried on under various names, and with different partners, until 1846. The subjects embraced what was by now becoming a traditional range, with a partiality for religious, mythological, literary and classical themes. Many of the figures have tree backgrounds, a vogue which was taken up by several other potters.

Enoch's busts are thought by many to be his masterpieces; one of the most famous is that of John Wesley executed in 1791, after Wesley's death. After Enoch's death in 1840, his sons carried on the pottery at Fountain Place until about 1846, soon after which Pinder, Bourne and Hope (predecessors of Doulton at the Nile Street factory, Burslem) took it over. They reproduced figures from many of the Wood moulds.

Other Staffordshire figure-makers

Among the numerous other makers of figures in the Stoke area space allows mention of only a few of these best-known to present-day collectors. Humphrey Palmer, of Hanley, and his successor, James Neale, made many dainty well-modelled small figures with bright on-glaze enamel colouring and often gilding. The sprig patterns on many of the dresses were imitative of porcelain fashions.

Top Earthenware soldier figure of the Astbury/Whieldon type, *c*1745
Centre Earthenware shepherd and shepherdess by Ralph Wood, *c*1770
Bottom Earthenware group of the Walton/Salt type, *c*1820

John Walton (c 1780-1835) of Burslem is the best known, and was the most successful, of a group of early nineteenth century figure-makers, among them Ralph and Charles Salt, Charles Tittensor, and John and Ralph Hall. Characteristic features are *bocage* backgrounds of leaves and flowers, thick opaque enamel colours lavishly applied, sentimental and patriotic themes, and the strong influence of china models, especially Chelsea and Derby, on many of the designs. The output of Walton and his followers and imitators was immense; it included china as well as earthenware figures and other cottage ornaments, varying considerably in quality of modelling and enamelling. Some are amusing and attractive, others primitive and vulgar.

Obediah Sherratt (c 1775-1846) and his wife, Martha, of Burslem, combined potting with keeping an ale-house. Their work represented a rebound to folk-art and rustic realism. Many of the powerfully-modelled earthenware figures ascribed

Earthenware figure of Neptune, Obediah Sherratt type, *c*1820

Earthenware flat-back group, *The Prodigal Son*, *c*1860

Earthenware flat-back cricketer figures, *c*1880

to them reflect the earthy humour and occasional brutality of the patrons of the ale-house. Among the best known are the Bull-Baiting groups, the complicated Menagerie groups and the Gretna Green wedding groups.

Victoriana

From a purely aesthetic standpoint the bulk of the figures, mostly in earthenware, that flooded forth from the Potteries throughout most of the nineteenth century show a sad falling-away from the standard set by the Woods.

Samson Smith of Longton and the many other known and unknown makers of these figures probably would never have dreamed of claiming for them any artistic merit. Their aim was to provide—at a low, yet still profitable, price—ornaments which, in those days before the advent of the popular press, the cinema, radio and television, caught the public imagination. Their figures (inspired by striking episodes and well-known characters in Victorian social, political, religious, sporting, theatrical and other spheres) were probably 'the first entirely decorative wares to reach in quantity the simplest homes of the countryside and the towns'.

The majority of the naive but fascinating Victorian figures and groups are what are known as 'flat-backs'. They were easy to turn out from simple two-piece press-moulds; they were stingily coloured and the backs were left unpainted altogether; they could be rapidly made, even by children. Whatever one may think about their artistic merits, these figures tell a fascinating story of an epoch. Patriotism, sentiment, humour and sometimes a touch of satire are well to the fore. First of all, for the historically minded, there is a whole galaxy of British and foreign 'royals', together with many of their progeny; a parade of popular military and naval heroes; and an assortment of politicians. For those with a taste for tales of crime and murder, there were, for instance, William Corder, the notorious Red Barn murderer; his victim, Maria Marten, daughter of a Suffolk mole-catcher, and even a model of the notorious Red Barn itself. Among the very popular sporting figures, we find Fred Archer, the famous jockey who, before his death at the early age of thirty, had ridden 2,447 winners, including five Derbys and six St. Legers. The array of portrait-figures includes authors—Shakespeare, Milton, Burns, Scott; divines and evangelists—the Protestant martyrs Ridley and Latimer shown at the stake, Wesley (in many different portrayals and obviously a great favourite) Spurgeon, Booth (founder of the Salvation Army), Sankey and Moody (the American evangelists and hymn writers). Among the actors are Garrick, Kean, Kemble and Quinn. And one could continue the inventory with heroines Grace Darling and Florence Nightingale, actresses Jenny Marston, Jenny Lind, Charlotte and Susan Cushman, and many, many others—celebrated or notorious, still remembered or nearly forgotten, except in clay!

CHAPTER 4
Doulton of Lambeth

The year 1815, when Napoleon Bonaparte was finally defeated at Waterloo, is a memorable one in British history. Compared with the issues at stake in that fateful battle, the fact that John Doulton, a young man of twenty-two, had just ventured his life-savings of £100 on a one-third partnership in an obscure backyard stoneware pot-house, with two small kilns, in Vauxhall Walk, Lambeth, was seemingly of little moment. From that humble beginning, none the less, was to evolve the now world-famous Royal Doulton Group, whose name and products have become household words.

John Doulton, 1793–1873

Sir Henry Doulton, 1820–1897

John Doulton

John Doulton, who was born at Fulham, still a small Thames-side village, on 17th November 1793, served his apprenticeship from 1805 to 1812 at the famous pottery founded by Dwight. It was then still owned by one of Dwight's descendants on the female side. In later years, John Doulton recalled that, during his apprenticeship, he often worked from seventy to eighty hours a week, and that, apart from Christmas Day, Good Friday and Sundays, he had only one day off in the year. In 1806, he spent it watching the funeral procession of Admiral Lord Nelson to St Paul's Cathedral.

In 1812, after leaving Fulham, John, who by then had acquired the reputation of being one of the best practical potters in the Metropolis, found work at the small pot-house of which, three years later, he became part proprietor. It was one of three or four in the same street and almost faced one of the entrances to the famous Vauxhall Gardens.

The story of how John Doulton came to be associated with the Vauxhall pot-house is an unusual one. Martha Jones, the proprietress, was a widow who had carried on the small business after her husband's death, intending to hand it over eventually to her son, Edward, who was then learning the craft. Unfortunately for her plans, young Edward was involved one night in 1812 in some trouble with the law which led to his decamping hastily to the London docks, where he managed to get taken on as one of the crew in a ship about to sail for South America.

The flight of her son left Mrs Jones short of labour, and she asked her foreman, John Watts, to find a replacement. It happened that Doulton, an acquaintance of Watts, had just come out of his apprenticeship and was seeking work. An interview

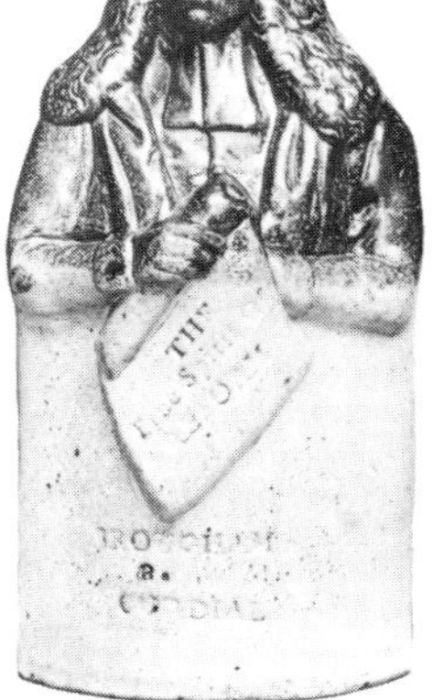

Doulton stoneware 'Reform Flasks', 1832, *top* William IV, *bottom* Lord Brougham

and a demonstration proved that he was not only adept at throwing pots on the wheel but he had acquired at Fulham a good all-round knowledge of other pottery processes. And so he was engaged. He worked hard and consistently, and was always ready in an emergency to take on any job that needed doing, from preparing the clay mix to setting, firing and drawing the kilns, apart from his own work as a thrower. In this way, he amplified the experience he had already gained at Fulham, laying the foundation of his future success as a master potter.

Early in June 1815, Martha Jones, not having heard a word from her son for over three years, took John Watts and John Doulton into working partnership, and the firm became Jones, Watts and Doulton. Watts, who was not a potter, tested the ware, helped pack it, and kept the accounts. It was an exciting, challenging and often anxious time for a young man on the threshold of his life's work. A short-lived post-war boom was followed by an economic crisis. Wages were cut, exports fell, and a catastrophic drop in prices ruined many small farmers and small industrial enterprises. Competition from other potteries in London and the Provinces was intense. Some days John Doulton worked at his wheel from six in the morning until late in the evening; other days he would spend the morning calling on customers to take orders and collect bills, returning in the afternoon to help the other thrower and the apprentice to make the ware. In 1820, Mrs Jones withdrew from the business. A notice appeared in the *London Gazette* for 5th February of that year, announcing that John Watts and Doulton would carry on the business.

Early Products

Among the early products of the Vauxhall Walk pottery, apart from plain salt-glaze stoneware bottles, jars, and other packaging containers, were some brown figure-mugs and figure-jugs in the likenesses of Nelson, Wellington and Napoleon. Of particular interest, too, are the relief-figure 'hunting' jugs and mugs (often described as Toby Ware); these were of a traditional type made in Fulham and Lambeth for generations. Unlike the anthropomorphic Staffordshire Toby, modelled as a seated or standing figure, the London types were of conventional jug or mug shape but decorated with applied reliefs of topers with foaming tankards, hounds and horsemen, stags, foxes, hares, windmills, and cottages.

This type of ware was made throughout the whole period the Lambeth Pottery was in existence, as were many commemorative wares in salt-glaze stoneware. Among the rarest of these are the 'Reform Bottles' and 'Reform Flasks' made in 1832 to celebrate the passing of the first Reform Act. These were large semi-flat bottles and smaller spirit flasks with necks depicting the heads of those associated with the Bill—William IV and the Lords Grey, Brougham and Russell. Other items of a similar kind modelled at Lambeth in the early nineteenth century portrayed Queen Caroline, the young Queen Victoria, the Prince Consort and Daniel O'Connell. These were the predecessors of a whole series of stoneware commemorative figures, figure-jugs, busts, flasks and jugs.

Doulton stoneware figures of Queen Victoria and Prince Albert, *c*1840

Doulton and Watts Pottery, High Street, Lambeth, *c*1840

By 1826 the business had so outgrown the little Vauxhall pot-house that it was gradually transferred to High Street, Lambeth, where the property taken over had the largest garden in all Lambeth except for that of the Archbishop of Canterbury, whose ancient Palace lay at the end of the street.

The first important impetus to the expansion of the Doulton enterprise had come from the demands of the rapidly developing chemical and allied industries for acid-resisting plant material to enable engineers to reproduce, on an industrial scale, processes evolved in the laboratory. It was found that salt-glaze stoneware, because of its wonderful resistance to corrosion, was unequalled for this purpose, and unequalled it remained for many decades.

Henry enters the firm

If in 1835, when he was fifteen years old, Henry Doulton had decided, as his parents half expected, to stay on at University College School in London, and thereafter to study to become a Baptist minister, there would in all probability be no Royal Doulton Potteries today and, of course, no Royal Doulton figures.

Henry had an astonishingly retentive memory and at the age of four already knew long passages of the Bible by heart. His father was a devout Nonconformist, and a great admirer of the oratory of Robert Hall, a celebrated Baptist preacher. Young Henry was sometimes taken to hear him. One of John's most treasured possessions was a Staffordshire figure, probably by Enoch Wood, showing a 'two-decker' pulpit with the somnolent vicar dozing above while the clerk reads the Lesson below. It may have been this figure which inspired Henry to rig up a 'three-decker,' with one brother below as leader of the responses, another in the middle as clerk, and he himself at the top thumping a sofa-cushion while he held forth.

It is not surprising then that his family should have anticipated that Henry would wish to go into the Church. But, much to their surprise, he resolutely declined this suggestion. He refused just as firmly to study to become a doctor or a lawyer. What he really wanted, he made quite clear, was to enter his father's factory and to become like him a practical potter. His insistence was such that his desire could not be gainsayed, and thus it was that, soon after his fifteenth birthday, he entered an informal but strict apprenticeship, under his father's guidance, at the Lambeth Pottery, as it was now called, in the High Street.

Now that Henry had decided to become a potter, his father was determined that he should become a good one. He had to be up at six in the morning, his first task an hour later being to ring the factory bell which called the men together. Then he took his place among them, receiving no favours or privileges, learning every aspect of the potter's craft, as it was then practised, from preparing the clays and other raw materials, through the various processes of shaping—throwing, turning, modelling, moulding, casting—to the stacking of the ware in the kilns, followed by the firing, salting and drawing. After about two years, he was making twenty-gallon vessels on the wheel, and in this and similar ways he gained that practical and intimate knowledge which was one of the secrets of his later phenomenal success. This was just the kind of training he desired, and he found the work no hardship. 'I preferred', he said, 'the fascination of the potter's wheel to the routine of the counting house. I felt, too, that if I were to be the judge of pottery work, I should at least have a practical acquaintance with it'. He celebrated his twenty-first birthday in 1841 by completing an enormous Ali-Baba type 300-gallon jar—which his father proudly exhibited in front of the pottery with a notice reading: 'The largest stoneware vessel in the world'. (It was still there in 1875 when a German journalist reported it as being 'big enough to hold five or six of the forty thieves'.)

In the earlier part of his career, Henry Doulton had concentrated all his energies on the development and perfection of various industrial ceramics for the use of chemical, electrical and sanitary engineers, architects and builders. In the late 1860s, however, somewhat to his father's dismay, he became closely involved in the activities of the Lambeth School of Art. Up to about 1867, little attempt had been made at the Lambeth Pottery to produce decorated wares but at the Paris Exhibition, held in that year, were shown a few simply decorated but well-formed salt-glaze stoneware vases, designed by George Tinworth and other students of the Art School, and fired in the Doulton kilns. At the International Exhibition in South Kensington, London, four years later, about seventy similar pieces were shown. These made a marked impression upon both art critics and public; they also attracted the attention of an important visitor, Queen Victoria, who ordered some to be sent to Windsor. Throughout the remainder of her long reign, the Queen took a great interest in the achievements of the Doulton artists.

From this modest beginning, there developed a veritable renaissance of salt-glaze decorated stoneware in England. During the next twenty years, the number of designers and artists at the Lambeth Pottery grew into hundreds and 'the Doulton Ware', as it came to be known, was shown at one great Exhibition after another, taking highest international honours. In this development of the decorated wares, Henry Doulton worked in close association with the Lambeth School of Art and its brilliant principal, John Sparkes, who later became Head of the National Art Training School at South Kensington (now the Royal College of Art).

By the time of the Philadelphia Exhibition, in 1876, immense progress had been made. Nearly 1,500 pieces of Doulton Ware were shown there, compared with some seventy in London in 1871. The *New York Times* wrote:

> 'The collection of Doulton pottery, about which the critics are wild, is indeed beautiful . . . Doulton has produced out of simplest elements a creation which may be considered the Etruscan Vase of the nineteenth century'.

From the outset of this revival, Henry Doulton determined that each artist should be given the greatest possible scope for free individual expression. The leading artists—George Tinworth, the Barlow sisters Hannah and Florence, Arthur B. Barlow, Mark V. Marshall, Frank A. Butler, Emily J. Edwards, Eliza Simmance, John Broad, Willie Rowe and others—became as well known as the firm which sponsored them.

It is one of these in particular, George Tinworth, who was destined to become the creator of the first generation of Doulton figures.

CHAPTER 5

George Tinworth

The Wheelwright's Son

Among the many unusual characters who have been allured by the modeller's craft, perhaps none has had a stranger upbringing, background and destiny than George Tinworth. His life illustrates how grit and genius can overcome the greatest obstacles.

George Tinworth was born on Guy Fawkes Night, 5th November, 1843, the fourth son to Jane and Joshua Tinworth but the first to survive infancy. His mother vowed that if the child to be born in 1843 were spared to her she would dedicate him to the service of the Lord. Tinworth wrote in his old age: 'Well, I *did* live and she tried to keep her vow but in time I got out of her control and went my own way'. In fact, his 'own way' though different from the path his mother had envisaged, was a life-long dedication to the ideals which she had instilled into him.

Tinworth spent more than half his life in a somewhat sombre, and in parts squalid environment in and around Walworth, Lambeth and Stockwell, adjoining districts of south-east London. His parents were of humble origin. His mother, before her marriage, had worked in a pastry-cook's shop. His father began work as a slater's boy and later with a brother, started a small wheelwright's business. This did not prosper and by the time George was eight the family became more or less destitute. George had little regular schooling and none at all beyond the age of twelve. He was, it could be said, brought up on the Bible. In such an environment, it is hardly surprising that his evolution as an artist followed an unconventional course.

At the age of fourteen, George worked daily except Sundays from 7 am to 9 pm at a hot presser's in Watling Street, earning four shillings a week which he handed over to his mother. He had to leave home each morning soon after six to walk to work, taking with him some slices of bread and a penny pocket-money. He had always had a disposition for whittling, and now he began to carve some butter-stamps out of wood and to mould figures in red clay which he retrieved from a sewer-trench some men were excavating.

By the time he was sixteen, George had begun to work for his father in the wheelwright's shop. Joshua looked on his son's carvings as a wanton waste of time. He could quote Scriptures for his own ends when he chose and used to say to George: 'Thou shalt not make any graven image'. Mrs Tinworth, on the other hand, quietly encouraged the youth, despite struggles with her conscience as to whether his activities were strictly in accord with scriptural precepts, for she belonged to an ultra-strict Nonconformist sect.

When he was in his nineteenth year Tinworth seems to have heard of the Lambeth School of Art for the first time. Here is how he himself described his initial experience there: 'I saw an old lady going into the school and she invited me in. When I got inside and saw the statues and the water-colour portraits I felt in a new world! I told this woman that if I had the stone I could carve the statues before us . . . I thought I would come and see Mr Sparkes, the headmaster, so I went the next night and a boy lifted me up to see through the window . . . It was modelling night and I said if there were no more people in the room the next night I would go in. The next night I had another lift up to look in. It was full of people as it was painting night. I had brought a bust of Handel that I had carved in Portland stone... I went round to the side door and Mr Sparkes was coming out and I showed it to him. . . I asked him if I could come and be taught modelling. He said: 'Come in and see what we are doing'. He introduced me to Mr Bale, the modelling master, saying: 'Here's a new student for you, Mr Bale'.'

Student Days

Tinworth's first exhibited piece at the school's annual show was a pigeon carved in wood. After a time he won a prize—the first of several while at the school—for a carved panel of *The Saviour being mocked by the Soldiers*. In 1864, after three years studying under Sparkes and other teachers, Tinworth won entrance to the Antique School of the Royal Academy with a figure of Hercules. His progress as a modeller and sculptor was extraordinarily rapid and successful, especially when one considers the complete incongruity between his humdrum daily work, making and repairing wheels, and his academic studies. He spent three or four hours in the wheelwright's shop before breakfast, after which he walked to the Academy; then back to the shop to work several hours more in the evening.

In 1866, after having won several prizes and medals, Tinworth exhibited at the Royal Academy for the first time. Sparkes was greatly concerned about Tinworth's future. It grieved him to see this gifted student having to devote most of his time to mending hackney cabs and wheelbarrows, and it was a great joy to him when he

George Tinworth working in his studio, 1887

persuaded Henry Doulton to offer, and Tinworth to accept, a job at the Lambeth Pottery.

A Prodigious Worker

In 1874 Tinworth exhibited three large terracotta panels at the Royal Academy. The following year eight smaller panels were shown. Further exhibition successes followed and then came two important commissions, the first of many such, for a reredos for York Minster Cathedral and a series of 28 semi-circular lunettes for the Guard's Chapel in Birdcage Walk, Westminster. In 1894, Tinworth informed a colleague that by then he had done at least 500 terracotta panels 'of important size' and many more smaller ones. He continued to produce panels, busts, statues, figure groups, medallions, vases and other creations in terracotta and salt-glaze stoneware until his sudden death in 1913 when on his way to work. Examples of his religious sculpture are to be found in cathedrals, churches and chapels in many parts of the world.

Figures and Animal Models

Stoneware group *Scandal* modelled by George Tinworth, *c*1891

From the mid-1870s onwards, Tinworth found welcome relaxation and diversion from his larger sculptural work in a haphazard flow of small figures, especially of children, and of whimsical studies of mice, frogs and other creatures parodying all kinds of amusing and intriguing human situations and activities. No detailed or chronological record of these has survived; new and hitherto unsuspected productions come to light from time to time, bearing the well-known GT monogram and, fortunately, often dated. For a visitor such as George Eliot, Gladstone, the Crown Prince of Germany or the Archbishop of Canterbury Tinworth would sometimes model a special piece of which no copies would be made. Other figures and animal models were reproduced in small quantities from moulds, Tinworth himself adding the finishing touches while they were still in the unfired clay state, before incising his initials. There are thus many slight (and, occasionally, some major) variations in these partly moulded and partly modelled pieces. Joseph Mott, former art director of the Lambeth Studios, who knew Tinworth for over thirty years, doubted if as many as a hundred—in some cases as many as a score—of each of these miniature items were made. A few models were also cast in china at the Doulton Burslem factory.

Tinworth, although he had none of his own, was a great lover of children, and they, too, loved him. It is not surprising that the majority of known Tinworth figures feature children. Some are free-standing figures on circular and other shaped bases; others are incorporated as supports for spill-vases, candlesticks, menu-holders, salt-cellars and the like. The famous brown salt-glaze 'Merry Musician' series, produced a few at a time between about 1889 and 1912, was preceded in the early 1880s by somewhat similar studies of boys and girls also playing musical instruments but forming decorative features of salt-cellars and other objects. The 'Merry Musicians' themselves are among the most delightful and charming works that Tinworth ever produced.

Existing photographs of the original unglazed models show that there were at least fifty-five different figures, most of them between 3½ and 5½ inches high, including two conductors, playing thirty-seven instruments. Some forty appear to have been produced for sale, part moulded and part modelled in the way already described, with many variations in facial expressions, styles of hats and positioning of limbs. About a hundred different figures with white instead of brown faces were made specially for an Australian customer.

Charles J. Noke, art director of the Burslem studios and reviver of the Staffordshire figure tradition was greatly attracted by these 'Merry Musicians' and had many

Stoneware 'Merry Musician' figures, from the series modelled by George Tinworth

of them in his private collections. He would have liked Tinworth to create some child models in similar vein for him. But Tinworth died suddenly just at the time the first china figures in the HN-series were coming on the market; otherwise there is little doubt that his services as a sculptor of an entirely original style of figure would have been in great demand at Burslem. As it was, he was indirectly responsible for the initiation of what became, and still is, one of the most popular series of Royal Doulton figures—those depicting twenty-four well known Dickens characters. One of the few books, other than the Bible and some of Shakespeare's plays, which Tinworth ever found pleasure in reading was *The Pickwick Papers*. He designed various small models depicting Mr Pickwick, one showing him seated in an arm-chair, another standing on a chair and about to make a speech; other figures of Pickwick were incorporated in a menu-holder, an ink-stand, a salt-cellar and a spill-vase. When the young Leslie Harradine was working in Tinworth's studio, during part of his apprenticeship as a modeller, it was Tinworth's figure of Pickwick that first gave him the idea of creating a series of Dickens characters in salt-glaze stoneware. These were later adapted, in collaboration with Noke, for production in china and earthenware and the original series of six was gradually expanded.

Left Stoneware bust of Charles Dickens, *right* Stoneware figure of Sam Weller, both modelled by L. Harradine in *c*1912

CHAPTER 6 *Doulton of Burslem*

The story of the genesis of the Royal Doulton figures now returns to Staffordshire. In December 1877 Henry Doulton launched out in a new development of far-reaching significance for the future of the Doulton enterprise itself and for the eventual restoration of the former importance of Staffordshire in the field of figure-making. Encouraged by the spectacular progress of the decorated Lambeth wares, which had rapidly achieved success far beyond his expectations, he decided to extend his interests in ceramics into the sphere of fine earthenware. An old-established factory in Nile Street, Burslem, then owned by Pinder, Bourne & Co was acquired. In 1882 the name was changed to Doulton & Co, Burslem, and Doulton took over complete control.

Steps were then taken to bring together a distinguished staff of designers, artists, modellers and engravers under the able direction of John Slater who came of an old Derby stock of ceramic painters. Slater was not only a gifted artist himself, who had been trained at the Minton factory under their famous art director, Léon Arnoux, but he also had a great flair for discovering and training others, encouraging them to develop their particular gifts. He was the ideal man to help Henry Doulton follow out the policy, already proved so fruitful at Lambeth, of drawing upon the best available talent locally and further afield, and then according the artists the utmost possible freedom of expression. Never before in any Staffordshire pottery had such a large and gifted group of creative artists come together who were so little tied to a particular 'factory style'. Among the array of talent were men who could draw not only upon the inspiration of traditional schools but could open up new and original paths of their own, bringing fresh approaches to the whole conception of ceramic design.

Left The Royal Doulton Nile Street factory in Burslem, *c*1925, *right* C. J. Noke

In Burslem and other pottery towns of North Staffordshire dwelt a population with an inherited aptitude for pottery-making and the skills which seem almost to be inborn when, for generations, a community has pursued a specialised craft in a certain measure of isolation. However, at the time of what some of the old-established Staffordshire potters somewhat ironically called 'the Doulton invasion', the general standards of design, especially of ornamental wares, left much to be desired. 'It is impossible', said Charles Noke, who succeeded Slater as Art Director in 1914, 'for anyone of the present generation to conceive just what an impact Sir Henry Doulton (who was knighted by Queen Victoria in 1887, the first potter ever to be accorded such an honour) made on the Staffordshire industry. To talk to him was invigorating, challenging, demanding the best one could give. He was just what the industry needed . . . What the Elers, Whieldon, Wedgwood and Spode had been for the industry in the eighteenth century, this man—by his tremendous vitality, his irrepressible enthusiasm, and his genius for inspiring others—did in the nineteenth'.

Any doubts as to whether the new star which had appeared in the ceramic firmament was destined to endure were settled by the exhibits at the great Chicago 'World's Columbian Exposition' of 1893. 'Doultons have completely outstripped their rivals and are today the leaders in English potting' wrote an American critic. The *Art Journal* for April 1893, commenting on the Doulton exhibits, summarised succinctly the almost incredible strides made during just two decades:

> 'Seldom has it happened in the experience of a single generation to see the birth and complete development of an entirely new Art Industry. Yet, in the short space of twenty years, there has been originated and perfected at the Lambeth Potteries,

> without the aid of previous tradition, a wealth of ceramic method that seems likely to become a conspicuous feature of the Renaissance of English Art . . . At Burslem, on the contrary, the whole available skill and tradition of several generations has been brought successfully to bear. The most typical productions of these two Art Potteries form a striking and unique collection which, for range of material and versatility of design, cannot fail to help greatly the reputation of this country for skill in ceramic decoration'.

At Chicago were shown publicly for the first time several large vases, ceramic figures and other pieces modelled by Charles J. Noke who had joined Slater's team of designers only four years previously but whose talents as a ceramic sculptor had already made a marked impact and were destined to play a major role in the revival of Staffordshire's reputation for the art of figure-making.

Charles J. Noke

Charles J. Noke was born in Worcester in 1858 in the very atmosphere of pottery. His birthplace was almost in the shadow of the famous china factory; his father, a dealer in antiques in that city, was a well-known connoisseur and had one of the largest private collections in the Midlands of old English and Continental pottery and porcelain. Included in this were some fine examples of Chelsea, Bow, Derby, Sèvres and Meissen figures and vases. These came to have a considerable fascination for young Charles who, as he grew older, begged to be allowed to handle them and was always plying his father with questions about them, as well as about the many other specimens of china which passed in and out of the antique shop in the course of ordinary business. He was also intrigued to listen sometimes to discussions between his father and other collectors about the authenticity or the provenance of some particular piece.

Charles's father had friends and acquaintances among the directors and staff of the Royal Worcester Porcelain Company which in 1862 succeeded variously-titled earlier china factories that had been active in the city since the mid-eighteenth century. Among these friends were the head of the firm, R. W. Binns, and the gifted modeller, James Hadley, whose work had attracted notable attention at the International Exhibition in South Kensington in 1871 and at the Vienna Exhibition two years later. Permission was readily given for Charles to visit the factory and during his school holidays the lad liked nothing better than to spend a few hours roaming quietly and unobtrusively from one workshop and studio to another, asking a pertinent question here and there, and gradually absorbing a great deal of knowledge about the designing and making of china. He was especially attracted to the modellers' studios where he liked to watch Hadley and others at work on sometimes very elaborate vases in Japanese, Renaissance and other styles, and occasionally on figures and animal models.

Charles was allowed to take home some modelling clay and with this he began to shape some small elephants and other animal models and human figures, including —prophetically!—one of a Jester. These were said by Hadley to show promise and there was soon no doubt as to what career the youth wanted to follow. When he was not quite sixteen, he started work as an apprentice-modeller under Binns and Hadley; at the same time he began a long course of study at the Worcester School of Design.

In 1875, Hadley set up as an independent designer and modeller but for the next twenty years practically his entire output was bought by the Royal Worcester Company which naturally did not wish to lose to a rival factory the services of such an outstandingly talented ceramic sculptor. Noke now came under the direction of George Evans, George Owen and other Worcester modellers but he was occasionally seconded, with other apprentices, to help Hadley with some of his more elaborate pieces. He had a great admiration for Hadley whose influence is clearly to be seen in some of his early work for Doulton.

The Chicago Exhibition

Noke remained with Worcester for some sixteen years until 1889 when John Slater, who had been impressed by some of his work that he had seen at exhibitions, invited him to join Doulton & Co. of Burslem. By this time the decoration of china and earthenware at the Nile Street pottery was of a very high order and, as Frederick Rhead wrote in the American Journal, *Pottery and Glass*, in December 1912, 'it was in the combination of this fine decoration and (Noke's) experience of shape and line that a special field was opened for his efforts... Full advantage was taken of this opportunity to co-ordinate the two factors'.

The fruits of Noke's first two or three years of activity as Doulton's chief modeller were revealed and acclaimed at the Chicago Exhibition of 1893. His gifts as a modeller were evident in many of the tablewares and ornamental wares, and most notably in a series of large vases, specially conceived as 'Prestige pieces' for the occasion, modelled by Noke in a general Renaissance style and richly painted by Labarre, Mitchell, Wilson, Piper and other leading artists.

It was in the modelling of the figures incorporated in these vases that Noke's gifts in this particular genre were first seen. The 'Columbus' vase, for instance, standing nearly six feet high, was surmounted by a bold and picturesque figure of the great navigator; above the handles were two other finely sculpted figures—one symbolising 'Emancipation', seen freeing a bird, and the other 'Sleep' with owl head-dress. The American *Trenton Sunday Advertiser* wrote that this 'suggested rather the atelier of the sculptor and painter than the workshop of a pottery . . . elevated as it is to the highest pinnacle of art'. The local home newspaper, the *Staffordshire Sentinel*, described it as 'a triumph of pottery . . . the whole composition a marvel and delight'.

Only a few independent *free-standing* figures modelled by Noke were shown. The potential importance of this particular field does not seem to have been appreciated at this time; the figures that *were* shown are not mentioned in any of the known press references to the exhibition, and, what is stranger still, they are not referred to even in an elaborately produced and well-illustrated 64-page Doulton publication featuring the exhibits. However, it is fairly certain that the following figures modelled by Noke were shown in Chicago in 1893: *Jack Point*, *Moorish Minstrel* (with stringed instrument), *Lady Jester*, *A Jester* (seated and clasping raised leg) and, most unusual of all, *Mirth and Melancholy* (also known as *The Laughing Philosopher* but not actually inscribed with any title), a duplex or double-sided figure of a jester, standing by a column, one face joyful, the other sad.

Between 1893 and 1897 a few other figures were added to the range, all modelled by Noke. They include: *A Jester* (standing), a seated *Pierrot*, *Shylock*, *Ellen Terry as Queen Catherine* and *Henry Irving as Cardinal Wolsey* (both in two different decorations), a duplex figure depicting *Mephistopheles and Marguerite*, *A Geisha*, and yet another duplex model, this time depicting a judge and a woman standing back to back, entitled *Oh! Law!*

These figures were generally much larger than those produced later on in the HN-series; they ranged from about 8 to 20 inches in height, and instead of being in the usual china or earthenware body they were made in a Doulton variety of Parian porcelain, containing felspar. This was tinted an ivory or vellum shade and had only a slight 'smear' of surface glaze. The usual decoration was with pink and green sheens and gilding. Their colour and style showed the continuing influence of James Hadley on Noke. Examples of these early figures can be seen on pages 54, 77, 107, 112 and 165.

It is recorded that a *Jack Point* figure, some 16 inches high, was sold at Chicago to an American collector for $400. These early Noke figures were probably too large and too expensive to have a widespread appeal, and although the modelling was of a high order the style of decoration was dull and anaemic compared with the gay enamelling of the popular smaller French and German figures. Judging from the infrequency with which they appear either in the salesrooms or the antique shops they were apparently not made in any large editions. The rarity of references to them in the general or trade press tends to confirm this impression. It was not until some twenty years later that some of the Noke models produced in the 1890s, and re-introduced after 1913, in a much bolder, more attractive and extensive range of colours, began to achieve wider recognition although, even then, none of them, except perhaps a smaller version of the *Jester*, attained anything remotely like the popularity of such new models as *Darling*, *The Parsons' Daughter*, *Polly Peachum*, *The Balloon Seller* and the *Dickens* series, to name but a few of the now world-famous HN-series.

Between about 1897 and 1909, Noke seems to have put aside temporarily any ambition he may have had earlier on to revive Staffordshire's former fame for figure-making. He became, instead, deeply involved in a series of new projects, some of which demanded many months to bring them to perfect fruition. They included his much sought after 'Enamelled Pottery'—a combination of relief modelling with glowing enamel colours, resembling *champlevé*, his 'Holbein' and 'Rembrandt' wares, his 'Lactolian' wares with a type of *pâte-sur-pâte* decoration, and a whole range of what were to prove immensely popular 'series wares' based on *The Jackdaw of Rheims*, *The Bayeux Tapestry*, and scenes from Shakespeare's plays and Dickens' novels. Above all, demanding long and patient research, came the wonderful *flambé* wares with their astonishingly lovely transmutation glaze effects.

It was not until these developments were successfully launched and firmly established that Noke resumed any active interest in figure-modelling.

CHAPTER 7 *The Renaissance of Staffordshire Figure-making*

As early as 1909, Charles Noke began to turn his attention once again to figure-modelling, and to pondering how best a revival of interest in this long neglected but once greatly admired Staffordshire *genre* could be brought about. The time had come, Noke felt, for a major revival in original and simpler styles, more appropriate for the new century; embodying the best features of older traditions, both English and Continental, but avoiding the fussiness and over-ornamentation that marked the work of many earlier figure-modellers in both the earthenware and the china media. He saw clearly that such an ambitious undertaking would demand the collaboration of other sculptors and artists and a long period of costly experimentation and judicious testing of public response. The history of china-figure production in England, generally speaking, had been an unfortunate one financially —most of the factories which specialised in it going bankrupt after a few years.

As a first step, having obtained the approval of Henry Lewis Doulton, Sir Henry's son and successor, to spend a certain sum on a 'trial run', Noke began to invite well-known sculptors to visit the Burslem factory and studios, and to discuss the feasibility of their modelling specially some figures and figure-groups which could be reproduced in the ceramic medium. Some sculptors, accustomed mainly to creating large works in marble or stone, proved unable or unwilling to adapt their conceptions to the small scale and the technical problems involved; others proved more amenable.

Even today a year or more may elapse between the designer's original conception of a figure and its final successful emergence from the enamelling oven as a *fait accompli*. At the beginning of the Doulton figure revival it took even longer. Several of the models submitted had to be tactfully rejected for one reason or another and it was early in 1913 before Noke felt confident enough to launch some twenty models in the new series—several of them decorated in more than one way. These were the work of Noke himself and of five sculptors: Phoebe Stabler, George Lambert, F. C. Stone, ARCA, Charles Vyse, ARCA, and William White.

White was a winner of the coveted Royal Academy Gold Medal and the Goldsmiths' Prize. Phoebe Stabler and Vyse had both exhibited at the Royal Academy, the Paris Salon and other important exhibitions; Stone and Lambert were masters at the Burslem School of Art. Vyse was already well-known to Noke, who had followed his successful career with almost fatherly interest, for he had been apprenticed to Doulton, under Noke, as a modeller and designer in 1896 when he was just fourteen. For the next few years he combined his practical work in Noke's studio with part-time studies in the Burslem School of Art. From there he went on to the Royal College of Art where he obtained two National Scholarships (1905-7 and 1907-10) for sculpture. A travelling Scholarship enabled him to pursue his studies in Italy. In 1911 he was elected a member of the Royal Society of British Sculptors. After his marriage a few years later, he and his wife set up their own studio in Chelsea where they produced over fifty figures and figure-groups in small limited editions, besides a great number of vases, bowls and other individually hand-decorated pots.

Picardy Peasant figures modelled by Phoebe Stabler in *c*1911, prior to their production at Burslem

A Royal Visit

The new range of Doulton models had been completed by the end of 1912, some even earlier. The latter included *The Diligent Scholar*, *The Sleepy Scholar* and *Coquette* by White; *Elizabeth Fry* and *The Return of Persephone* by Vyse; *Picardy Peasants* and *Madonna of the Square* by Phoebe Stabler. The original of *Elizabeth Fry*, 'a dignified, natural and noble figure', had been exhibited at the Royal Academy in 1912. They were all held back from the public exhibition and sale until after the visit of King George V and Queen Mary to Doulton's Burslem Pottery in April, 1913. At the time of the Royal Visit, the little figure now known as *Darling* had been named *Bedtime*. The Queen, singling it out, took it in her hands and exclaimed 'Isn't he a darling!' She ordered reproductions for herself and some of her friends, and the figure has ever since been known to many thousands of collectors all over the world as *Darling*. Although it was not in fact the first of the new series to be completed it was, because of its Royal 'christening', given the number HN-1 when this system of numbering was introduced. It proved to be far and away the most popular figure Vyse ever created, and a smaller version of it is still in production today.

Noke had, towards the end of the previous century, already adapted *Jack Point* and *A Jester* (seated) in an earthenware body, decorated with underglaze colours, but for some reason they were not given numbers in the HN-series until after 1913. A version of *King Charles* was in existence by 1912 or earlier but first appeared with an HN-number (404) in 1920. There may be a few other isolated instances of this kind, including possibly coloured versions of *Queen Catherine* and *Cardinal Wolsey*, later given the numbers HN344 and 379.

It will be seen from the Alphabetical Index that the names of many figures, especially early ones like *Madonna of the Square* and *The Welsh Girl*, appear again and again under new HN-numbers. New numbers for similar models were usually given because of changes in decoration, less frequently because of modifications in modelling or a change of body. It is evident that for several years a good deal of experimenting was going on to try to strike the right note which would make the figures commercially viable.

Between 1914 and 1921 several other sculptors made contributions to the range. They included Albert Toft, L. Perugini and two resident artists, Harry Tittensor, RI, and E. W. Light, both local art masters. Tittensor's *The Gainsborough Hat*, *Pretty Lady* and *The Parson's Daughter;* Light's *Lady of the Fan*, *Lady with Rose*, *The Curtsey* and *The Flounced Skirt;* Perugini's '*Shy Anne*' and other child studies; and Noke's *Carpet Vendor*, *Guy Fawkes* and *An Old King* opened up new directions which were to inspire many subsequent creations. In helping Noke to establish the new figure department on a sound basis, Tittensor—one of the most versatile all-round artists ever employed by Doulton—played an inestimably important part. The same applies to Harry Nixon, another resident artist. The painting of the early HN-figures was entrusted to Harry Allen, Charles Nixon and Eric Webster who formed the nucleus of what was to become years later a large studio of artists specialising in this work. Webster also painted many of the animal models created by Noke and Harradine and, later on, the well-known *Championship Dogs* modelled by Frederick T. Daws, and the horses modelled by W. M. Chance—of which the most famous is that of the Royal steeple-chaser, *Monaveen*, made for HM Queen Elizabeth II (then The Princess Elizabeth) in 1949.

Partly because of inevitable teething troubles and disappointments in the slow public response to most of the new models, partly because of the First World War and its repercussions, restricting marketing opportunities both at home and overseas, production remained on a very limited scale for several years. An exact record was kept of the models (including colour variations) completed by the modellers and the three painters between 2nd June, 1913 and 8th September 1917. It will probably interest collectors to have the details. The total number completed was 680—an average of about three a week. During the whole of 1916 only 117 figures were painted and these included hardly any new models. *Darling* and *The Crinoline* were clear favourites as will be seen from the following list:

> *Darling*, 148; *The Crinoline*, 51; *Spooks* (several varieties), 40; *Madonna of the Square*, 35; *Picardy Peasant* (female), 22; *Pussy*, 21; *Sleep*, 20; *Lilac Shawl*, *Picardy Peasant* (male) and *Shy Ann*, 18 each; *Under the Gooseberry Bush*, 15; *Dunce*, 14; *Lady of the Georgian Period* and *Moorish Minstrel*, 13 each; *Coquette*, 12; *Lavender Woman*, 11; *Baby*, *Lady of the Time of Henry VI*, *Diligent Scholar*, *Lady with Rose* and *Elizabeth Fry*, 9 each; *An Arab* (later re-named *The Moor*), *Sleepy Scholar*, *Land of Nod* and *The Gainsborough Hat*, 8 each; *A Child's Grace*, *The Little Land*, *Milking Time*, *Pedlar Wolf*, *The Welsh Girl*, *Elizabethan Lady* and *The Return of Persephone*, 7 each; *Katharine*, *Lady of the Fan*, *Lady Ermine*, *Pretty Lady* and *Upon her Cheeks she Wept*, 6 each; *Motherhood* and *Child and Crab*, 3 each; *Sentimental Pierrot*, *Carpet Vendor*, *Curtsey*, *Robert Burns*, *Jester*, *Charley's Aunt*, 2 each; *Orange Vendor* and *The Flounced Skirt*, 1 each.

Some of these were not introduced until 1916-17 so naturally not so many of them would have been completed. The general trend indicated, none the less, is significant and must have given Noke food for thought. It is interesting to note that on some of the early models a hand-written number (apart from the HN-number and the impressed case-number) appears; these numbers seem to indicate the order in which the figures were painted.)

Darling, *Madonna of the Square*, the two *Picardy Peasants*, *Pussy* and *Shy Anne* long remained favourites. Here again were significant pointers for the future. *Darling*, *Pussy* and *Shy Anne* proved to be the precursors of a long series of child studies (there are over 30 in the current collection). *Madonna of the Square*—suggested to Phoebe Stabler by seeing a woman selling lavender on the pavement of a London square—was the first of many delightful studies of balloon-sellers, flower-sellers, street vendors and other characters in similar vein. The *Picardy Peasants*, modelled from life in France, have their successors in a host of characters such as *Lambing Time*, *The Master*, *Country Lass* and *The Huntsman*.

The Crystal Palace

The first significant impact made upon the buying public was in 1920, when the range of figures available, including several new models, was shown at the British Industries Fair in the Crystal Palace. It was then that a percipient contributor to the *Staffordshire Sentinel* voiced the acclamation which was soon repeated, in its original or in slightly altered form, by admirers in Australia, New Zealand and the United States: 'A renaissance of Staffordshire figure-ware after long neglect. . . . Since the days of Ralph Wood there has been produced in Staffordshire nothing so craftsmanlike and so eminently right'. Queen Mary again bought copies of *Darling* and also of *Contentment*, a new figure by Leslie Harradine. She became a great admirer of Harradine's work and bought many of his models at subsequent exhibitions over a long period of years.

Despite the publicity gained by the Crystal Palace display, production remained on a severely limited scale until well into the 1920s. In 1923 Norman Woodings joined the small band of painters and, about the same time, John Pierpoint, who has given me the following interesting information: 'The second range of Doulton figures began about 1920 when C. J. Noke acquired some models by L. Harradine, a former Lambeth modeller and designer. He had them cast at Burslem in bone china. Harry Nixon suggested the colours for these new models and Charles Nixon (no relation to Harry Nixon) interpreted them, and later became his assistant. There was great emphasis on the obtaining of subtle colour effects by repeated paintings and firings and *the special way in which the colours were fused together into the glaze was the first time that enamel colours had ever been used in this way, and was unique to Doulton*'.

By 1927 the number of figure-painters had grown to ten. When one considers that the figures were largely hand-painted and that several firings and fusings of colours were needed to obtain the desired results, it is clear that the total output could not have been great. The studios were extended in the mid-1930s but even by 1939 there were only twenty-seven painters. The Second World War brought inevitably many problems, not least the calling-up of several of the artists. Between 1941 and 1949 many of the earlier figures were discontinued; these are naturally among the most sought after today. Of those figures which had been withdrawn by 1949, it is unlikely that as many as 2,000 of any one had been made—probably far fewer of many of them.

Leslie Harradine

Arthur L. Harradine (usually known by his second name, Leslie) was born in 1887. In 1902 he joined Doulton's Lambeth Studios as an apprentice modeller, working under the supervision, at different times, of Tinworth, Marshall and Broad.

In 1902 also he entered the Camberwell School of Art as a part-time student under the well-known sculptor, Albert Toft.

Tinworth's large biblical panels had little attraction for the young artist but he loved the 'Merry Musicians' and the amusing mice and frog studies. He once said that, if he had been Tinworth, he would have 'stuck to that kind of thing' which would probably be still admired after his 'dreary terracotta panels' had been forgotten. Marshall's 'grotesques' he could appreciate but had no desire to emulate; he found his occasional crinoline ladies more attractive. Broad, a versatile and prolific artist, equally at home with large and small works, appealed to him the most of his three mentors. Harradine learned a good deal from Broad whose striking studies of Boer War soldiers probably inspired him to produce his own salt-glaze figures of Spahis and Foreign Legionaries.

Left Three hard-paste porcelain figures modelled by John Broad at Lambeth in *c*1912

Right Stoneware figures, *Market Woman* and *The Toiler*, modelled by L. Harradine at Lambeth in *c*1912

Harradine had to spend more time than he liked in designing vases for reproduction. He was much more interested in ceramic sculpture. Among the salt-glaze pieces he produced between 1907 and 1912 were some well-modelled spirit flasks depicting Dr Johnson, Lord Balfour, Lord Haldane, Austen Chamberlain, David Lloyd George, John Burns and President Theodore Roosevelt. Other creations, revealing an original and vigorous talent were figures of a sower and a reaper, a Dutch woman, two peasants, a coalman, a study entitled *Motherhood* and another of Sidney Carton, hero of Dickens' *Tale of Two Cities*, standing trial. The figures which particularly appealed to Charles Noke, who had been following Harradine's development with interest, were those of several of the best known characters from Dickens' novels—Pickwick, Micawber, Squeers, Pecksniff, Sam Weller, the Fat Boy, Uriah Heep and Sairey Gamp. These wonderfully expressive characterisations greatly attracted Noke who was himself a great lover of Dickens.

Much to the surprise of some of his Lambeth colleagues, Harradine resigned suddenly towards the end of 1912. A virile, somewhat Bohemian young man, a great lover of the open-air life, he found working in Lambeth too constricting and longed to be fully independent. He had a vision of one day setting up his own studio but in the meantime was attracted by a proposition put up to him by his brother, Percy, that the two of them should go off to Canada and take advantage of the enticing opportunities to acquire land for large-scale farming then being offered by the Canadian Government. And so it came about that the two brothers between them began to farm some 4,000 acres of land in Saskatchewan.

Much of the soil was poor and they found it difficult to produce good crops of wheat. They made mistakes due to their inexperience but learned from them. They built their own log cabin from trees they had felled themselves. Their nearest neighbours were several miles away; help was not easy to find. They broke in their own horses and sometimes spent many hours a day on horseback. They kept cows and chickens, grew vegetables, and lived entirely on what they could produce themselves. Life was hard but they were strong and healthy and thoroughly enjoyed the change from the big city and from indoor work.

Leslie continued to paint and draw in any spare time he could find and, having come across some fairly suitable modelling clay on his land, passed many a winter's evening creating figures of real and imaginary people, including some amusing caricatures. Unfortunately he never managed to build a kiln which could fire these pieces successfully. During the winter, too, when work on the farm slackened, the two young men toured Saskatchewan, giving concerts and marionette shows. They made the marionettes themselves. Leslie, who was a brilliant conjuror, demonstrated his abilities in this direction also.

In 1914 came the Great War and some two years later the two brothers joined Lord Strathcona's Horse Regiment and eventually found themselves in action in France. There Leslie had his horse shot from under him twice. The first time he managed to jump clear but the second time the horse fell on top of him and one of his legs was badly injured. Then came long spells in hospital. Before the war ended, Leslie had married and had his first child. He decided, when he came out of the army, that a lonely log cabin in Canada was no place for a woman and young child. He handed his land over to his brother and decided to try to realise his earlier dream of establishing a studio and working as an independent artist.

Often when Charles Noke was in London to visit an exhibition or art gallery he would call at the Lambeth Pottery for a chat with his opposite number there, art director Joseph Mott. Hearing from Mott that Harradine was back in England, he tried to get into touch with him. Harradine was living at this time in Bedfordshire but was spending a working holiday in Jersey, sketching and painting and modelling some figures from life. Eventually he was contacted and an interview with Noke was arranged in Mott's neo-Gothic eyrie in the top turret of the remarkable building which still stands at the corner of Lambeth High Street.

Noke offered him every inducement he could think of to come and work in Burslem but Harradine was unyielding in his refusal. After his experiences in Canada and in the army he valued his new-found freedom too much to tie himself down again. He believed that he could live, simply perhaps but happily, and support a family, by selling his paintings and models. He had already had some success in this direction and he aimed in due course to set up a small studio in London. Noke was disappointed naturally at Harradine's refusal to work in Burslem but gladly accepted his offer to model some figures at home and send these up to the Potteries to see if Noke could use them for reproduction in bone china. Thus began one of the most fruitful collaborations between a sculptor and a china factory in the whole history of figure-making—one which was to continue unbroken for nearly forty years, first with Charles Noke, then with his son Jack (Cecil J. Noke) who succeeded him as Art Director, and finally, after 1955, with the present Director of Design, Joseph W. Ledger, ARCA.

The porcelain figure offered Harradine the possibility, of which he took the utmost advantage, of depicting in the round a seemingly unlimited variety of expressions, forms and poses. He developed a wonderful gift for suggesting movement—wind-blown outdoor ladies, flouncing indoor damsels. Amongst his first models for Noke were *Contentment*, *Marie*, *Betty*, *The Goose Girl*, *Fruit Gathering*, and a famous series—*Polly Peachum* and other characters from the Beggar's Opera, which, like the first Dickens figures, were modelled first of all in stoneware at Lambeth. Six large and sixteen small Dickens characters (later increased to twenty-four) were developed in close collaboration with Noke who had made a long study of Dickens personalities. And down through the years the new models came in almost unbroken succession: 'I sent at least one model a month, sometimes two or three, for nearly 40 years', he said, shortly before his death in Gibraltar in 1965, 'then I wrote and told them I couldn't do any more'. A former figure-painter has recalled how, when the monthly parcel arrived, artists and painters would crowd into Noke's studio to see what Harradine 'had come up with this time'.

The Old Balloon Seller, The Flower Seller's Children, Fruit Gathering, The Chelsea Pair, The Perfect Pair, Harlequinade, The Mask, A Yeoman of the Guard, A Chelsea Pensioner, Mam'selle, A Victorian Lady, The Dandy, The Belle, The Modern Piper, Miss 1926, Lido Lady, Lady Jester, The Wandering Minstrel, Tête-à-Tête, Carnival, Yum-Yum, Midinette, Bo-Peep, Sweet Anne, Sunshine Girl, The Mendicant, The Little Mother, Darby, Joan, Pantalettes, Sweet and Twenty and *The Beggar's Opera* series—these are but a few of the many Harradine figures which had gone into production by 1931, figures which have given great joy and pleasure to a multitude of collectors. Noke and Harradine between them consolidated the revival of Staffordshire figure-making which had begun in 1913.

Advertisement from the *Pottery Gazette*, December 1922

Pages from a 1930s catalogue, showing figure table-lamps

It is a great tribute to Harradine's flair for creating models which do not date that so many of them are still in production and still popular after so many years. His child studies still transport one to a world of innocence. His *Top o'the Hill, Autumn Breezes, The Old Balloon Seller, The Flower Seller's Children* and the Dickens characters are among the most popular Royal Doulton figures ever made. He preserved his vigorous creative faculty to the end and during the last four years of his life, which he spent in Spain, he did a great many terracotta figures of Spanish peasants, most of which are still in the possession of Mrs Harradine. Before going to Spain they had lived for many years in Sark, one of the smaller Channel Islands.

Leslie Harradine once remarked that, of all the earlier china figures, he preferred those of Vincennes to Meissen or Chelsea. One wonders if he had ever come across the advice given by Vincennes' artistic director in 1751: 'Diversity of Tastes is the guardian angel of a factory which revolves round products intended to please; what does not please one pleases others. . . Graciousness, variety, novelty should be its watch-word. Graciousness in this sense means a light touch. What is wanted is, as it were, the gentle "sneezes" of genius like those of a pretty woman, that is to say, smiling and pleasant'. Whether he had read this or not, it well expresses Leslie Harradine's own philosophy of figure-making.

Leslie Harradine liked reading Bertrand Russell, Fred Hoyle and Walt Whitman and, in his younger days, was a great admirer of Bernard Shaw. His favourite painters were Matthew Smith and Augustus John. He thought the French sculptor, Maillol, was wonderful but more than any other—strange as it may seem—

he admired Epstein. Indeed he did some almost life-size sculptures himself in a style that many people thought was considerably influenced by Epstein. A man of simple and often unconventional tastes he loved cricket, shove halfpenny and snooker, and was always ready to entertain a group of children with his conjuring tricks. His broad outlook on life and his warm humanity are reflected in his work.

The Garbe Figures

Between 1934 and 1939 a number of figures, wall-masks and other ceramics, modelled for Doulton by Professor Richard Garbe, RA, were produced in limited editions as follows: *Spring* (100 at £3.00 each); *Salome* (100 at £1.50 each); *West Wind* (25 at £8.40 each); *Spirit of the Wind*, (50 at £4.20 each); *Beethoven* (25 at £15.00 each); *Macaw* (25 at £4.20 each); *Lady of the Snows* (25 at £3.25 each); *The Cloud* (25 at £4.20 each); and a number of wall-masks in limited editions of 100 each (price not recorded). The prices quoted above, converted to decimal currency, were those charged to china dealers; the retail prices would have been more but even so they must have been astonishingly low for such works by a well-known artist who, at that time, was Professor of Sculpture at the Royal College of Art. The ceramics were made in a special porcelain body and had an ivory glaze. Coloured versions of the figures were also produced, apparently for fitting up with lamps like many of the other figures, also coloured wall-masks. These were not limited in numbers but sales were disappointingly few.

It may interest collectors to have a few wholesale export prices of figures in a 1939 list: HN-549, *Polly Peachum:* £0.80; HN-728, *A Victorian Lady:* £1.00; HN-1392, *Paisley Shawl:* £1.00; HN-1482, *Pearly Boy:* £0.45; HN-1493, *The Potter:* £2.25; HN-1528, *Bluebeard:* £1.00; HN-1649, *Sweet and Twenty:* £1.60; HN-1713, *Daffy-down-Dilly:* £1.25; HN-1745, *Rustic Swain:* £2.00; HN-1747, *Afternoon Tea:* £2.25; HN-1814, *The Squire:* £2.50. When one sees the prices which obsolete figures now fetch in the salesrooms, one realises just how true were the words written in the 1930s by Edward R. Cross, a great admirer of the Doulton figures: 'The Connoisseurs of tomorrow will seek out these exquisite creations of the potter just as today they give fabulous prices for the pieces of bygone days. So that in giving a Royal Doulton figure one gives an heirloom. It will be handed down—with its memories'.

CHAPTER 8

An On-going Story

During World War II severe restrictions were imposed by the British Government on the manufacture of decorated ceramics. This, plus the fact that many artists were in the Armed Forces, or serving the war effort in other ways, inevitably restricted the number of new models that could be added to the by then already world-famous figure collection.

But since 1945, under the direction of Jack Noke, Jo Ledger and, more recently, Eric Griffiths, there has come forth from the Nile Street Studios, year after year, a colourful procession of exquisitely modelled and decorated figures—some of them novel variations on traditional and perennially popular themes; others introducing altogether new concepts in both themes and techniques; and all of them adding fresh lustre to the Royal Doulton annals.

Peggy Davies, Mary Nicoll, Eric Griffiths and Robert Jefferson have in recent years contributed an exciting new chapter, full of promise for the future, to the story which began all those years ago with Tinworth, Noke and the rest who, with the support of Sir Henry Doulton and his successors, ventured into a field of ceramics in which many before them came to grief. Valuable contributions, though fewer in number, have also been made by John Bromley, William Harper, David Lovegrove and Douglas Tootle.

Margaret May Davies

Margaret Davies—Peggy, as she is generally known to her many admirers—was born in Burslem, the 'mother-town' of the Potteries. As a child, owing to bovine tuberculosis, caused by unpasteurised milk, she spent more time at home, and in hospitals and convalescent homes, than at school. She recalls that it was when she was only seven years old, and confined to bed in Hanchurch Convalescent Home, that her dawning promise as an artist was first recognised. She had drawn a very detailed and striking picture of a mermaid and, since most children at that age draw just 'stick' figures, the nurse in charge was astonished. She sent for the matron—who sent for the doctor—who sent for his wife—until the bed was surrounded by admirers.

Allowed back to school she found herself hopelessly behind her class-mates in the more intellectual subjects but, fortunately, an enlightened school-mistress, recognising her artistic talents, did not worry about this and encouraged her to draw and paint to her heart's content.

Peggy went to live with grandparents who were in a better position than her parents to provide the special attention and expensive extras needed for a delicate child. Her grandfather was an engineer at a pot-bank; his house was attached to the factory and so, at an early age, she became familiar with the bottle ovens, slip-house, pug-mills, presses and potters' wheels of an old factory of the kind which has long since disappeared but whose activities are being revived in the Gladstone Pottery Museum in Longton,—a 'Living Museum' where the old methods of manufacture can be demonstrated to the visitor. Here future generations will be able to see the old bottle ovens, once the most characteristic feature of the Stoke-on-Trent landscape in which Peggy grew up, and learn how the pottery industry developed from primitive peasant beginnings.

All this is in Peggy's blood. She well remembers the smoke and the grit, the quaint old-fashioned attire of the workers, some carrying heavy saggars full of ware on their heads, others, with a fascinating single motion, plunging plates into a tub of glaze, then lifting them out and by dexterous swerves and twists causing the glaze to run equally over the whole surface. Most of all perhaps the making of pots on the wheel intrigued her, with their seemingly magical growth under the skilful manipulation of the thrower's hands,—'now expanding, now contracting', as the poet Longfellow put it. Then there were the kilns, their intense heat, and the firemen who tended them faithfully day and night—even on Sundays when they wore their 'chapel clothes' so that they could take it in turn, devout followers of Wesley that they were, to attend either the morning or evening service. From her bedroom window, while resting, she could see the workmen making the saggars—fireproof containers in which the pots were placed to protect them from the direct flames of the ovens. She knows that a 'saggar maker's bottom knocker' was a real man with a real job, not just a myth or a music-hall joke. It was the coarse sticky marl used for making saggars that provided the means for her first attempts at rough modelling.

When she was only twelve, Peggy won a scholarship to the Burslem College of Art, where her gift for modelling had scope to develop. After some years, first as a junior student, then as a senior under Gordon Forsyth (who was not only a distinguished teacher but a practical craftsman and designer for several pottery firms), family circumstances made it necessary for her to earn some money. She became an assistant to Clarice Cliff, a well-known local designer and modeller but was able to keep her scholarship going by attending the college one full day and three evenings a week.

In 1939 Peggy went to Doulton's Burslem Studios as an assistant to Cecil J. Noke, thus beginning a long and fruitful association which has added numerous new figures to the Royal Doulton Collection. A small studio which she set up at home was destroyed by incendiary bombs. As a contribution to the war effort she then decided to take up nursing but being under five feet and weighing merely seven stone she found great difficulty in being accepted by any hospital! In the end her persistence triumphed. During her training, she was able to study anatomy in greater detail than at the art school, and this has stood her in good stead in her subsequent career as a ceramic sculptor.

After the war, Peggy became an independent artist, but has continued, under contract, to create for Royal Doulton a host of delightful figures, as well as several large figures and groups, in a very individual and distinctive style of modelling. She has a 'workroom studio' at the bottom of her garden, where she continues to develop her craft just as the early Burslem potters did, sometimes digging her own clay, throwing her pots on the wheel, modelling figure upon figure, firing them in her own small experimental kiln. She loves to produce complicated pieces such as *The Matador and Bull*, *Indian Brave* and *The Palio*. She takes infinite pains to research her subjects thoroughly, whether they involve the attire of medieval Queens, techniques of a Spanish bull-fighter, the intricacies of a Sioux Indian ritual sun dance, or the costume of a sixteenth-century Italian knight on horseback. Her group *The Marriage of Art and Industry* was the centre-piece of the Doulton stand at the Brussels International Exhibition of 1958 at which Royal Doulton was the only pottery firm to win a *Grand Prix*. Modelled by Peggy, to a suggestion by Art Director Jo Ledger, this group symbolised the theme of the exhibition; it depicted a young man and woman by the tree of knowledge with doves of peace, and, at the base, symbols of the arts and sciences.

Peggy has had a portrait of the Queen accepted by Her Majesty. In addition to the many small models and the large 'prestige pieces' specially designed for Royal Doulton she produces individual pieces of sculpture for herself and paints portraits of children (she has three sons of her own). Still keen on experimenting, she believes that people always love to see beautiful and unusual things expertly produced. Her favourite hobbies are collecting old glass and 'other people's work'; her relaxations include reading, interior decoration, painting, cooking unusual dishes, theatre and concert going, caravanning in beautiful lonely places, and walking.

Peggy Davies' bevy of 'fair ladies', each a distinct individual portrayal of archetypal femininity, carries on the Royal Doulton pre-eminence in this field, yet each is an original conception and none of them could be mistaken for the work of Harradine who was also a brilliant exponent of the manifold variations possible in this particular type of figure. Besides all these, she has given the world of collectors several outstanding series featuring themes such as *Period Figures in English History*, *Ballet*, *Figures of Williamsburg* and *Lady Musicians*.

The Enchantment of the figure thus aptly named, the fantasy of *Sea Sprite;* the mature beauty of *Southern Belle*, the lively freshness of *Sweet Seventeen*; the endearing studies such as *Sweet Dreams* and *Nanny*; these show but a few aspects of Peggy Davies' brilliancy as a ceramic sculptor who is not surprisingly considered by many collectors to be one of the world's best figure artists in the porcelain medium.

Among her latest contributions to the Royal Doulton Collection are the first figures in a new series *Dancers of the World* (limited to 750 of each), and the first in a series of Kate Greenaway figures, capturing the infinite delicacy, tenderness and grace of the famous artist's sketches of children.

Mary Nicoll

Mary Nicoll's death in February 1974, at the far too early age of 52, was a shock to her many admirers in Britain and overseas, and was a sad loss for Royal Doulton. In vividness of imagination, and in the vitality with which she imbued her sculptures and paintings, she always remained a young woman. Her work will undoubtedly live on, to give joy and pleasure to future collectors as it has done to those of the recent past. It has that indefinable quality which is the result of close observation of many different types of human nature, combined with wholesome imagination and considerable artistic and technical ability; it reflects her own unique blend of human sympathy, gentleness, tenderness, romance and humour, with now and then a touch of lovable eccentricity.

Mary's artistic gifts, especially in the field of sculpture and modelling, manifested themselves at an early age. Her first professional commission came when she was only twelve, from the architect, Mr Guy Church, who asked her to model seven figures for him. Her artistic education was loving supervised by her father, Gordon Nicoll, RI, himself a widely-known and gifted painter in oils and watercolours. After a period of study at the Central School of Arts and Crafts in London she began to exhibit at the Walker Galleries, the Royal Academy and other art centres. Several examples of her work were shown at the Festival of Britain in 1951.

Desmond Eyles was partly responsible for introducing Mary Nicoll to Royal Doulton, and the story of how this came about is best told in his own words:

> 'Mary Nicoll's figures for the Royal Doulton Collection have always had a special interest for me personally. Her father, who did some magnificent paintings to illustrate my books *Pottery through the Ages* and *Pottery in the Ancient World*, became a valued friend of mine. He showed me one day two or three arresting figures which Mary had modelled in buff unglazed terracotta, and asked me whether I thought that these might be of any interest for Doulton. Mary herself later brought along several others, carefully packed in two rather ancient hat boxes. These figures appealed to me very much indeed but they were in such a different *genre* from any Doulton figures that I had seen up to that time, I wondered what the reaction of Jack Noke, the then Art Director at Burslem, would be. An appointment was duly made and one fine day, twenty years ago, I took Mary up to Burslem to meet him. His first reaction was more or less what I had expected it might be. He admired the figures but they were not suitable for reproduction in fine earthenware or bone china, however attractive they might be in a somewhat rugged terracotta. He was, none the less, obviously impressed by Mary's talent and some weeks later asked me to bring her up again. He then arranged for her to spend some time in the Burslem studios and factory to familiarise herself with the particular techniques demanded by the finer ceramic 'bodies' made there. Thus began a long, happy and successful collaboration between Mary Nicoll and Royal Doulton.'

The following tribute by Eric Griffiths is taken from *Insight*, Spring 1974—the house magazine of Royal Doulton Tableware Limited:

> Perhaps some of the craftsmen and women who make and paint the Royal Doulton character figures will recall a small gentle-voiced lady of middle years who, once a year, could be seen being conducted round the factory, and who took more than a usual interest in these figures. They may have wondered at her pleased cry of recognition when she saw *The Judge* or *The Dreamweaver*. But probably not—for that is a common reaction from the thousands of visitors who see at the factory the same figures that grace their homes.
>
> Yet there *was* something special in this particular visitor. For here was an artist greeting the children of her creative talent. Mary Nicoll had last seen these characters, inspired from her imagination, in the form of clay models in her studio. These she would then pack, with loving care, to be sent to the Nile Street factory, two hundred miles away.
>
> For twenty years Mary Nicoll had lived two separate lives. To her family, in their Devon home, she was a loving wife and mother. In her studio she created

another family from lumps of raw clay—dream children from a world full of cheer and gentle humour. A motherly old lady, pouring a saucer of milk for her tabby cat, grows into *The Favourite*; the companionship between a shepherd and his dog gives us *The Master*. These figures express with warm humanity Mary Nicoll's views on life.

She drew inspiration, too, from the small Devon harbour she knew so well, portraying the characters she observed with a kindly but discerning eye—as in *Sea Harvest*, *The Boatman* and *Tall Story*. To thousands of homes *The Lobster Man* brings a salty tang of sea air. . .

Whether an artist's worth is to be judged by the esteem of her fellows or by the appreciation of her public, the name of Mary Nicoll can justly claim to rank high indeed.

Eric J. Griffiths

Under a reorganisation of the Design Centre for the Royal Doulton Group in 1972, design activities were separated into three main divisions, each with its own Art Director, under the overall direction of Jo Ledger as Design Director. Eric J. Griffiths became the head of the Ceramic Sculpture Division.

Born of working-class parents, Eric Griffiths spent his childhood in a North Wales mining village. Most of his relations worked either on small-holdings on the barren mountainside or down the pits that dominated the village landscape with their stark silhouettes of winding machinery. The village's only claims to fame were that its male voice choir regularly won awards in the Welsh Eisteddfods, and that, in proportion to its population, it produced more teachers than any other village in the land. This was hardly surprising when all the mothers there constantly preached the gospel of escape from the mines by way of a scholarship to the local grammar school. But a terrible accident which almost cost Eric his life, followed by a long convalescence of two years, changed his whole course and gave him time to discover his true vocation—that of an artist.

There followed some years at Shrewsbury Art School and Wolverhampton Art College but Griffiths was not the type to take readily to conventional academic teaching; he regards himself as a largely self-taught artist. For a time he earned a living as a cartoonist while training as a portrait painter. He found no great demand for his portraits but his evident talent for modelling found him an opening with a local manufacturer of toys and ornaments. This was the beginning of his career as a sculptor in industry. During the next twenty years he worked for several concerns as chief designer, head of development or design consultant, modelling all manner of subjects from tractors to toy dogs, from life-size figures to merry-go-round horses, from portrait busts to inch-high toy soldiers. He created sculptures in ceramics, plastics and metals, played a leading part in developing several new industrial processes, and obtained patents on two inventions. He has also undertaken independent research into technological processes used in industry in the reproduction of shapes—such as mould-making materials and methods, and the lost-wax casting of metals.

To his new appointment as Head of Sculpture at Royal Doulton, Eric Griffiths thus brought not only his considerable experience as a sculptor but also an essentially practical outlook gained in leading teams of skilled craftsmen to success in the competitive world of commercial achievement.

A designer in industry is limited in what he can do by the skills of the organisation for which he designs. To have at his disposal the skills developed over generations at Royal Doulton has been for him, he says, a marvellous experience, rather like changing over to a Rolls-Royce from some not so outstanding a car.

During the few years he has been at Burslem, Eric Griffiths has already made some notable contributions of a highly distinctive calibre to the Royal Doulton Collection. Among these are *Cavalier*, the *Haute Ensemble* series, and the magnificent *Soldiers of the Revolution* limited edition figures.

Soldiers of the Revolution

This magnificently detailed collection of porcelain military sculptures has been produced by Royal Doulton in close association—at every stage of designing, modelling and painting—with the Colonial Williamsburg Foundation. It has given Griffiths a wonderful opportunity, which he has grasped with great enthusiasm, to make a significantly new statement in the somewhat neglected field of ceramic military figures.

From the days of Napoleon, Nelson and Wellington down to the recent Silver Jubilee of HM Queen Elizabeth II, Doulton artists and craftsmen have created a vast collection of figure jugs, loving cups, figures, busts and other pieces commemorating notable people and significant historical events. It was altogether fitting then that such an outstanding occasion as the Bicentennial Celebration of the United States should call forth something really special.

Six years of effort by Royal Doulton and the Colonial Williamsburg Foundation, and its researchers and consultants, have gone into the development of this Collection which has justly been described as 'a masterpiece of historical accuracy sculptured in porcelain'. Every detail of uniforms and equipment down to the number and kind of buttons, the number of eyelets in the boots, has been scrutinised for accuracy.

Eric Griffiths has himself modelled all thirteen pieces depicting the first American soldiers from the first thirteen States. He models in wax which, although more difficult to work than clay, retains fine detail better through the moulding process. In addition, he has supervised personally every step and procedure required to bring each piece to completion. Only 350 of each of the thirteen Revolutionary Soldiers are being made; the master moulds will then be destroyed. Collectors have been quick to recognise in this unique Collection the artistry, authenticity and integrity of a great endeavour.

In the drawers and cupboards of the Griffiths Studio are numerous new models in various stages of preparation, including some intriguing experimental pieces. In his Department one may see enthusiastic young modellers at work developing their own ideas and following up suggestions made by their Art Director. 'The best preparation for the future', wrote George MacDonald, 'is the present well seen to'. With all the experimentation that is going on in the Royal Doulton Design Centre, with all the new ideas that are in the air, it is evident that the present is being well seen to and that the collector may look forward to some exciting new developments.

Eric Griffiths at work in his studio

Artistry in Action

The making of a Royal Doulton Figure

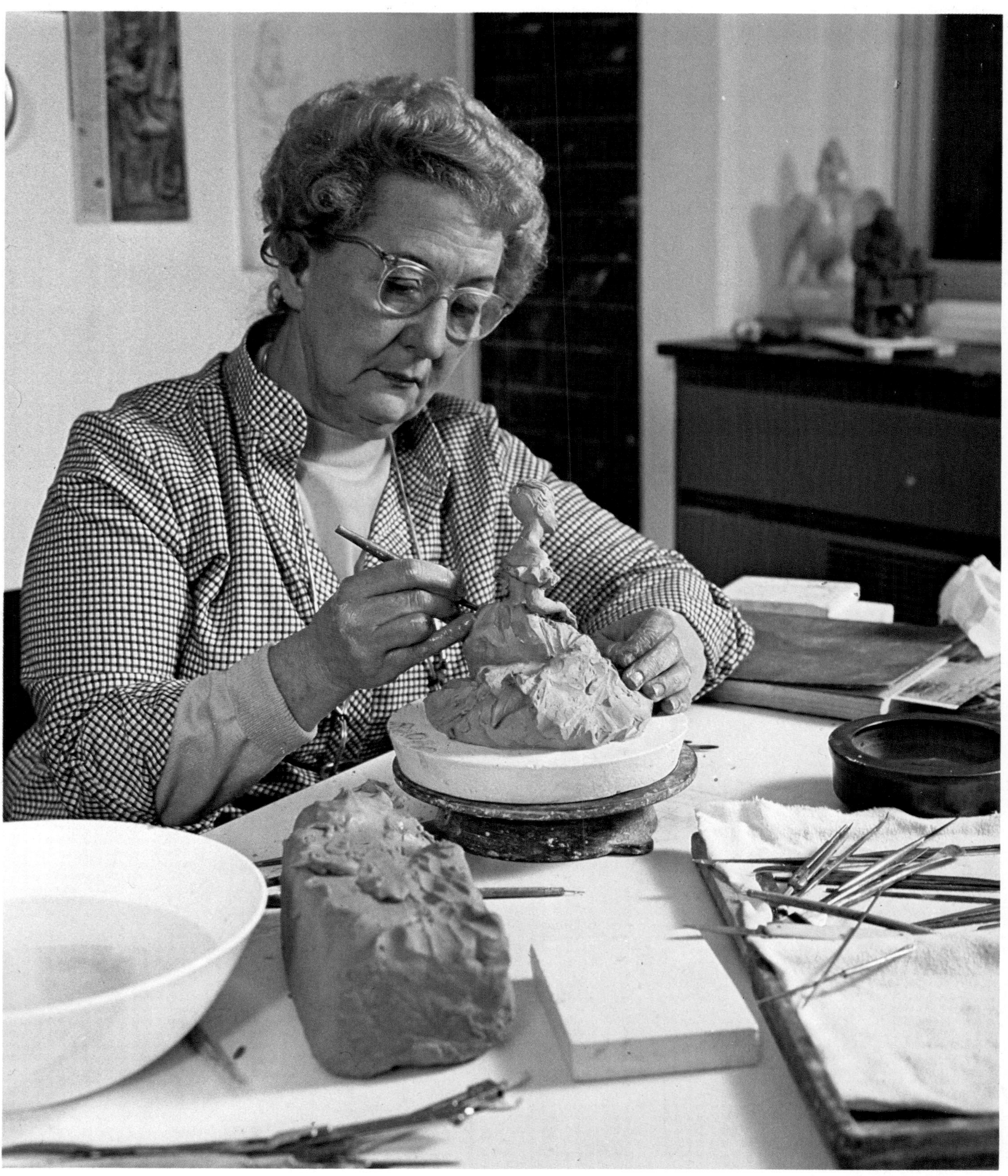

The process of creating a Royal Doulton Figure is a long and painstaking one, involving the blending together of imagination, artistry, craftsmanship and technical expertise. Every figure begins life as an idea in the artist's mind. First the broad outlines and then the finer details are developed as the artist gradually creates the first master model from clay or wax. The shape and detail of this model will determine exactly the appearance of the finished figures and so a sure touch, a trained eye, and an absolute precision are necessary. Here Peggy Davies can be seen at work on the original master model for a new Doulton lady.

Every figure is made from three basic ingredients, namely china clay, Cornish stone and calcined bone ash. These basic materials are rigorously checked to ensure consistency and purity, and are then blended together with water to form a fine 'body' that will be capable of withstanding all the high temperature firings necessary to produce a superfine yet strong translucent ceramic material.

From the master model is made the master mould, or block, from which all the subsequent plaster of paris moulds necessary for the casting of the figure will be made. The mould maker, in converting all the details of the artist's original figure into a reproducible form, will use his skills and experience to determine exactly where to cut the figure, and how many

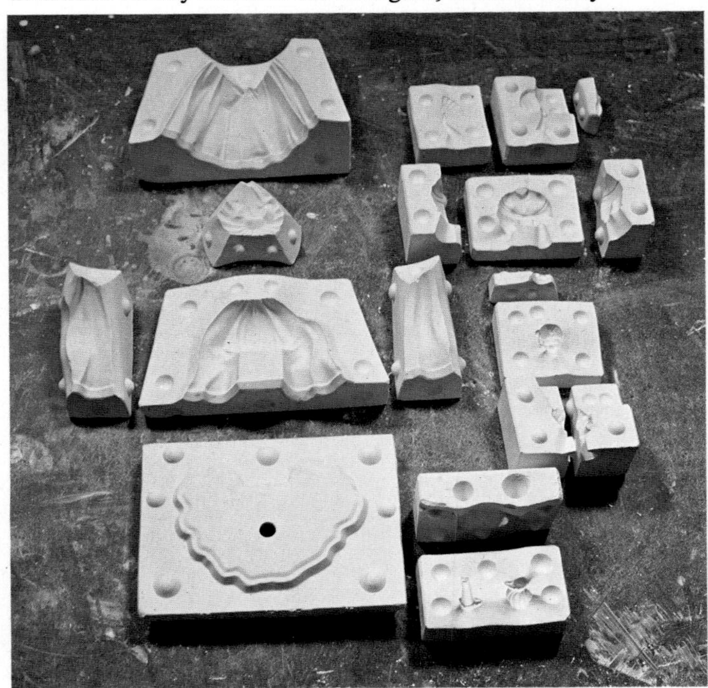

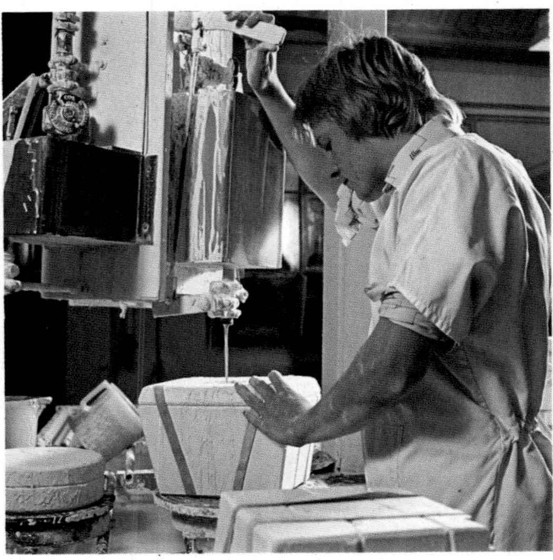

separate moulds will be necessary. These moulds are masterpieces of ingenuity for each part must fit exactly when assembled to recreate precise replicas of the original figure.

The carefully prepared clay slip is then poured, either by hand or mechanically, into all the separate moulds. The porous moulds absorb water from the slip until all the inner surfaces are lined with a coating of 'set clay'. The slip has to remain in the moulds for a precisely controlled time to ensure that the cast pieces have the correct thickness and strength. Superfluous slip is then poured away, the moulds are opened up and the various pieces are removed and trimmed by experienced assemblers who build them up by hand into complete figures.

The assembled figure is now slowly dried to remove surplus water before being subjected to its first passage through the kilns. This first, or biscuit firing, takes place at temperatures up to 1,240° Centigrade, and during this firing a massive shrinkage takes place, reducing the volume of the figure by over 10 per cent.

On leaving the kiln the biscuit china figure has a matt surface. Depending on type, it then either passes directly to the painters for initial decoration, or it is dipped by hand into a vat of liquid glaze, carefully formulated to marry perfectly with the china body. The glazed figures then pass through the kiln again and emerge with a fused coating that gives them a crystal sheen.

From this stage onwards, the white translucent figure is back in the hands of the artists who paint it with specially prepared ceramic pigments, evolved mainly from metal bases, to achieve the delicate harmony of colours and realistic skin tones which are among the distinctive features of these figures.

As different colours withstand different temperatures, some figures may have to be fired several times in the enamel kilns. Tones have to be carefully built up and some especially delicate colour effects need as many as six or seven firings to achieve them. All decoration is applied by hand, for the skill of the painter has always been found to be far superior to the various methods of mechanical decoration that have occasionally been tried in the past. Only by using this skill and experience can each figure be made into an individually finished work of art.

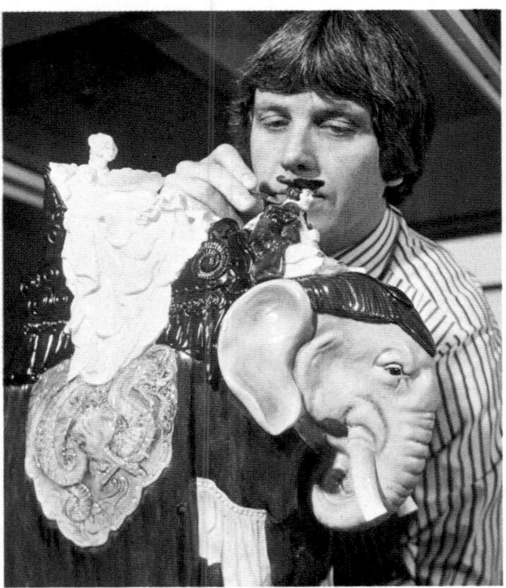

Finally, each figure has to pass the rigorous scrutiny of the inspector who will decide whether or not the collector will ever see it. One tiny crack or flaw, the slightest colour fault, the least blemish in the glaze, and it will be ruthlessly rejected as unfit to carry the Royal Doulton name.

Using the Book

The HN Number Sequence

The initials 'HN' do not, as some writers on the subject have assumed, mean 'House Number'. They are the initials of Harry Nixon, who was in charge of the first small group of artists concerned with painting the figures. A gifted artist himself, he was largely responsible for the choice of colours for the early models and for the training of the younger figure painters. He also suggested many of the subjects for modelling.

The figures were apparently first given HN-numbers in 1913, although a few had been modelled a year or so earlier.

In the following lists almost all the names are those either noted on actual figures or clearly stated in the Doulton records. In a few instances, where it has not so far been possible to trace the name, a description in *italics* has been given, eg *Gypsy Woman with Child.* Wherever possible, the significance or background of a figure's name has been explained. However, many figures, especially those with girls' names, have only a local significance, having been named after Doulton employees, or the family or friends of Doulton employees.

It should not be assumed that all the HN-numbers follow one another in chronological order. This was more or less so up to about 1940 but since then the system of numbering has been changed, partly because batches of consecutive numbers are now allocated to different modellers, to be available for their use over a period, possibly of years. Moreover, many figures which have been given numbers for market survey purposes have not gone into actual production. It sometimes happens, too, that a figure modelled and given a number one year is, for various reasons, first produced several years later.

Although some recent models have HN-numbers in the 2,800s, this does not mean that over 2,800 different ones have been produced. Numbers 100 to 299 and 800 to 1200, for instance were reserved for animal and bird models, and there are many gaps in the 2,000s for the same reason and also, of course, because of the method of allocation mentioned in the preceding paragraph.

Some misleading dates of withdrawal of figures from production have been published in unauthorised lists, based on the assumption that if certain figures appeared, say, in a 1933 catalogue but not in a 1935 one, they had been withdrawn during the intervening period. There is no basis whatever for such an assumption. Up to the 1950s none of the published catalogues gave more than *a small selection* of the figures available at the time of issue. An internal record of current prices in 1938 clearly shows, for example, that 373 different models were then available but of these only 59 were described or illustrated in a current catalogue. Although it probably did not often happen, almost any early figure could be supplied to special order until well into the 1930s; the moulds and painting instructions were all available and occasionally an order would be received for a figure which had not been made for many years.

How to use this book

In the catalogue that follows, figures are listed by number in their HN sequence, starting with HN 1 *Darling*, and continuing to HN 2865 *Tess* (the last number to be issued before this book went to press).

After the HN series there is a similar catalogue of all the M series miniature figures. There is also a small Miscellaneous section, which includes a number of figures not included in either HN or M series.

In the HN and M series catalogues the entries are in numerical order, with each successive new number in bold type. However, where a number of alternative colour versions of the same figure have been produced, often over a period of years, these are not always in numerical order. To simplify identification and comparison, alternative versions have been printed in the catalogue immediately after the first version of any figure to have been produced. Thus, the alternative versions of *A Victorian Lady* can be found immediately after HN 726, the first example of this figure. Alternative versions are not printed in bold type, unless they actually occur in correct numerical order in the HN or M sequence.

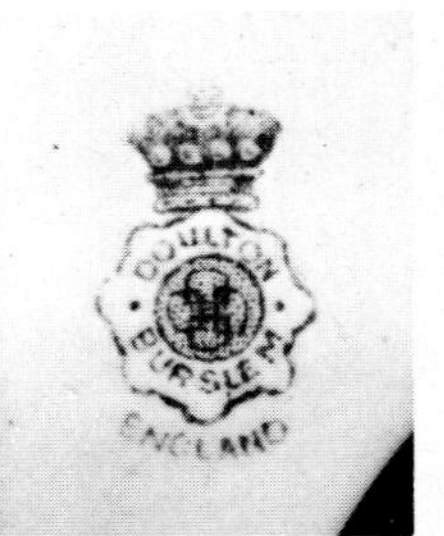

Printed Doulton mark, in use about 1891-1901. This mark is to be found on the early Noke figures, made during the 1890s

Alternative versions are also printed in their correct numerical sequence, with a cross reference to the page in the book where the details can actually be found. Thus, the entry in the sequence for HN 745, an alternative version of *A Victorian Lady*, will be followed by the words, *See page 161*.

To use the book, it is therefore necessary to know either the name or the HN number of the figure in question. To trace the figure by number, simply look up the number in the HN or M sequence. To trace it by name, look it up in the name index, which will give its correct HN or M number.

In the alphabetical name index, the key word is the first word in the name, other than 'A', 'An' or 'The'. *Tony Weller*, for instance, will be found under *Tony*, *An Old King* under *Old*, *Captain MacHeath* under *Captain*, and *Mr Pickwick* under *Mr*. In the titling of some figures the definite and indefinite articles are sometimes interchanged or even omitted.

Many of the earlier figures carry the modeller's name and such inscriptions as *Potted by Doulton and Co* or *Potted by Royal Doulton*. The use of these inscriptions became less frequent in the 1930s and seems to have ceased altogether after 1939. Dates were *impressed* on many figures, giving either the full date when the moulds were made (not necessarily when the figure itself was made) eg 6-10-21 (6th October 1921) or just the month and year, eg 10-21 (October 1921). These impressed dates seem to have been discontinued in the 1930s. A printed numeral may be found on

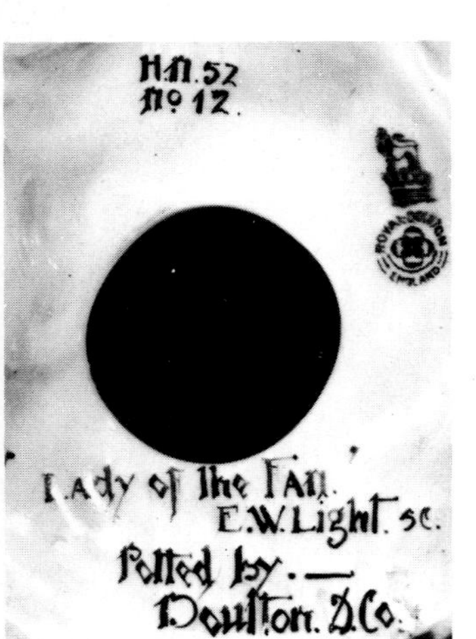

Printed Royal Doulton mark, in use about 1902-1932, with hand-written figure name, HN number, factory mark and artist identification of the style in use 1913—about 1920

Printed Royal Doulton mark, in use about 1902-1932, with hand-written figure name, HN number and factory mark of the style in use from about 1920-1930

Printed Royal Doulton mark, in use 1932—about 1945, with printed figure name and design registration number, and hand-written HN number. The figure 12 to the right of the printed mark indicates the actual year of manufacture as 1939

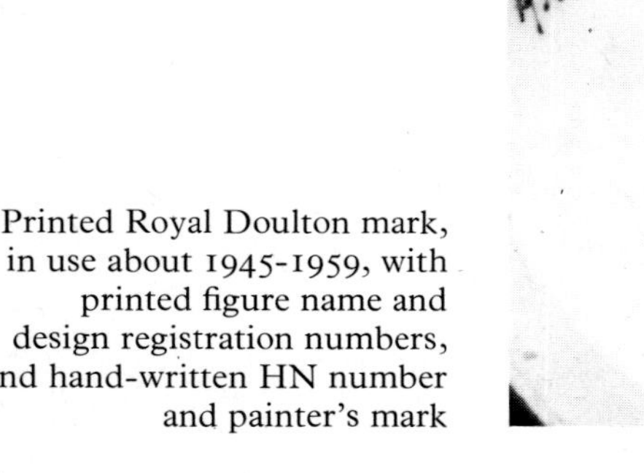

Printed Royal Doulton mark, in use about 1945-1959, with printed figure name and design registration numbers, and hand-written HN number and painter's mark

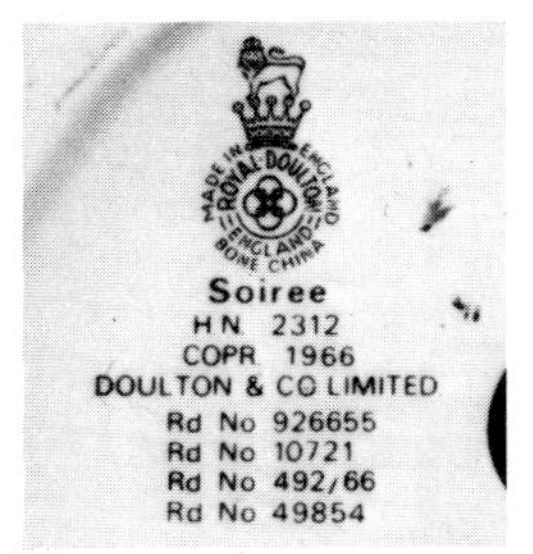

Printed Royal Doulton mark in use 1959-present day, incorporating printed figure name, HN number and design registration numbers

Printed Royal Doulton mark and hand-written figure name and HN number as used on the M series miniature figures, 1932-1949. Because of the limited space available, these marks are often incomplete, as in this example

some figures beside the Royal Doulton backstamp. These numbers run from 1 in 1928 to 27 in 1954 but were often omitted. Where they do appear, a simple rule is to add the number to 1927—so that 14 would indicate the year 1941. The use of the words *Bone China* appears to have been introduced in the trade-mark about 1932. The dates of registration of the design are given on all the more recent productions. Since 1940 there has usually been an interval of at least one year between the date of registration and that of general production. Before then the gap was often only a few months.

The number of the shape, or model, as distinct from the decoration is often found *impressed* on the bases of the figures but may be difficult to decipher. Where there are two or more figures with the same name but entirely different shapes the model number, where known, is indicated in the catalogue entry. Unfortunately the records do not always show the model numbers.

A mystifying feature of some early figures is that although almost all the examples bearing the same name and shape are correctly ascribed to, say, Light or Tittensor, one is occasionally found bearing the name of C. J. Noke. One can only surmise how this could happen. A possible explanation is that Noke, as Art Director, had made some slight modification in shape or colouring, and that whoever was responsible for inscribing the sculptor's name assumed that he had created the original design. It was the custom, too, to register designs in the name of the Art Director who naturally had the last word on questions of design and would at times, for technical production reasons, make changes in the sculptors' original models.

The details that follow have been derived, partly from the examination of more than 700 actual figures in the Royal Doulton Collection and elsewhere, partly from printed and written records in the Royal Doulton archives and partly from editorial and advertising references in old newspapers and magazines. The dates of introduction and withdrawal of each figure have been given where it has been possible to establish these with near certainty; in some cases there may have been some overlap between one year and the next. For figures produced before 1938 and between 1941 and 1949, it has not in many cases been possible to establish the exact date of withdrawal; in these cases, the date of withdrawal is given as *By 1938* or *By 1949*.

Designers have been identified when known. Sizes given refer to height, to the nearest quarter inch. Minor variations in the height of any particular model are likely to occur. Designers and sizes have been omitted when not known.

Illustrations of nearly all models are included, wherever possible in colour. In most cases, actual examples have been illustrated in proportion to each other, in order that the reader may judge their relative size. Where no actual example has come to light, illustrations have been taken from the figure design books, old catalogues or advertisements.

Alternative colour versions have been included when actual examples have been discovered, but if no example has been traced, a brief description of its colour scheme has been given, from details recorded in the figure design books. Minor variations in the painting and colour scheme of any particular model are also likely to be found.

Thus, throughout the catalogue, a figure entry without a colour description has been illustrated, while an entry followed by a description has not been illustrated. For example, the entry for HN 739, a non-illustrated alternative version of *A Victorian Lady*, includes the words, *As HN 726, but mottled red, blue and yellow skirt, yellow scarf.*

The authors and Royal Doulton will be delighted to hear from collectors owning actual examples of figures not illustrated in this book. Similarly, information that will fill any of the gaps, such as heights, designers' names or the correct title of a figure, will be gratefully welcomed.

Index of Figure Names

D

E

F

G

H

I

J

N

O

P

Q

R

S

Miscellaneous Figures

Illustrated below are a number of figures produced at Burslem that for various reasons were not included in the HN series. In some cases, little is known about them as they have not been traced in the figure design books or the mould record book. Those included in this section are by no means comprehensive, and so either the authors of this book or Royal Doulton would be delighted to hear of any other unrecorded figures that come to light.
The illustrations are not reproduced in scale.

The Sketch Girl

Front of the *Sketch* magazine, showing the familiar cover girl

The Sketch Girl (model 444)
Designer: L. Harradine
Size: 7in (17.7cm)
Introduced: About 1923
Withdrawn: By 1938
This figure was apparently made for *The Sketch* magazine, and was based on the cover girl drawing usually associated with the magazine. It was not included in the HN series, but does seem to have been produced in some quantity and sold publicly. It was included among a number of figures illustrated in an article in the issue of *Eve, the Lady's Pictorial* dated May 7th, 1924.
The Sketch, 'a magazine of art and actuality', was first published on February 1st, 1893, and remained in production until June 1959. The items on the girl's tray, a devil, a jockey, a ballerina, a soldier and a cupid, represent the fields of interest covered by the magazine.

Standing Beefeater

Girl with Sunshade

Standing Beefeater (model 505)
Size: $7\frac{3}{4}$in (19.6cm)
Introduced: About 1924
Withdrawn: By 1938
This figure is holding a facsimile of the first edition of the *Illustrated London News*, first published in 1842, and so it is possible that the model was commissioned by the magazine for advertising purposes. The reproduction of the type is actually readable on the model.

Girl with Sunshade
Size: 5in (12.7cm)
Introduced: About 1928
Withdrawn: By 1938
Although there does not appear to be any record of the production of this stylish model, it is similar to many figures of the late 1920s and early 1930s.

Diana and Stag

Monaveen

Diana and Stag
Designer: David Evans
Size: 14½ in (36.8 cm)
Date: 1928
Although not recorded, a number of models of this figure are known to exist, including one in the Victoria & Albert Museum, London. In style, it is close to the figures designed by Richard Garbe, and was obviously produced at about the same time. The figure carries the designer's name, painted and incised, and the incised date.

Monaveen
Designer: W. M. Chance
Date: 1949
This model of the famous steeplechaser, Monaveen, owned jointly by HM the Queen Mother and HRH Princess Elizabeth (as she then was) was specially made to present to Princess Elizabeth after her visit to the Burslem factory. During the design of the model W. M. Chance worked closely with Captain Peter Cazalet, the horse's trainer, and in the end 26 separate moulds and five firings were necessary to complete it. Shortly after the presentation, a letter was received in Burslem from the Princess's Equerry, which said: 'As you already know, this model has given Her Royal Highness very great pleasure. She would be very happy if you would convey her thanks and gratitude to all who had anything to do with this very beautiful model'. The only other examples made were for display in the Royal Doulton showrooms.

Shylock

Shylock
Designer: C. J. Noke
Size: 16 in (40.6 cm)
This ivory-finished model was produced at Burslem in small numbers during the early 1890s. Unlike many of the other Noke models of this early period, it was not subsequently added to the HN series. *Shylock*, HN 79, is a quite different model. The figure carries Noke's incised signature.

HRH Prince Charles

HRH Princess Anne

HM Queen Elizabeth II and HRH the Duke of Edinburgh

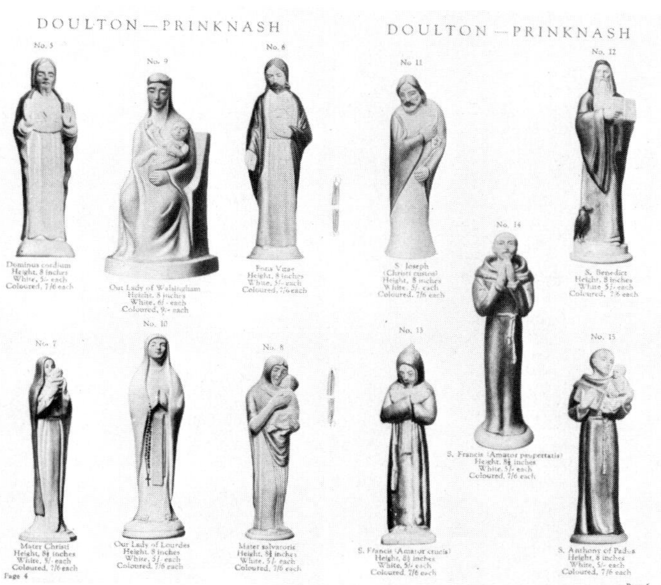

DOULTON—PRINKNASH

No. 5
Dominus cordium
Height, 8 inches
White, 5/- each
Coloured, 7/6 each

No. 9
Our Lady of Walsingham
Height, 8 inches
White, 6/- each
Coloured, 9/- each

No. 6
Fons Vitae
Height, 8 inches
White, 5/- each
Coloured, 7/6 each

No. 7
Mater Christi
Height, $8\frac{1}{2}$ inches
White, 5/- each
Coloured, 7/6 each

No. 10
Our Lady of Lourdes
Height, 8 inches
White, 5/- each
Coloured, 7/6 each

No. 8
Mater salvatoris
Height, $8\frac{1}{2}$ inches
White, 5/- each
Coloured, 7/6 each

Page 4

DOULTON—PRINKNASH

No. 11
S. Joseph
(Christi custos)
Height, 8 inches
White, 5/- each
Coloured, 7/6 each

No. 12
S. Benedict
Height, 8 inches
White, 5/- each
Coloured, 7/6 each

No. 14
S. Francis (Amator paupertatis)
Height, $8\frac{1}{2}$ inches
White, 5/- each
Coloured, 7/6 each

No. 13
S. Francis (Amator crucis)
Height, $8\frac{1}{2}$ inches
White, 5/- each
Coloured, 7/6 each

No. 15
S. Anthony of Padua
Height, 8 inches
White, 5/- each
Coloured, 7/6 each

Page 5

Pages from the Doulton Prinknash catalogue, c 1936

Sir Winston Churchill

Prinknash Figures
Between 1936 and about 1945 seventeen different religious statues, designed and modelled by the Benedictines of Prinknash Priory, Gloucestershire, were reproduced by Royal Doulton. They ranged in height from 6in (15.2cm) to 20in (50.8cm) and were available either white or coloured.

HRH Prince Charles
Designer: J. Bromley
Size: $10\frac{3}{4}$in (27.3cm)
Introduced: 1969, limited edition of 150
Made to commemorate the Investiture of Prince Charles as Prince of Wales at Caernarvon in 1969

HM Queen Elizabeth II and HRH the Duke of Edinburgh
Designer: E. J. Griffiths
Size: Elizabeth $10\frac{1}{2}$in (26.6cm) Philip $11\frac{1}{4}$in (28.5cm)
Introduced: 1972, limited edition of 750
Made to commemorate the Royal Silver Wedding Anniversary in 1972

HRH Princess Anne
Designer: E. J. Griffiths
Size: 11in (27.9cm)
Introduced: 1973, limited edition of 750
Made to commemorate Princess Anne's marriage to Captain Mark Phillips on 14th November, 1973.

Sir Winston Churchill
Designer: E. J. Griffiths
Size: $11\frac{1}{4}$in (28.5cm)
Introduced: 1974, limited edition of 750
Made to commemorate the centenary of Sir Winston's birth in 1974.

APPENDIX *Animal and Bird Models*

Many animal and bird models have been included in the HN list. Although these are outside the scope of this book, the following list has been included as an Appendix to help collectors identify these models. It will also show the importance of animals and bird models in Royal Doulton's figure production today, as in the past.

HN 100 Fox in red frock coat
HN 101 Hare in red coat
HN 102 Hare in white coat
HN 103 Double Penguins
HN 104 Single Penguin
HN 105 Alsatian (sable)
HN 106 Alsatian (white and sable)
HN 107 Hare, crouching
HN 108 Rabbit
HN 109 Cat (white)
HN 110 Titanian bowl, jade, decorated with butterfly in on-glaze colours
HN 111 Cockerel on stand
HN 112 Alsatian (pale grey)
HN 113 Penguin
HN 114 Drake (malachite head)
HN 115 Drake (blue head)
HN 116 Drake (bright colours overall)
HN 117 Two Foxes
HN 118 Monkey
HN 119 Polar Bear, sitting on green cube
HN 120 Cat (white)
HN 121 Polar Bear, sitting
HN 122 Two Turtle Doves
HN 123 Pelican
HN 124 Cockerel, sitting
HN 125 Guinea Fowl
HN 126 Hare, crouching
HN 127 Pekinese
HN 128 Puppy
HN 129 Bulldog, sitting
HN 130 Fox
HN 131 Kingfisher on rock
HN 132 Drake on rock
HN 133 Double Penguins
HN 134 Single Penguin
HN 135 Raven on rock
HN 136 Robin on rock
HN 137 Blue Tit on rock
HN 138 Squirrel
HN 139 Falcon on rock
HN 140 Ape
HN 141 Rhinoceros
HN 142 Hare, crouching
HN 143 Chaffinch on its back
HN 144 Wren
HN 145 Small yellow bird on rock, beak open
HN 145A ditto, beak closed
HN 146 'Old Bill' Bulldog with helmet and haversack
HN 147 Fox on rock
HN 148 Two Drakes
HN 149 Swallow on rock
HN 150 Duck
HN 151 Rabbit
HN 152 Kingfisher on rock
HN 153 As HN 146 but with tammy instead of helmet
HN 154 Character Cat
HN 155 Owl
HN 156 Monkey, listening
HN 157 Cockerel
HN 158 Toucan
HN 159 Toucan
HN 160 Owl and Young
HN 161 Four Thrush Chicks
HN 162 Butterfly (blue and gold)
HN 163 Budgerigar
HN 164 Cockerel, crowing
HN 165 Kingfisher
HN 166 Beagle, sitting
HN 167 Tern Duck
HN 168 Tern Drake
HN 169 Owl
HN 170 Brown Bear, Titanian Ware
HN 171 Four Baby Birds
HN 172 Buffalo
HN 173 'Wise Old Owl' in red cloak and ermine collar
HN 174 No record
HN 175 Great Crested Grebe
HN 176 Bloodhound
HN 177 Powder Bowl with small ape figure seated on lid
HN 178 Cockerel, crouching
HN 179 Two Foxes
HN 180 Cockerel, crouching
HN 181 Elephant
HN 182 Character Monkey, green jacket
HN 183 Character Monkey, blue jacket
HN 184 Cockerel, crowing
HN 185 Parrot on rock
HN 186 Elephant
HN 187 Character Owl (check shawl, ermine collar)
HN 188 Duckling (yellow and brown)
HN 189 Duckling (black and yellow)
HN 190 Duckling (green and blue)
HN 191 Parrot, Baby (blue and purple)
HN 192 Parrot, Baby (red and orange)
HN 193 Tortoise
HN 194 Terrier Puppy
HN 195 Tern Duck
HN 196 Toucan
HN 197 Bird on rock
HN 198 Penguin and Young
HN 199 Budgerigar on stand (green and yellow)
HN 200 Parrot, Baby (decorated in enamel flowers)
HN 201 Tabby Cat and Mouse
HN 202 Black Cat and Mouse
HN 203 Tortoiseshell Cat on pillar
HN 204 Tortoiseshell Cat
HN 205 Two Ducklings (black and white)
HN 206 Two Ducklings (brown and white)
HN 207 Character Mouse
HN 208 Character Toucan
HN 209 Two Rabbits
HN 210 Black and White Cat

HN 211	Black-headed Gull
HN 212	Black-headed Gull
HN 213	Two Pigs
HN 214	Bird and four Chicks (black, pink and brown)
HN 215	Bird and four Chicks (grey, blue and lemon)
HN 216	Bird and four Chicks (green, blue and lemon)
HN 217	Two Rabbits (brown patches on faces)
HN 218	Two Rabbits (brown and black patches on faces)
HN 219	Two Rabbits (brown, black and yellow patches on faces)
HN 220	Bird on rock
HN 221	Cat (black and white)
HN 222	Owl in boat
HN 223	Lion, sitting
HN 224	Kingfisher on rock
HN 225	Tiger, lying
HN 226	Character Mouse (blue coat)
HN 227	Tabby Cat, asleep
HN 228	Character Mouse (yellow coat)
HN 229	Teal Duck
HN 230	Not issued
HN 231	St Bernard
HN 232	Puppy with bone
HN 233	Kitten
HN 234	Two Cats
HN 235	Duckling
HN 236	Two Baby Birds
HN 237	Character Mouse with basketful of Babies
HN 238	Two Pigs
HN 239	Two Ducks
HN 240	Bird on Rock
HN 241	Eagle (brown and gold)
HN 242	Eagle (lighter colouring, white head and neck)
HN 243	Piggy Bowl
HN 244	Cat and Mouse (cat black and white)
HN 245	Cat and Mouse (cat all black)
HN 246	Character Pig
HN 247	Guinea Fowl
HN 248	Drake, large size
HN 249	Mallard Drake, large size
HN 250	Heron
HN 251	Heron

HN 252	Drake, large size
HN 253	Small Ape, sitting
HN 254	Two small Apes
HN 255	Not issued
HN 256–66	Miniature Character Penguins and Puffins
HN 267	Cockerel, sitting
HN 268	Kingfisher
HN 269	Blue Bird on Rock
HN 270	Brown Bear, sitting up
HN 271	Duck
HN 272	Bird with three Chicks
HN 273	Rabbit
HN 274	Green Bird
HN 275	Two Orange Birds
HN 276	Rabbit
HN 277	Wren
HN 278	Two Green Birds
HN 279	Green Bird on Rock
HN 280	Three Chicks
HN 281	Yellow Bird on Rock
HN 282	Blue Bird
HN 283–93	Miniature Character Penguins and Puffins
HN 294	Toucan, large size (black and white, red beak)
HN 295	Toucan, large size (black and green, red beak)
HN 295A	Toucan, large size (black and green, brown beak)
HN 296	Penguin
HN 297	Penguin and Young
HN 298	Duck, sitting
HN 299	Drake, lying
HN 800	Pig, asleep
HN 801	Pig asleep, larger version
HN 802	Two Pigs
HN 803	Rabbit
HN 804	Miniature Pup, playing (pale orange)
HN 805	Miniature Pup, playing (malachite and purple)
HN 806	Miniature Drake (white)
HN 807	Miniature Drake (malachite and purple)
HN 808–12	Miniature Character Pups
HN 813	Miniature White Bird
HN 814–15	Miniature Character Pups
HN 816–17	No record
HN 818	Character Cat 'Lucky' (black and white)

HN 819	Miniature Cat 'Lucky' (white)
HN 820–22	Miniature Kittens
HN 823–25	Miniature Kittens
HN 826	Character Pup
HN 827	Character Cat (tortoiseshell)
HN 828	Character Cat (tabby)
HN 829	Character Cat (black and white)
HN 830	No record
HN 831	Beagle Puppy
HN 832	Pekinese Puppy, sitting
HN 833	Pekinese Puppy, standing
HN 834	Pekinese Puppy on stand (black and brown)
HN 835	Pekinese Puppy on stand (lighter brown)
HN 836	Pekinese Puppy on stand (light coloured)
HN 837	Chow on stand (brown)
HN 838	Chow on stand (lighter brown)
HN 839	Chow on stand (white and grey)
HN 840–45	Character Ducks
HN 846	Toucan
HN 847	Yellow Bird
HN 848	No record
HN 849	Duck and Ladybird
HN 850	Duck, standing on rocks
HN 851	Bird on Tree Stump
HN 852	Penguin, standing on rocks
HN 853	Small Mallard Drake on rocks
HN 854	Budgerigar
HN 855	Small Bird on Tree Stump
HN 856	Penguin on rocks
HN 857	No record
HN 858	Kingfisher on rock
HN 859	Tortoise on rocks
HN 860	Small Bird on Tree Stump
HN 861	Polar Bear
HN 862A	Kingfisher on stand with Primroses
HN 862B	Kingfisher on stand with Kingcups
HN 863–65	Ducks, quacking
HN 866	Fox, sitting
HN 867–74	Small Birds
HN 875	Kingfisher on Tree Stump

HN 876	Tiger on Rock
HN 877	Baby Parrot
HN 878	Cockerel (white)
HN 879	Cockerel (blue and green)
HN 880	Cockerel (brown and orange)
HN 881	Bulldog, sitting
HN 882	Penguin, large size
HN 883	Two Monkeys
HN 884	Cockatoo (blue and orange)
HN 885	Cockatoo (pink, purple and orange)
HN 886	Cockatoo (red, blue and orange)
HN 887	No record
HN 888	Cockatoo (pale blue and yellow)
HN 889	Dog, Dobermann type (black and white)
HN 890	Dog, Dobermann type (brown)
HN 891	Elephant, large size (silver grey)
HN 892–97	Character Pigs (in Clown Costume)
HN 898	Alsatian's Head
HN 899	Alsatian, sitting
HN 900	Fox Terrier (white and brown)
HN 901	Fox Terrier (white and black)
HN 902–3	Character Pigs
HN 904	Terrier Puppy
HN 905	Small Frog
HN 906	Spaniel Puppy (black and white)
HN 907	Spaniel Puppy (brown and white)
HN 908	Spaniel Puppy's Head
HN 909	Fox Terrier, standing
HN 910	Fox Terrier, sitting
HN 911	Tiger, lying
HN 912	Tiger, sitting
HN 913–18	Toucan Heads on round bowl-like Bodies
HN 919	Leopard, sitting
HN 920	Two Foxes (brown)
HN 921	Alsatian, sitting, large size
HN 922	Character Hare
HN 923	Fox Terrier, standing
HN 924	Fox Terrier, sitting, large size
HN 925	Two Foxes (grey and brown)
HN 926	Two Foxes (miniature model)
HN 927	Two Pekinese Dogs
HN 928	Large Toucan Bowl
HN 929	Miniature Terrier Pup, sitting
HN 930	Miniature Alsatian, sitting
HN 931	Miniature Terrier Pup
HN 932	Miniature Scotch Terrier
HN 933	Miniature Scotch Terrier
HN 934	Miniature Scotch Terrier
HN 935	Pip, Squeak and Wilfred Ash-tray
HN 936	Teal, swimming
HN 937	Alsatian on stand
HN 938	Alsatian on stand, sitting
HN 939	Large and small Brown Bears
HN 940	Large and small Brown Bears (light brown)
HN 941	Elephant, large size (black)
HN 942	Terrier
HN 943	Terrier
HN 944	Fox Terrier
HN 945	Fox Terrier
HN 946	Penguin Chick
HN 947	Penguin Chick
HN 948	Bulldog, large size (brown)
HN 949–52	Baby Elephants
HN 953	Terrier Pup (brown and black)
HN 954	Terrier Pup (darker brown and black)
HN 955	Brown Bear, standing
HN 956	Mallard Drake, large size
HN 957	Spaniel (liver and white)
HN 958	Spaniel (black and white)
HN 959	Not used
HN 960	Character Ape with book, eyes open
HN 961	Character Ape with book, eyes closed
HN 962	Terrier's Head
HN 963	Fox, sitting
HN 964	Scotch Terrier, large size (black)
HN 965	Scotch Terrier, large size (brown)
HN 966	Elephant, large size (brown and grey)
HN 967	Tabby Cat
HN 968	Pig, black and white
HN 969	Two Rabbits
HN 970	Dachshund
HN 971	'Lucky' Cat Ash-tray
HN 972	Character Ape in Dunce's cap, reading book
HN 973	Character Duck (orange)
HN 974	Character Duck (lemon yellow)
HN 975	Collie (silver grey)
HN 976	Collie (brown)
HN 977	Duck
HN 978	Fox, lying
HN 979	Hare, lying
HN 980	Scotch Terrier (black)
HN 981	Scotch Terrier (light grey and brown)
HN 982	Sealyham Terrier (black patches on face)
HN 983	Sealyham Terrier (brown patches on face)
HN 984	Hare, lying (white)
HN 985	Hare, lying (grey)
HN 986	Alsatian sitting on lid of Lustre Bowl
HN 987	Bulldog sitting on lid of Lustre Bowl
HN 988	Airedale Terrier (brown)
HN 989	Sealyham Terrier (grey)
HN 990	Tiger, crouching
HN 991	Tiger, crouching (smaller model)
HN 992	Sealyham Terrier (black)
HN 993	Cat asleep on Cushion
HN 994	Fox on Pedestal
HN 995	Pekinese (brown)
HN 996	Airedale Terrier (black, blue and brown)
HN 997	Terrier, seated (black and brown)
HN 998	Penguin and Baby
HN 999	Persian Cat (black and white)
HN 1000	Cocker Spaniel, large size (black)
HN 1001	Cocker Spaniel and Pheasant, large size
HN 1002	Cocker Spaniel (liver and white)
HN 1003	Pekinese (dark colouring)
HN 1004	Blue Tit on Bough with Blossom
HN 1005	Thrush on Bough with Blossom
HN 1006	No record

HN 1007 Ch. 'Crackley Startler' Rough Haired Terrier, large size
HN 1008 Ch. 'Albourne Arthur' Scottish Terrier, large size
HN 1009 Hare and two Leverets
HN 1010 Ch. Biddee of Ifield 'Pekinese', large size
HN 1011 Ch. Biddee of Ifield 'Pekinese', medium size
HN 1012 Ch. Biddee of Ifield 'Pekinese', small size
HN 1013 Ch. 'Crackley Hunter' Fox Terrier, medium size
HN 1014 Ch. 'Crackley Hunter' Fox Terrier, small size
HN 1015 Ch. 'Albourne Arthur' Scottish Terrier, medium size
HN 1016 Ch. 'Albourne Arthur' Scottish Terrier, small size
HN 1017 Scottish Terrier, sitting (black)
HN 1018 Scottish Terrier, sitting (black)
HN 1019 Scottish Terrier, sitting (black)
HN 1020 Ch. 'Lucky Pride of Ware' Cocker Spaniel, medium size
HN 1021 Ch. 'Lucky Pride of Ware' Cocker Spaniel, small size
HN 1022 Ch. 'Cotsfold Topsail' Airedale Terrier, large size
HN 1023 Ch. 'Cotsfold Topsail' Airedale Terrier, medium size
HN 1024 Ch. 'Cotsfold Topsail' Airedale Terrier, small size
HN 1025 Ch. 'Tring Rattler' Foxhound, large size
HN 1026 Ch. 'Tring Rattler' Foxhound, medium size
HN 1027 Ch. 'Tring Rattler' Foxhound, small size
HN 1028 Cocker Spaniel and Pheasant, medium size
HN 1029 Cocker Spaniel and Pheasant, small size
HN 1030 Ch. 'Scotia Stylist' Sealyham, large size
HN 1031 Ch. 'Scotia Stylist' Sealyham, medium size
HN 1032 Ch. 'Scotia Stylist' Sealyham, small size
HN 1033 Ch. 'Charming Eyes' Cairn, large size
HN 1034 Ch. 'Charming Eyes' Cairn, medium size
HN 1035 Ch. 'Charming Eyes' Cairn, small size
HN 1036 Cocker Spaniel, medium size (liver and white)
HN 1037 Cocker Spaniel, small size (liver and white)
HN 1038 Scottish Terrier, begging
HN 1039 Pekinese, sitting, large size
HN 1040 Pekinese, sitting, small size
HN 1041 Sealyham, lying, large size
HN 1042 Bulldog, large size (brindle)
HN 1043 Bulldog, medium size (brindle)
HN 1044 Bulldog, small size (brindle)
HN 1045 Bulldog, large size (brown and white)
HN 1046 Bulldog, medium size (brown and white)
HN 1047 Bulldog, small size (brown and white)
HN 1048 West Highland White Terrier, large size
HN 1049 Ch. 'Maesydd Mustard' English Setter, large size
HN 1050 Ch. 'Maesydd Mustard' English Setter, medium size
HN 1051 Ch. 'Maesydd Mustard' English Setter, small size
HN 1052 Sealyham, lying, medium size
HN 1053 Sealyham, lying, small size
HN 1054 Irish Setter, large size
HN 1055 Irish Setter, medium size
HN 1056 Irish Setter, small size
HN 1057 Ch. 'Ashstead Applause' Collie, large size
HN 1058 Ch. 'Ashstead Applause' Collie, medium size
HN 1059 Ch. 'Ashstead Applause' Collie, small size
HN 1060 Not used
HN 1061 Not used
HN 1062 Cocker Spaniel and Pheasant, small size (black and white)
HN 1063 Cocker Spaniel and Hare, medium size (liver and white)
HN 1064 Cocker Spaniel and Hare, small size (liver and white)
HN 1065 Greyhound, large size (brown)
HN 1066 Greyhound, medium size (brown)
HN 1067 Greyhound, small size (brown)
HN 1068 Smooth-haired Fox Terrier, large size
HN 1069 Smooth-haired Fox Terrier, medium size
HN 1070 Smooth-haired Fox Terrier, small size
HN 1071 Hare, lying
HN 1072 Bulldog, large size (white)
HN 1073 Bulldog, medium size (white)
HN 1074 Bulldog, small size (white)
HN 1075 Greyhound, large size (black and white)
HN 1076 Greyhound, medium size (black and white)
HN 1077 Greyhound, small size (black and white)
HN 1078 Cocker Spaniel, small size (black and white)
HN 1079 Gordon Setter, large size
HN 1080 Gordon Setter, medium size
HN 1081 Gordon Setter, small size
HN 1082 Tiger, stalking, large size
HN 1083 Tiger, stalking, medium size
HN 1084 Tiger, stalking, small size
HN 1085 Lion, large size
HN 1086 Lion, medium size
HN 1087–1093A Ashtrays
HN 1094 Leopard
HN 1095–1095A Ashtrays
HN 1096 Character Fox with stolen Goose (green cloak and hat)
HN 1097–1101 Character Dogs
HN 1102 Character Fox with stolen Goose (red cloak and hat)
HN 1103 Character Dog
HN 1104 Cairn, large size (black)
HN 1105 Cairn, medium size (black)
HN 1106 Cairn, small size (black)
HN 1107 Cairn, large size (black) (earthenware)
HN 1108 Cocker Spaniel, large size (black and white)

HN 1109 Cocker Spaniel, medium size (black and white)

HN 1110 Not used

HN 1111 Ch. 'Goworth Victor' Dalmatian, large size

HN 1112 Lion, large size

HN 1113 Ch. 'Goworth Victor' Dalmatian, medium size

HN 1114 Ch. 'Goworth Victor' Dalmatian, small size

HN 1115 Ch. 'Benign of Picardy' Alsatian, large size

HN 1116 Ch. 'Benign of Picardy' Alsatian, medium size

HN 1117 Ch. 'Benign of Picardy' Alsatian, small size

HN 1118 Tiger on Rock, large size (earthenware)

HN 1119 Lion on Rock, large size (earthenware)

HN 1120 Fighting Elephant, large size (earthenware)

HN 1121 Elephant, large size

HN 1122 Elephant, large size

HN 1123 Elephant, medium size

HN 1124 Elephant, large size

HN 1125 Lion on Alabaster Base

HN 1126 Tiger on Alabaster Base

HN 1127 Ch. 'Shrewd Saint' Dachshund, large size

HN 1128 Ch. 'Shrewd Saint' Dachshund, medium size

HN 1129 Ch. 'Shrewd Saint' Dachshund, small size

HN 1130 Fox, large size

HN 1131 Staffordshire Bull Terrier, large size

HN 1132 Staffordshire Bull Terrier, medium size

HN 1133 Staffordshire Bull Terrier, small size

HN 1134 Cocker Spaniel, large size (liver and white)

HN 1135 Cocker Spaniel, medium size (liver and white)

HN 1136 Cocker Spaniel, small size (liver and white)

HN 1137 Cocker Spaniel and Pheasant, large size (black and white)

HN 1138 Cocker Spaniel and Pheasant, medium size (black and white)

HN 1139 Dachshund, large size

HN 1140 Dachshund, medium size

HN 1141 Dachshund, small size

HN 1142 Ch. 'Bokus Brock' Bull Terrier, large size

HN 1143 Ch. 'Bokus Brock' Bull Terrier, medium size

HN 1144 Ch. 'Bokus Brock' Bull Terrier, small size

HN 1145 to HN 1157 and HN 1160 to HN 1185 are Animal Studies modelled by Raoh Schorr

HN 1145 Moufflon, standing (green matt)

HN 1146 Calf, sleeping (green matt)

HN 1147 Calf, standing (green matt)

HN 1148 Buffalo (green matt)

HN 1149 Donkey, small size (green matt)

HN 1150 Young Doe (green matt)

HN 1151 Swiss Goat (green matt)

HN 1152 Horse (green matt)

HN 1153 Moufflon, lying (green matt)

HN 1154 Jumping Goat (green matt)

HN 1155 Donkey, large size (green matt)

HN 1156 Suspicious Doe (green matt)

HN 1157 Antelope (green matt)

HN 1158–1159 Character Dogs

HN 1160 Moufflon, standing (cream matt)

HN 1161 Calf, sleeping (cream matt)

HN 1162 Calf, standing (cream matt)

HN 1163 Buffalo (cream matt)

HN 1164 Donkey, small size (cream matt)

HN 1165 Young Doe (cream matt)

HN 1166 Swiss Goat (cream matt)

HN 1167 Horse (cream matt)

HN 1168 Moufflon, lying (cream matt)

HN 1169 Jumping Goat (cream matt)

HN 1170 Donkey, large size (cream matt)

HN 1171 Suspicious Doe (cream matt)

HN 1172 Antelope (cream matt)

HN 1173 Calf, sleeping (natural colours)

HN 1174 Calf, standing (natural colours)

HN 1175 Buffalo (natural colours)

HN 1176 Donkey, small size (natural colours)

HN 1177 Young Doe (natural colours)

HN 1178 Swiss Goat (natural colours)

HN 1179 Moufflon, standing (natural colours)

HN 1180 Horse (natural colours)

HN 1181 Moufflon, lying (natural colours)

HN 1182 Jumping Goat (natural colours)

HN 1183 Donkey, large size (natural colours)

HN 1184 Suspicious Doe (natural colours)

HN 1185 Antelope (natural colours)

HN 1186 Cocker Spaniel, large size (golden brown)

HN 1187 Cocker Spaniel, medium size (golden brown)

HN 1188 Cocker Spaniel, small size (golden brown)

HN 1189 King Penguin

HN 1190 Penguin

HN 1191 Mallard

HN 1192 Duck

HN 1193 Tern

HN 1194 Tern

HN 1195 Seagull

HN 1196 Seagull

HN 1197 Gannet

HN 1198 Drake

HN 1199 Penguin

HN 1200 No record

HN 2500 Cerval

HN 2501 Lynx

HN 2502 Deer (green). This number also used for *Queen Elizabeth II*

HN 2503 Deer (white)

HN 2504 Lamb (green)

HN 2505 Lamb (white)

HN 2506 Asiatic Elephant

HN 2507 Zebra

HN 2508–2511 Character Dogs

HN 2512 Ch. 'Chosen Dan of Notts' smooth-haired Terrier, large size

HN 2513 Ch. 'Chosen Dan of Notts' smooth-haired Terrier, medium size

HN 2514 Ch. 'Chosen Dan of Notts' smooth-haired Terrier, small size

HN 2515 Ch. 'Dry Toast' Springer Spaniel, large size
HN 2516 Ch. 'Dry Toast' Springer Spaniel, medium size
HN 2517 Ch. 'Dry Toast' Springer Spaniel, small size
HN 2518 'Pride of the Shires', mare and foal (brown)
HN 2519 'The Gude Grey Mare,' with foal, large size
HN 2520 'The Farmer's Boy' (on dappled Shire)
HN 2521 'The Dapple Grey' (girl on Shire Pony)
HN 2522 'The Chestnut Mare', with foal, large size
HN 2523 'Pride of the Shires', mare and foal (dapple grey)
HN 2524 American Foxhound, large size
HN 2525 American Foxhound, medium size
HN 2526 American Foxhound, small size
HN 2527 Fox (sitting)
HN 2528 'Pride of the Shires' replacing 2518
HN 2529 English Setter and Pheasant
HN 2530 'Merely a Minor', large size (brown)
HN 2531 'Merely a Minor', large size (grey)
HN 2532 'The Gude Grey Mare', with foal, medium size
HN 2533 'The Chestnut Mare', with foal, small size
HN 2534 'Pride of the Shires', mare and foal, small size (brown)
HN 2535 Tiger on Rock
HN 2536 'Pride of the Shires', mare and foal, small size (grey)
HN 2537 'Merely a Minor, medium size (brown)
HN 2538 'Merely a Minor', medium size (grey)
HN 2539 Persian Cat (white)
HN 2540 Kingfisher
HN 2541 Kingfisher
HN 2542 Baltimore Oriole. This number also used for *Boudoir*
HN 2543 Blue Bird. This number also used for *Eliza*
HN 2544 Mallard. This number also used for *A la Mode*
HN 2545 Pheasant. This number also used for *Carmen*
HN 2546 Yellow Throated Warbler. This number also used for *Buddies*
HN 2547 Budgerigars (pair)
HN 2548 Golden Crested Wren
HN 2549 Robin
HN 2550 Chaffinch
HN 2551 Bullfinch
HN 2552 Young Thrushes (pair)
HN 2553 Young Robins (group)
HN 2554 Cardinal Bird. This number also used for *Masque*
HN 2555 Drake Mallard
HN 2556 Mallard
HN 2557 Welsh Corgi, large size
HN 2558 Welsh Corgi, medium size
HN 2559 Welsh Corgi, small size
HN 2560 Great Dane, large size
HN 2561 Great Dane, medium size
HN 2562 Great Dane, small size
HN 2563 'Pride of the Shires' (no foal), large size (brown)
HN 2564 'Pride of the Shires' (no foal), medium size (brown)
HN 2565 'The Chestnut Mare' (no foal), large size
HN 2566 'The Chestnut Mare' (no foal), small size
HN 2567 'Merely a Minor', small size (grey)
HN 2568 'The Gude Grey Mare' (no foal), large size
HN 2569 'The Gude Grey Mare' (no foal), medium size
HN 2570 'The Gude Grey Mare' (no foal), small size
HN 2571 'Merely a Minor', small size (brown)
HN 2572 Drake Mallard, small size
HN 2573 Kingfisher, small size
HN 2574 Seagull, small size
HN 2575 Swan
HN 2576 Pheasant, small size
HN 2577 Peacock
HN 2578 Horse as HN 2520, without Boy (dapple grey)
HN 2579–2584 Character Cats
HN 2585–2590 Character Dogs
HN 2591 Drake Mallard
HN 2592–2594 Hares
HN 2595–2598 Lambs
HN 2599 English Setter and Pheasant
HN 2600 Cocker Spaniel and Pheasant, small size
HN 2601 American Great Dane, large size
HN 2602 American Great Dane, medium size
HN 2603 American Great Dane, small size
HN 2604 Peacock Butterfly
HN 2605 Camberwell Beauty Butterfly
HN 2606 Swallowtail Butterfly
HN 2607 Red Admiral Butterfly
HN 2608 Copper Butterfly
HN 2609 Tortoiseshell Butterfly
HN 2610 Hen Pheasant
HN 2611 Chaffinch
HN 2612 Baltimore Oriole
HN 2613 Golden Crested Wren
HN 2614 Blue Bird
HN 2615 Cardinal Bird
HN 2616 Bullfinch
HN 2617 Robin
HN 2618 Yellow Throated Warbler
HN 2619 Grouse
HN 2620 English Setter, large size (liver and white)
HN 2621 English Setter, medium size (liver and white)
HN 2622 English Setter, small size (liver and white)
HN 2623 Horse as HN 2520, without Boy (brown)
HN 2624 Pointer
HN 2625 Poodle, large size
HN 2626 Poodle, medium size
HN 2627 Poodle, small size
HN 2628 Chow, large size
HN 2629 Chow, medium size
HN 2630 Chow, small size
HN 2631 French Poodle
HN 2632 Cock Pheasant
HN 2633 Penguin, large size
HN 2634 Pheasant, large size
HN 2635 Mallard, large size
HN 2636 Indian Runner Drake
HN 2637 Polar Bear
HN 2638 Leopard on Rock
HN 2639 Tiger on Rock
HN 2640 Fighter Elephant
HN 2641 Lion on Rock

HN 2642 Squirrel
HN 2643 Ch. 'Warlord of Mazelaine' Boxer
HN 2644 Elephant
HN 2645 Dobermann Pinscher
HN 2646 Tiger
HN 2647 Drake
HN 2648–2653 Character Piglets
HN 2654 Character Dog

'Chatcull Range'

HN 2655 Siamese Cat, sitting
HN 2656 Pine Martin
HN 2657 Langur Monkey
HN 2658 White-tailed Deer
HN 2659 Brown Bear
HN 2660 Siamese Cat, standing
HN 2661 Mountain Sheep
HN 2662 Siamese Cat, lying
HN 2663 River Hog
HN 2664 Nyala Antelope
HN 2665 Llama
HN 2666 Badger
HN 2667 Ch. 'Bumblikite of Mansergh' Black Labrador

Jefferson Sculptures

HN 2668–2670
HN 3500–3511
HN 6448 Huntsman Fox

K-Numbers Miniatures

1 Bulldog
2 Bull Pup
3 Sealyham
4 Sealyham
5 Airedale
6 Pekinese
7 Foxhound
8 Terrier
9 Cocker Spaniel
10 Scottish Terrier
11 Cairn
12 Cat
13 Alsatian
14 Bull Terrier
15 Chow Chow
16 Welsh Corgi
17 Dachshund
18 Scottish Terrier
19 St Bernard
20–25 Penguins
26 Mallard
27 Yellow-Throated Warbler
28 Cardinal Bird
29 Baltimore Oriole
30 Blue Bird
31 Bull Finch
32 Budgerigar
33 Golden Crested Wren
34 Magpie
35 Jay
36 Goldfinch
37–39 Hares

Royal Doulton Figures

The HN and M Series

HN 2 Elizabeth Fry

HN 1 & HN 1319 Darling (first version) HN 1985 Darling (second version)

HN 1 Darling (first version, model 89)
Designer: Charles Vyse
Size: 7½ in (19 cm)
Introduced: 1913
Withdrawn: 1928
Perhaps the best known figure in the Doulton series, *Darling* has been in continuous production from the start of the range in 1913 to the present day.
Inspired perhaps by poems by A. A. Milne or Robert Louis Stevenson, the figure was given its name after Queen Mary had picked it out at an early display of Doulton figures, exclaiming 'Isn't he a darling!'
According to the factory records, the first example of HN 1 was produced in April 1913.
Charles Vyse, 1882–1971, was born in the Potteries. Apprenticed to Doulton's in 1896 as a modeller and designer, he quickly showed his skills, winning several gold medals and scholarships and exhibiting his work widely, including at the Royal Academy. He designed three figures for Doulton, including the very successful *Darling*, before establishing his own studio in Chelsea in 1919 where he produced figures and experimented with oriental glazes. Several later Doulton figures, for example *The Balloon Woman*, *The Tulip Woman* and *The Carpet Seller*, seem to have much in common with Vyse's Chelsea models.

HN 1319 Darling (first version, model 89)
Introduced: 1929
Withdrawn: 1959

HN 1341 Darling (first version, model 89)
Introduced: 1930
Withdrawn: By 1938
As HN 1, but green nightshirt

HN 1372 Darling (first version, model 89)
Introduced: 1930
Withdrawn: By 1938
As HN 1, but pink nightshirt

HN2 Elizabeth Fry
Designer: Charles Vyse
Size: 17 in (43 cm)
Introduced: 1913
Withdrawn: By 1938
Elizabeth Fry, 1780–1845, known as 'the Genius of Mercy', achieved an international reputation for her work in prison reform, and for her concern for the poor, infirm and destitute. Coming from a comfortable East Anglian Quaker family, she braved the horrific world of early nineteenth century prisons, and gradually improved the conditions she found through her efforts, which finally resulted in Parliamentary reforms.
The model was based on a statue of Mrs. Fry by A. Drury, R.A., now standing outside the central criminal court in the Old Bailey, London, which in turn was taken from the famous portrait by Gibson.

HN 2A Elizabeth Fry
Introduced: 1913
Withdrawn: By 1938
As HN 2, but blue base

Above
An engraving of the well-known painting of Elizabeth Fry by Gibson
Right
The Old Goat Woman, designed by Phoebe Stabler and made by Royal Worcester in 1931, an identical figure to *Milking Time*

HN 3 Milking Time
Designer: Phoebe Stabler
Introduced: 1913
Withdrawn: By 1938
Phoebe Stabler first produced stoneware figures with her husband Harold at their Hammersmith studio. Some of these were made later at the Poole Pottery, in which Harold Stabler was a partner. Phoebe Stabler exhibited widely as a sculptor, and sold the reproduction rights of some of her models to several companies, including Royal Doulton, Royal Worcester, Poole Pottery and the Ashstead Pottery.
This particular figure was also produced by Royal Worcester in 1931, with the title, *The Old Goat Woman*.

HN 3 Milking Time (illustration from the figure design book)

HN 306 Milking Time
Introduced: 1913
Withdrawn: By 1938
As HN 3, but pale costume with black printed markings

HN 4 Picardy Peasant (female)
Designer: Phoebe Stabler
Size: 9½ in (24 cm)
Introduced: 1913
Withdrawn: By 1938
As HN 351, but white hat and blue skirt
Picardy, an agricultural province in Northern France, became well-known during the 1914–18 war because of the Battles of the Somme. The pre-war features of the area were made famous by songs such as *Roses of Picardy*, a hit of 1916.
Phoebe Stabler modelled this figure, and its male pair, at her London Studio before selling reproduction rights to Doulton in about 1911. Despite the many Doulton versions, Poole Pottery were still producing very similar Picardy Peasant figures as late as 1922.

HN 5 Picardy Peasant (female)
Introduced: 1913
Withdrawn: By 1938
As HN 351, but dove grey costume

HN 17A Picardy Peasant (female)
Introduced: 1913
Withdrawn: By 1938
As HN 351, but green hat and green costume

HN 19 Picardy Peasant (male)
Introduced: 1913
Withdrawn: By 1938
As HN 13, but green costume

HN 13 Picardy Peasant (male)
Designer: Phoebe Stabler
Size: 9½ in (24 cm)
Introduced: 1913
Withdrawn: By 1938

HN 17 Picardy Peasant (male)
Introduced: 1913
Withdrawn: By 1938
As HN 13, but green hat and green trousers

HN 351 & HN 13 Picardy Peasants

HN 351 Picardy Peasant (female)
Introduced: 1919
Withdrawn: By 1938

HN 513 Picardy Peasant (female)
Introduced: 1921
Withdrawn: By 1938
As HN 351, but blue blouse, spotted skirt

HN 6 Dunce
Designer: C. J. Noke
Size: 10½ in (26.6 cm)
Introduced: 1913
Withdrawn: By 1938

HN 310 Dunce
Introduced: 1918
Withdrawn: By 1938
As HN 6, but black and white patterned costume, green base

HN 357 Dunce
Introduced: 1919
Withdrawn: By 1938
As HN 6, but grey costume with black pattern

HN 7 Pedlar Wolf
Designer: C. J. Noke
Introduced: 1913
Withdrawn: By 1938

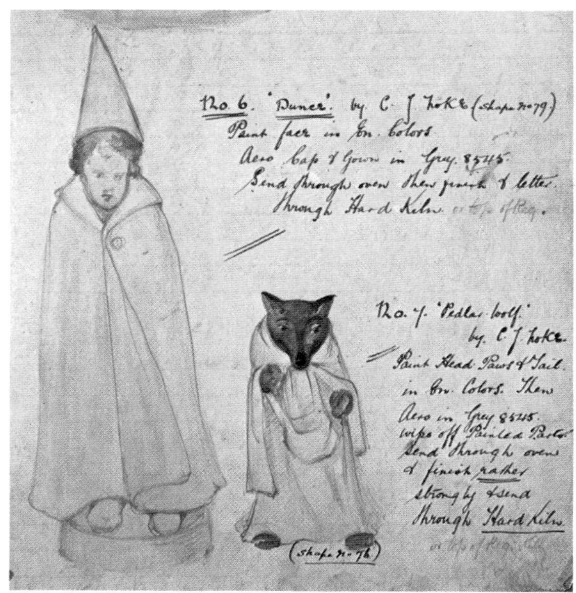

HN 6 Dunce & HN 7 Pedlar Wolf
(illustration from the figure design book)

HN 8 The Crinoline
Designer: George Lambert
Size: 6¼ in (15.8 cm)
Introduced: 1913
Withdrawn: By 1938
This, the first of the many Doulton ladies, takes its name from crinoline, a stiff fabric made from a combination of horsehair and cotton or linen, first produced in 1830. The material gave its name to a stiff, widely distended skirt supported by whalebone or iron hoops that became the height of fashion in the 1860s. By the early years of this century, the crinolined girl had become a popular figure in romantic fiction and in musical comedy. *The Crinoline Girl* was an American musical first performed in 1914. George Washington Lambert, 1873–1930, was born in Russia, the son of an American father and an English mother. His family moved to England in 1878, and he then studied in Australia and Paris before taking up a teaching post in London in 1910. Before returning finally to Australia in 1928 he exhibited widely as a sculptor, including twenty-eight times at the Royal Academy.

HN 9 The Crinoline
Introduced: 1913
Withdrawn: By 1938
As HN 8, but pale green skirt with flower sprays

HN 9A The Crinoline
Introduced: 1913
Withdrawn: By 1938
As HN 9, but no flower sprays on skirt

HN 21 The Crinoline
Introduced: 1913
Withdrawn: By 1938
As HN 8, but yellow skirt with rosebuds

HN 21A The Crinoline
Introduced: 1913
Withdrawn: By 1938
As HN 21, but no rosebuds on skirt

HN 413 The Crinoline
Introduced: 1920
Withdrawn: By 1938

HN 566 The Crinoline
Introduced: 1923
Withdrawn: By 1938
As HN 8, but cream skirt with green spots, green blouse

HN 628 The Crinoline
Introduced: 1924
Withdrawn: By 1938
As HN 8, but yellow and blue chequered bodice

HN 10 Madonna of the Square
Designer: Phoebe Stabler
Size: 7 in (17.7 cm)
Introduced: 1913
Withdrawn: By 1938
As HN 10A, but lilac costume
This, the first of the flower sellers and the most popular of the Phoebe Stabler models, was produced in many different styles. Apart from the early examples made by the Stablers at Hammersmith and those produced at Poole, there were fourteen different Doulton versions, one of which was still in production in 1950. Phoebe Stabler based many of her models on local Chelsea characters, and so this figure could represent a flower girl who worked in Sloane Square. Probably for copyright reasons the version advertised in the Poole Pottery Catalogue of 1922–23 was called *The Lavender Woman*, not to be confused with the Doulton figure of the same name, HN 22, also designed by Stabler.

HN 10A Madonna of the Square
Introduced: 1913
Withdrawn: By 1938

HN 11 Madonna of the Square
Introduced: 1913
Withdrawn: By 1938
As HN 10A, but grey costume

HN 14 Madonna of the Square
Introduced: 1913
Withdrawn: By 1938
HN 14 is a renumbered version of HN 10A

HN 27 Madonna of the Square
Introduced: 1913
Withdrawn: By 1938
As HN 10A, but mottled green and blue costume

HN 326 Madonna of the Square
Introduced: 1918
Withdrawn: By 1938
As HN 10A, but grey-blue costume. This version was made in earthenware

HN 573 Madonna of the Square
Introduced: 1913
Withdrawn: By 1938
As HN 10A, but orange skirt and cubist-style shawl

HN 576 Madonna of the Square
Introduced: 1923
Withdrawn: By 1938
As HN 10A, but green skirt and patterned black shawl

HN 594 Madonna of the Square
Introduced: 1924
Withdrawn: By 1938
As HN 10A, but green skirt and patterned brown shawl

HN 613 Madonna of the Square
Introduced: 1924
Withdrawn: By 1938
As HN 10A, but striped pink skirt and spotted orange shawl

HN 764 Madonna of the Square
Introduced: 1925
Withdrawn: By 1938
As HN 10A, but blue and purple striped shawl, yellow skirt

HN 1968 Madonna of the Square
Introduced: 1941
Withdrawn: By 1949
As HN 10A, but pale green costume

HN 1969 Madonna of the Square
Introduced: 1941
Withdrawn: By 1949
As HN 10A, but lilac costume

HN 2034 Madonna of the Square
Introduced: 1949
Withdrawn: 1951
The late versions of this figure, HN 1968, HN 1969 and HN 2034 appear to be very similar to some of the early models, for example, HN 10 and HN 27

HN 8 & HN 413 The Crinoline

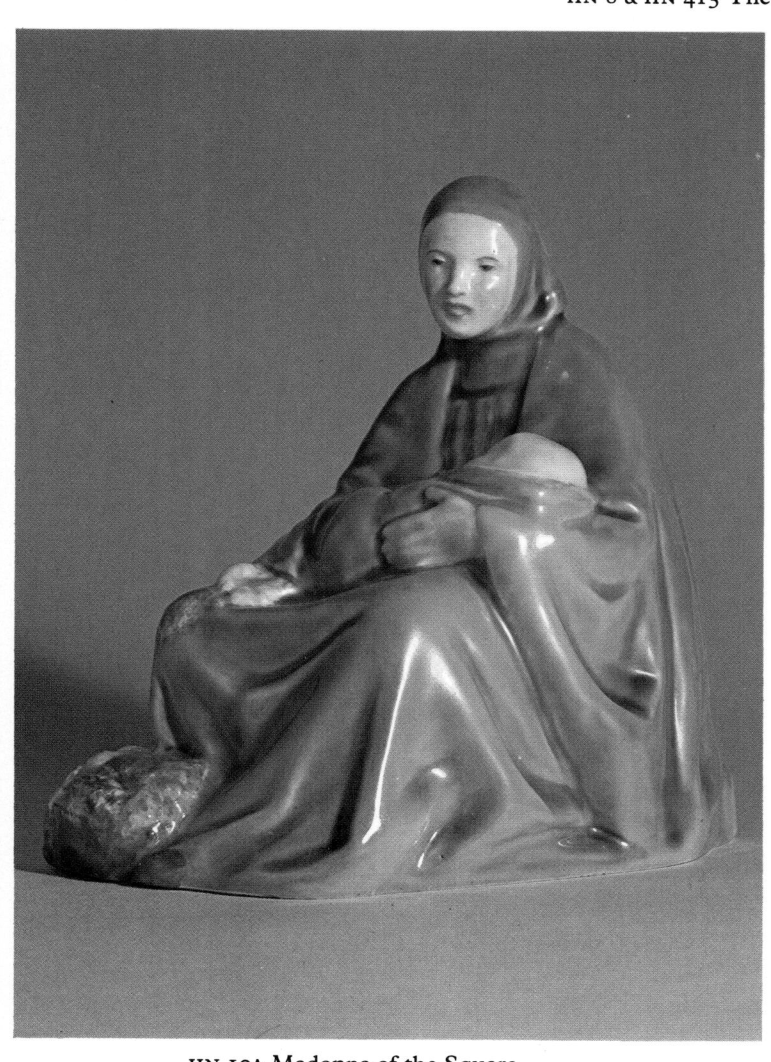

HN 10A Madonna of the Square

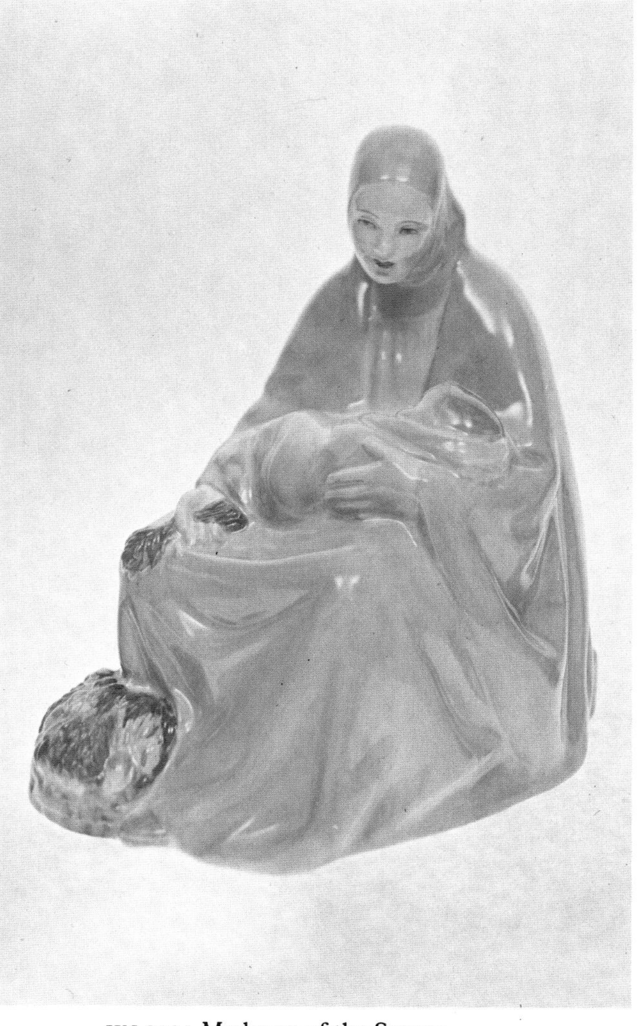

HN 2034 Madonna of the Square

HN 12 Baby
Designer: C. J. Noke
Introduced: 1913
Withdrawn: By 1938
This figure appears to be based on the Phoebe Stabler model entitled *The Bath Towel.*

HN 13 Picardy Peasant (male)
See page 66

HN 14 Madonna of the Square
See page 68

HN 15 The Sleepy Scholar
Designer: William White
Size: 6¾ in (17 cm)
Introduced: 1913
Withdrawn: By 1938
As HN 16, but blue costume
Also known as *The Idle Scholar*, this figure was designed as a pair to HN 26, *The Diligent Scholar*.
In the article published in *The Connoisseur* in 1912, J. F. Blacker wrote: 'I must call your attention to the group of three coloured figures exquisitely modelled by William White, a fellow student of Sir Thomas Brock. These are worthy of all praise, reproducing perfectly the spirit of the old Staffordshire style.'
White, born in Surrey, worked as a sculptor in London and Birmingham, exhibiting regularly in the 1880s and 1890s. Sir Thomas Brock, his teacher, carved the memorial statue of Colin Minton Campbell erected in Stoke in 1887, which stands today outside the headquarters of Royal Doulton Tableware.

HN 16 The Sleepy Scholar
Introduced: 1913
Withdrawn: By 1938

HN 29 The Sleepy Scholar
Introduced: 1913
Withdrawn: By 1938
As HN 16, but brown costume

HN 17 Picardy Peasant (male)
See page 66

HN 18 Pussy
Designer: F. C. Stone
Size: 7½ in (19 cm)
Introduced: 1913
Withdrawn: By 1938
Also known as *The Black Cat*
F. C. Stone was a little-known sculptor and modeller who lived in Chelsea, and exhibited at the Royal Academy in 1911.

HN 325 Pussy
Introduced: 1918
Withdrawn: By 1938
As HN 18, but white dress with black patterning

HN 507 Pussy
Introduced: 1921
Withdrawn: By 1938
As HN 18, but spotted blue dress

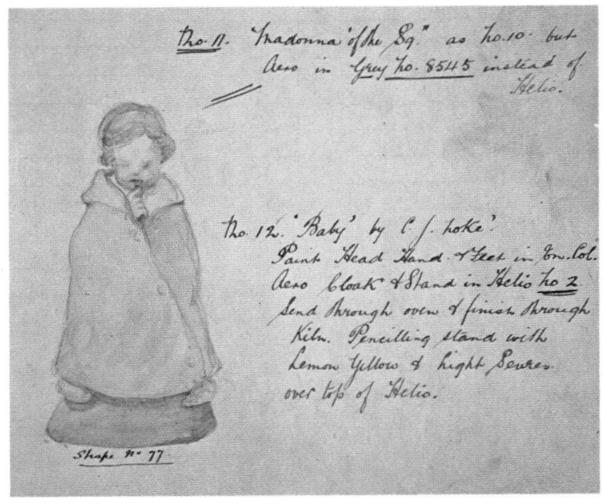

HN 12 Baby (illustration from the figure design book)

HN 16 The Sleepy Scholar

HN 18 Pussy (illustration from the figure design book)

HN 19 Picardy Peasant (male)
See page 66

HN 20 The Coquette
Designer: William White
Size: 9¼ in (23.5 cm)
Introduced: 1913
Withdrawn: By 1938

HN 37 The Coquette
Introduced: 1914
Withdrawn: By 1938
As HN 20, but green costume with flower sprays

HN 21 The Crinoline
See page 68

HN 22 The Lavender Woman
Designer: Phoebe Stabler
Size: 8¼ in (20.9 cm)
Introduced: 1913
Withdrawn: By 1938
This figure is also known as *The Lavender Girl*, or *Any Old Lavender*. It was also produced by Royal Worcester in 1931, with the title, *Flower Girl*.

HN 23 The Lavender Woman
Introduced: 1913
Withdrawn: By 1938
As HN 22, but green dress

HN 20 The Coquette

HN 569 The Lavender Woman

HN 22 The Lavender Woman

HN 24 Sleep

HN 23A The Lavender Woman
Introduced: 1913
Withdrawn: By 1938
As HN 22, but blue and green dress

HN 342 The Lavender Woman
Introduced: 1919
Withdrawn: By 1938
As HN 22, but patterned dress and lilac shawl

HN 569 The Lavender Woman
Introduced: 1924
Withdrawn: By 1938
For illustration, see previous page

HN 744 The Lavender Woman
Introduced: 1925
Withdrawn: By 1938
As HN 22, but blue spotted dress and striped shawl

HN 24 Sleep
Designer: Phoebe Stabler
Size: 8 in (20.3 cm)
Introduced: 1913
Withdrawn: By 1938
For illustration, see previous page

HN 24A Sleep
Introduced: 1913
Withdrawn: By 1938
As HN 24, but dark blue dress

HN 25 Sleep
Introduced: 1913
Withdrawn: By 1938
As HN 24, but blue-green dress

HN 25A Sleep
Introduced: 1913
Withdrawn: By 1938
As HN 25, but fewer firings

HN 424 Sleep
Size: 6 in (15.2 cm)
Introduced: 1921
Withdrawn: By 1938
As HN 24, but smaller figure with blue dress

HN 692 Sleep
Introduced: 1925
Withdrawn: By 1938
As HN 24, but smaller figure with gold dress

HN 710 Sleep
Introduced: 1925
Withdrawn: By 1938
As HN 24, but smaller figure with matt vellum finish

HN 26 The Diligent Scholar
Designer: William White
Size: 7 in (17.7 cm)
Introduced: 1913
Withdrawn: By 1938
Also known as *The Attentive Scholar*.
For illustration, see page 74

HN 27 Madonna of the Square
See page 68

HN 28 Motherhood
Designer: Phoebe Stabler
Introduced: 1913
Withdrawn: By 1938
As HN 30, but grey costume
This should not be confused with the figure of the same title, designed by Leslie Harradine, and produced in stoneware at the Doulton Lambeth factory in about 1911.

HN 30 Motherhood
Introduced: 1913
Withdrawn: By 1938

HN 30 Motherhood (illustration from the figure design book)

HN 303 Motherhood
Introduced: 1918
Withdrawn: By 1938
As HN 30, but white dress with black patterning

HN 29 The Sleepy Scholar
See page 70

HN 30 Motherhood
See above

HN 31 The Return of Persephone
Designer: Charles Vyse
Size: 16 in (40.6 cm)
Introduced: 1913
Withdrawn: By 1938
Persephone, the daughter of Zeus and Demeter, was carried off by Pluto to become Queen of Hades (the Underworld). Demeter grieved for her daughter and so Zeus allowed Persephone to return to earth on condition that she had eaten nothing while in Hades. Unfortunately she had eaten some pomegranate seeds and so had to spend a number of months in the Underworld each year. She was allowed to come to earth each spring, but had to return to Hades in the autumn, a pattern symbolic of the germination of seeds which are dormant in the ground all winter. The figure represents her return to her mother in the spring.

HN 31 The Return of Persephone

HN 26 The Diligent Scholar

HN 32 Child and Crab

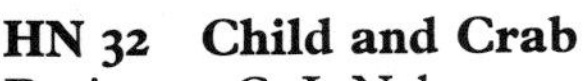

HN 32 Child and Crab
Designer: C. J. Noke
Size: 5¼ in (13.3 cm)
Introduced: 1913
Withdrawn: By 1938
Pale blue robe, green and brown crab
This curious figure appears to be an adaption of HN 12 *Baby*, and is probably based on contemporary children's book illustrations.

HN 33 An Arab
Designer: C. J. Noke
Size: 16½ in (41.9 cm)
Introduced: 1913
Withdrawn: By 1938
As HN 378, but green costume, blue cloak
This figure, still in production today in a different colour version and renamed *The Moor*, is the first of a series that reflect the increasing Western fascination with the Middle East that reached a peak during the 1920s. In England this was perhaps epitomised by Lawrence of Arabia, although the tradition may originally have stemmed from Shakespeare's play *Othello*.

HN 343 An Arab
Introduced: 1919
Withdrawn: By 1938
As HN 378, but striped yellow and purple costume.

HN 378 An Arab
Introduced: 1920
Withdrawn: By 1938

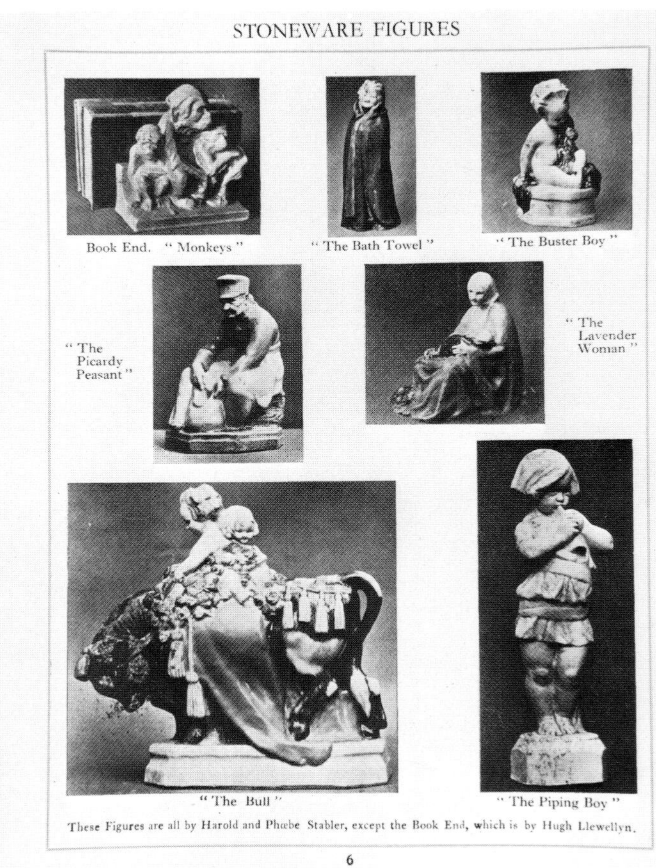

STONEWARE FIGURES

Book End. "Monkeys"

"The Bath Towel"

"The Buster Boy"

"The Picardy Peasant"

"The Lavender Woman"

"The Bull"

"The Piping Boy"

These Figures are all by Harold and Phœbe Stabler, except the Book End, which is by Hugh Llewellyn.

6

Page from the Poole Pottery catalogue of 1922–23, showing stoneware figures by Phoebe Stabler, including versions of *Madonna of the Square* and *Picardy Peasant*

HN 378 An Arab

HN 2082 The Moor

HN 1308 The Moor
Introduced: 1929
Withdrawn: By 1938
As HN 378, but patterned blue costume, mottled red cloak. The name is changed from *An Arab* to *The Moor*, but the model number, 159, remains the same.

HN 1366 The Moor
Introduced: 1930
Withdrawn: By 1949
As HN 378, but red costume with multicoloured patterning

HN 1425 The Moor
Introduced: 1930
Withdrawn: By 1949
As HN 378, but dark multicoloured costume

HN 1657 The Moor
Introduced: 1934
Withdrawn: By 1949
As HN 378, but striped waistband, black cloak

HN 2082 The Moor
Size: $17\frac{1}{2}$ in (44.5 cm)
Introduced: 1952
Still in production. This figure is slightly larger than the earlier versions, but the model number, 159, is unchanged.

HN 34 Moorish Minstrel
Designer: C. J. Noke
Size: $13\frac{1}{2}$ in (34.2 cm)
Introduced: 1913
Withdrawn: By 1938
This figure, and its pair, HN 301, *Moorish Piper Minstrel*, are examples of the small range designed by Noke and made at Burslem in the late nineteenth century, and later re-issued in the HN series. The original figures were usually made in an ivory-coloured body, with restrained decoration, in the style of the Hadley figures produced by Royal Worcester, and were issued in small numbers between about 1895 and 1900

HN 34 Moorish Minstrel & HN 301 Moorish Piper Minstrel

HN 364 Moorish Minstrel
Introduced: 1920
Withdrawn: By 1938
As HN 34, but blue, green and orange striped costume

HN 415 Moorish Minstrel
Introduced: 1920
Withdrawn: By 1938
As HN 34, but green and yellow striped costume

HN 797 Moorish Minstrel
Introduced: 1926
Withdrawn: By 1949
As HN 34, but purple costume

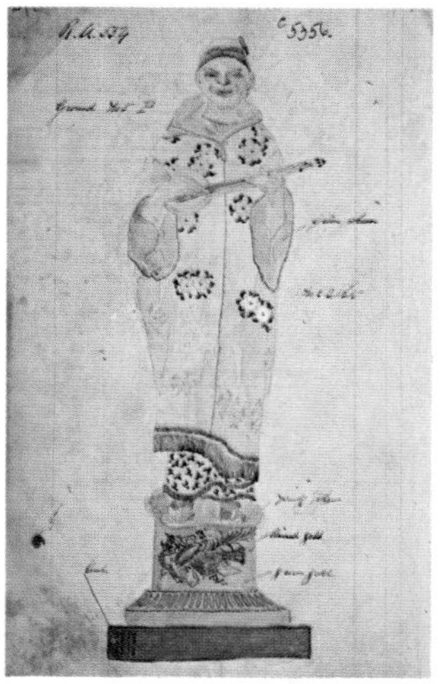

Design for an early version of HN 34, Moorish Minstrel, made during the 1890s

HN 35 Charley's Aunt (first version, model 161)
Designer: Albert Toft
Size: 7 in (17.7 cm)
Introduced: 1914
Withdrawn: By 1938
This figure has the following inscription on the base, '*W. S. Penley as Charley's Aunt*'; the designer's name is incised on the back.
Charley's Aunt, written by Brandon Thomas and first produced in 1892, is a very popular farce still frequently performed. The story revolves around a student who impersonates his visiting aunt from Brazil, a part played to perfection in the first performance by the comedy actor W. S. Penley, who wore a black satin gown over his trousers.

Albert Toft, 1862–1949, studied at Stoke School of Art before going to the Royal College. He exhibited widely as a sculptor, and his figure 'The Bather' was bought for the nation in 1915.

HN 640 Charley's Aunt (first version, model 161)
Introduced: 1924
Withdrawn: By 1938
As HN 35, but green and mauve spotted dress

HN 35 Charley's Aunt (first version) HN 1703 Charley's Aunt (third version)

HN 36 The Sentimental Pierrot
Designer: C. J. Noke
Size: $5\frac{1}{2}$ in (13.9 cm)
Introduced: 1914
Withdrawn: By 1938
As HN 307, but dove grey costume
This, the first of a number of clown or Pierrot figures, reflects the interest in French pantomime that was a feature of the late nineteenth and early twentieth centuries. The stage Pierrot, with his whitened face and loose-fitting clown's costume, usually represents wide-eyed innocence. His traditional female companion, Pierrette, was modelled in many later figures.
The great interest in these characters was also underlined by the many revues and seaside concert parties of the period, in which all the actors wore Pierrot and Pierrette costumes. An opera entitled *Pierrot and Pierrette* was first performed in London in 1909.

HN 307 The Sentimental Pierrot
Introduced: 1918
Withdrawn: By 1938

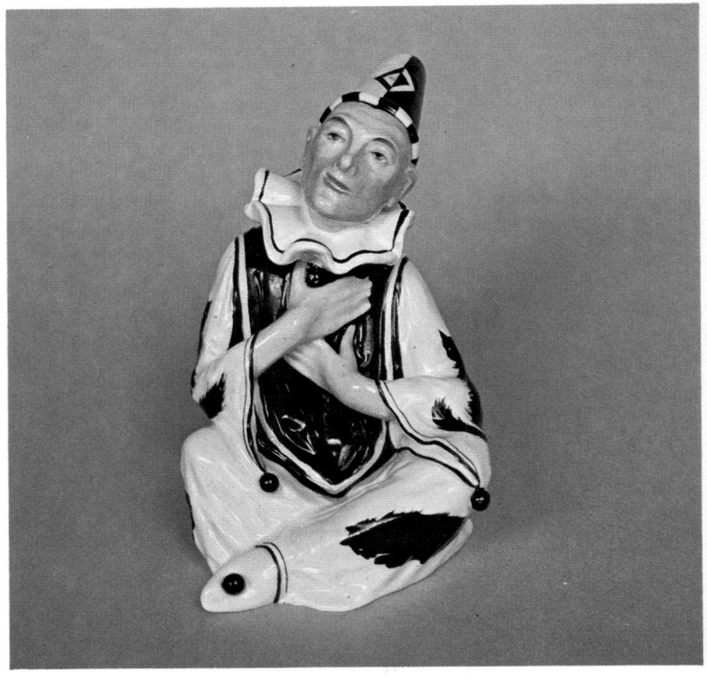

HN 36 The Sentimental Pierrot

HN 37 The Coquette
See page 71

HN 38 The Carpet Vendor (first version, model 163A)
Designer: C. J. Noke
Introduced: 1914
Withdrawn: By 1938
As well as expressing the general interest in the Middle East, this figure may also be based on the carpet seller in George Bernard Shaw's play, *Caesar and Cleopatra*, first produced in 1901. This character, a dashing Sicilian, Apollodorus, brings Caesar a carpet as a present from the Egyptian Queen. When he unrolls it, Cleopatra herself springs out, having concealed herself in its folds when she could not contain her curiosity about Caesar.

HN 38A The Carpet Vendor (first version, model 163A)
Introduced: 1914
Withdrawn: By 1938
As HN 38, but Persian-style carpet

HN 348 The Carpet Vendor (first version, model 163A)
Introduced: 1919
Withdrawn: By 1938
As HN 38, but blue-green costume, chequered base

A contemporary postcard view of a concert party of Pierrots and Pierrettes, dating from about 1910

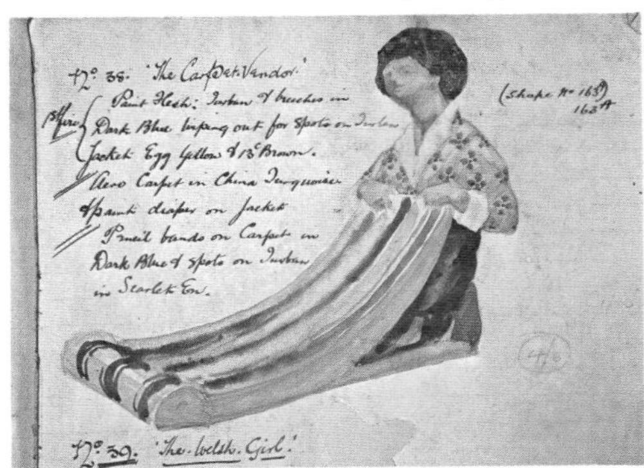

HN 38 The Carpet Vendor (first version, illustration from the figure design book)

HN 39 The Welsh Girl

HN 39 The Welsh Girl
Designer: E. W. Light
Size: 12 in (30.4 cm)
Introduced: 1914
Withdrawn: By 1938
Some, but not all versions of this figure are named on the base, *Myfanwy Jones from Llynwllanwllyn.* Myfanwy is a traditional Welsh name, but it was made particularly popular by the song *Myfanwy*, written by E. E. Davies. Still a favourite with many Welsh choirs, the song was first recorded by Webster Booth in 1913.
It is likely that this figure simply represents a typical Welsh girl, and not a particular character. Similarly, the place, Llynwllanwllyn, although typically Welsh, does not actually exist.
Ernest Light, who lived in Hanley, was well known locally as a sculptor and modeller. He exhibited quite widely, and produced a number of designs for Doulton. He was master-in-charge at Stoke School of Art from 1920 to 1932

HN 92 The Welsh Girl
Introduced: 1918
Withdrawn: By 1938
As HN 39, but blue-grey costume

HN 456 The Welsh Girl
Introduced: 1921
Withdrawn: By 1938
As HN 39, but green blouse and brown skirt

HN 514 The Welsh Girl
Introduced: 1921
Withdrawn: By 1938
As HN 39, but green skirt, spotted apron

HN 516 The Welsh Girl
Introduced: 1921
Withdrawn: By 1938
As HN 39, but chequered lilac dress, black spotted cloak

HN 519 The Welsh Girl
Introduced: 1921
Withdrawn: By 1938
As HN 39, but blue skirt, chequered lilac skirt

HN 520 The Welsh Girl
Introduced: 1921
Withdrawn: By 1938
As HN 39, but spotted lilac dress

HN 660 The Welsh Girl
Introduced: 1924
Withdrawn: By 1938
As HN 39, but spotted white costume, blue-lined cloak

HN 668 The Welsh Girl
Introduced: 1924
Withdrawn: By 1938
As HN 39, but chequered yellow costume, pink-lined cloak

HN 669 The Welsh Girl
Introduced: 1924
Withdrawn: By 1938
As HN 39, but spotted yellow costume, chequered green-lined cloak

HN 701 The Welsh Girl
Introduced: 1925
Withdrawn: By 1938
As HN 39, but striped costume, chequered blue-lined cloak

HN 792 The Welsh Girl
Introduced: 1926
Withdrawn: By 1938
As HN 39, but pink chequered costume, blue cloak

HN 309 & HN 411 A Lady of the Elizabethan Period (second and first versions)

HN 40 A Lady of the Elizabethan Period
(first version, model 165)
Designer: E. W. Light
Size: 9½ in (24.1 cm)
Introduced: 1914
Withdrawn: By 1938
As HN 411, but patterned orange and brown dress
Although there are two versions of this figure, with different model numbers, the variations are very insignificant. Also known as *Elizabethan Lady*.

HN 40A A Lady of the Elizabethan Period
(first version, model 165)
Introduced: 1914
Withdrawn: By 1938
As HN 40, but no pattern on the dress

HN 73 A Lady of the Elizabethan Period
(first version, model 165)
Introduced: 1917
Withdrawn: By 1938
As HN 411, but dark blue-green costume

HN 411 A Lady of the Elizabethan Period
(first version, model 165)
Introduced: 1920
Withdrawn: By 1938

HN 309 A Lady of the Elizabethan Period (second version, model 232)
Designer: E. W. Light
Size: 9½ in (24.1 cm)
Introduced: 1918
Withdrawn: By 1938
There are few differences between this, and the earlier version of the figure, HN 40, the most obvious being the raised pattern on the dress.

HN 41 & HN 331 A Lady of the Georgian Period

HN 41 A Lady of the Georgian Period
Designer: E.W. Light
Size: 10¼ in (26 cm)
Introduced: 1914
Withdrawn: By 1938

HN 331 A Lady of the Georgian Period
Introduced: 1918
Withdrawn: By 1938

HN 444 A Lady of the Georgian Period
Introduced: 1921
Withdrawn: By 1938
As HN 41, but green-blue spotted dress

HN 690 A Lady of the Georgian Period
Introduced: 1925
Withdrawn: By 1938

HN 702 A Lady of the Georgian Period
Introduced: 1925
Withdrawn: By 1938
As HN 41, but striped pink skirt, green overdress

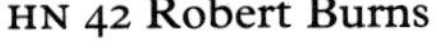

HN 42 Robert Burns

Robert Burns, miniature figure not recorded in the design book

HN 42 Robert Burns
Designer: E. W. Light
Size: 18 in (45.7 cm)
Introduced: 1914
Withdrawn: By 1938
Robert Burns, 1759–1796, is Scotland's national poet. Son of a small Ayrshire farmer, Burns worked first of all as a farm hand. He was educated by his father, developing early an interest in literature, and wrote many of his best poems while still a farmer. The publication of his poems in 1786 encouraged him to leave the land and move to Edinburgh, where he became a social and literary success, aided by his charm, modesty and ease of conversation. He contributed 200 songs to James Johnson's *Scots Musical Museum*, which included *Auld Lang Syne*, *Comin' thro' the Rye* and *The Banks of Doon*.
This figure, with Burns leaning on his plough, continues the tradition established by the anonymous Staffordshire figure modellers of the nineteenth century who frequently depicted Burns as the symbol of Scotland.

HN 43 A Woman of the Time of Henry VI
Designer: E. W. Light
Size: $9\frac{1}{4}$ in (23.4 cm)
Introduced: 1914
Withdrawn: By 1938
This figure was later adapted and re-issued as HN 2012, *Margaret of Anjou*.

HN 43 A Woman of the Time of Henry VI (illustration from the figure design book)

HN 44 A Lilac Shawl
Designer: C. J. Noke
Size: $8\frac{3}{4}$ in (22.2 cm)
Introduced: 1915
Withdrawn: By 1938
This figure was not only issued in a variety of versions, but was also produced with two alternative titles, *In Grandma's Days* and *The Poke Bonnet*. All the versions are the same model, 169, and so there is no obvious reason for the change.

HN 44A A Lilac Shawl
Introduced: 1915
Withdrawn: By 1938
As HN 44, but roses on shawl replaced by printed pattern

HN 339 In Grandma's Days
Introduced: 1919
Withdrawn: By 1938

HN 44 A Lilac Shawl

HN 339 In Grandma's Days

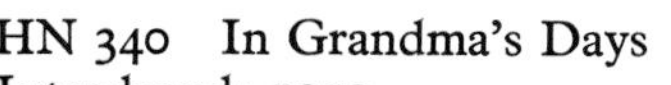

HN 340 In Grandma's Days
Introduced: 1919
Withdrawn: By 1938
As HN 339, but yellow and lilac costume

HN 362 In Grandma's Days
Introduced: 1919
Withdrawn: By 1938
As HN 339, but green, red, yellow striped skirt

HN 388 In Grandma's Days
Introduced: 1920
Withdrawn: By 1938
As HN 339, but patterned blue costume

HN 442 In Grandma's Days
Introduced: 1921
Withdrawn: By 1938
As HN 339, but white spotted skirt, green shawl

HN 612 The Poke Bonnet
Size: 9½ in (24.1 cm)
Introduced: 1924
Withdrawn: By 1938
Although the model is the same, the later versions of this figure appear to be slightly larger

HN 765 The Poke Bonnet
Introduced: 1925
Withdrawn: By 1938
As HN 612, but mottled dark green, blue and purple skirt

HN 612 The Poke Bonnet

HN 45 A Jester (first version)

HN 71 A Jester (first version)

HN 1295 A Jester (first version)

HN 45 A Jester (first version, model 170)
Designer: C. J. Noke
Size: 10 in (25.4 cm)
Introduced: 1915
Withdrawn: By 1938
Designed by Noke and first produced at Burslem in very small quantities during the 1890s, in both parian and tinted bone china, this figure was later re-issued in the HN series. The Jester is a traditional figure of English history and literature, known both as a joker, buffoon and Court fool, and as a teller of tales and romances. Although generally a comedian and entertainer, he is also essentially wise, a characteristic exploited by Shakespeare in plays such as *Twelfth Night* and *King Lear*. There is also an old proverb which runs, 'Jesters do oft prophets make.' The Jester has been a popular subject among ceramic modellers since the eighteenth century, and so Noke was following the tradition established by Chelsea, Derby and Meissen.

HN 71 A Jester (first version, model 170)
Introduced: 1917
Withdrawn: By 1938

HN 320 A Jester (first version, model 170)
Introduced: 1918
Withdrawn: By 1938
As HN 45, but green and black costume

HN 367 A Jester (first version, model 170)
Introduced: 1920
Withdrawn: By 1938

HN 412 A Jester (first version, model 170)
Introduced: 1920
Withdrawn: By 1938
As HN 45, but green and red striped tights

HN 426 A Jester (first version, model 170)
Introduced: 1921
Withdrawn: By 1938
As HN 45, but costume with pink markings, black tights

HN 446 A Jester (first version, model 170)
Introduced: 1921
Withdrawn: By 1938
As HN 45, but green sleeves, blue pedestal

HN 552 A Jester (first version, model 170)
Introduced: 1922
Withdrawn: By 1938
As HN 45, but black and red costume

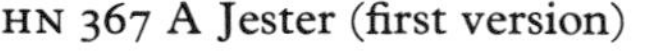

HN 367 A Jester (first version)

HN 2016 A Jester (first version)

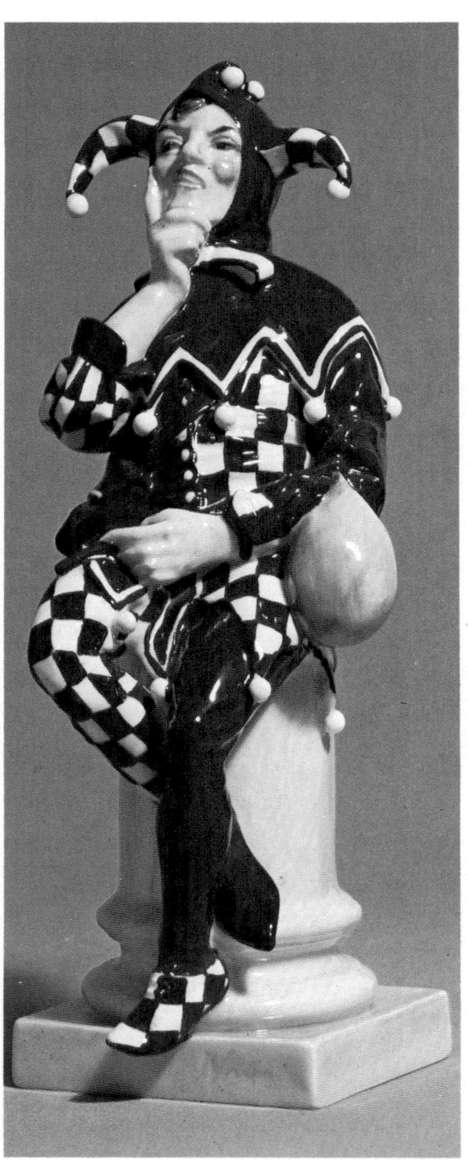

HN 45B A Jester (second version)

HN 616 A Jester (first version, model 170)
Introduced: 1924
Withdrawn: By 1938
As HN 45, but quartered heraldic tunic

HN 627 A Jester (first version, model 170)
Introduced: 1924
Withdrawn: By 1938
As HN 45, but brown chequered costume

HN 1295 A Jester (first version, model 170)
Introduced: 1928
Withdrawn: By 1949

HN 1702 A Jester (first version, model 170)
Introduced: 1935
Withdrawn: By 1949
As HN 2016, but minor variations

HN 2016 A Jester (first version, model 170)
Introduced: 1949
Still in production

HN 45A A Jester (second version, model 171)
Designer: C. J. Noke
Size: 10¼ in (26 cm)
Introduced: 1915
Withdrawn: By 1938
As HN 45B, but green and white chequered costume

HN 45B A Jester (second version, model 171)
Introduced: 1915
Withdrawn: By 1938

HN 55 A Jester (second version, model 171)
Introduced: 1916
Withdrawn: By 1938
As HN 45A, but black and lilac costume

HN 308 A Jester (second version, model 171)
Introduced: 1918
Withdrawn: By 1938
This appears to be a later version of HN 55, for a note below HN 308 in the figure design book says, 'same as 55.'

HN 630 A Jester (second version, model 171)
Introduced: 1924
Withdrawn: By 1938
As HN 45A, but brown striped tights

HN 1333 A Jester (second version, model 171)
Introduced: 1929
Withdrawn: By 1949
As HN 45A, but blue tunic with yellow and black stripes

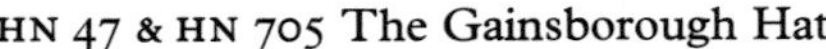

HN 47 & HN 705 The Gainsborough Hat

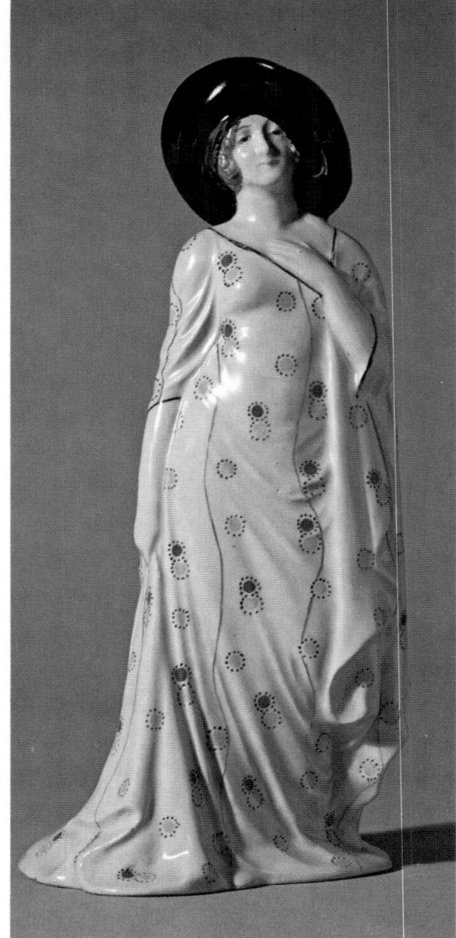

HN 675 The Gainsborough Hat

HN 46 The Gainsborough Hat
Designer: H. Tittensor
Size: 8¾ in (22.2 cm)
Introduced: 1915
Withdrawn: By 1938
As HN 47, but lilac dress
The painter Thomas Gainsborough, 1727–1788, was renowned for his romantic portraits of elegant women, many of whom were painted wearing large hats with nodding plumes. Particularly famous is the portrait of the actress Sarah Siddons, painted in 1784, which shows the actress, then at the height of her career, jauntingly wearing a huge hat over her powdered hair. When the fashion for large hats was revived during the Edwardian period as part of a broad interest in the elegance of the eighteenth century, it became the rule to refer to them as 'Gainsborough' hats.

Detail from a painting by Thomas Gainsborough of the actress, Sarah Siddons

HN 46N The Gainsborough Hat
Introduced: 1915
Withdrawn: By 1938
As HN 46, but black patterned collar added

HN 47 The Gainsborough Hat
Introduced: 1915
Withdrawn: By 1938

HN 329 The Gainsborough Hat
Introduced: 1918
Withdrawn: By 1938
As HN 47, but patterned blue dress

HN 352 The Gainsborough Hat
Introduced: 1919
Withdrawn: By 1938
As HN 47, but yellow dress and purple hat

HN 383 The Gainsborough Hat
Introduced: 1920
Withdrawn: By 1938
As HN 47, but striped dress

HN 453 The Gainsborough Hat
Introduced: 1921
Withdrawn: By 1938
As HN 47, but red, blue and green costume

HN 675 The Gainsborough Hat
Introduced: 1924
Withdrawn: By 1938

HN 705 The Gainsborough Hat
Introduced: 1925
Withdrawn: By 1938

HN 48 Lady of the Fan
Designer: E. W. Light
Size: 9½ in (24.1 cm)
Introduced: 1916
Withdrawn: By 1938
As HN 52, but lilac dress
This figure was designed to be a pair with *Lady with Rose*, and in many cases the two were issued with complementary colour schemes

HN 52 Lady of the Fan
Introduced: 1916
Withdrawn: By 1938

HN 53 Lady of the Fan
Introduced: 1916
Withdrawn: By 1938
As HN 52, but dark blue dress

HN 53A Lady of the Fan
Introduced: 1916
Withdrawn: By 1938
As HN 52, but green-blue dress

HN 335 Lady of the Fan
Introduced: 1919
Withdrawn: By 1938
As HN 52, but blue dress with brown patterning

HN 509 Lady of the Fan
Introduced: 1921
Withdrawn: By 1938
As HN 52, but green lilac and blue spotted dress

HN 52 Lady of the Fan

HN 48A Lady with Rose
Designer: E. W. Light
Size: 9½ in (24.1 cm)
Introduced: 1916
Withdrawn: By 1938

HN 52A Lady with Rose
Introduced: 1916
Withdrawn: By 1938
As HN 48A, but yellow dress

HN 68 Lady with Rose
Introduced: 1916
Withdrawn: By 1938
As HN 48A, but green and yellow dress

HN 304 Lady with Rose
Introduced: 1918
Withdrawn: By 1938
As HN 48A, but grey-lilac dress with brown patterning

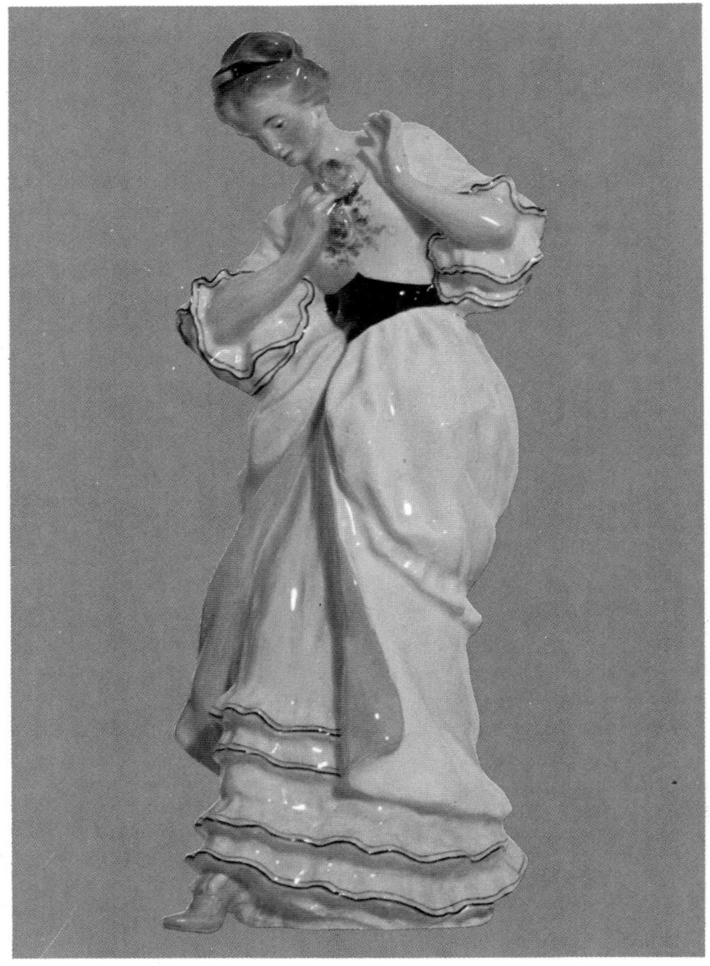

HN 48A Lady with Rose

HN 336 Lady with Rose
Introduced: 1919
Withdrawn: By 1938
As HN 48A, but multicoloured dress with brown patterning

HN 515 Lady with Rose
Introduced: 1921
Withdrawn: By 1938
As HN 48A, but striped lilac and green dress

HN 517 Lady with Rose
Introduced: 1921
Withdrawn: By 1938
As HN 48A, but lilac dress with orange spots

HN 584 Lady with Rose
Introduced: 1923
Withdrawn: By 1938
As HN 48A, but green and pink dress

HN 624 Lady with Rose
Introduced: 1924
Withdrawn: By 1938
As HN 48A, but green-blue skirt, pink and black cuffs

HN 49 Under the Gooseberry Bush
Designer: C. J. Noke
Size: 3½ in (8.8 cm)
Introduced: 1916
Withdrawn: By 1938

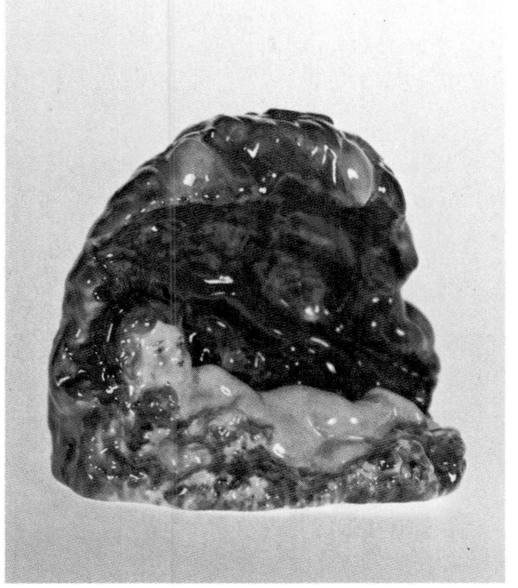

HN 49 Under the Gooseberry Bush

HN 50 A Spook
Designer: H. Tittensor
Size: 7 in (17.7 cm)
Introduced: 1916
Withdrawn: By 1938

HN 51 A Spook
Introduced: 1916
Withdrawn: By 1938

HN 51A A Spook
Introduced: 1916
Withdrawn: By 1938
As HN 51, but black cap

HN 51B A Spook
Introduced: 1916
Withdrawn: By 1938
As HN 51, but blue cloak

HN 58 A Spook
Introduced: 1916
Withdrawn: By 1938
Colour not recorded

HN 512 A Spook
Introduced: 1921
Withdrawn: By 1938
As HN 51, but spotted blue costume

HN 625 A Spook
Introduced: 1924
Withdrawn: By 1938
As HN 51, but yellow robe

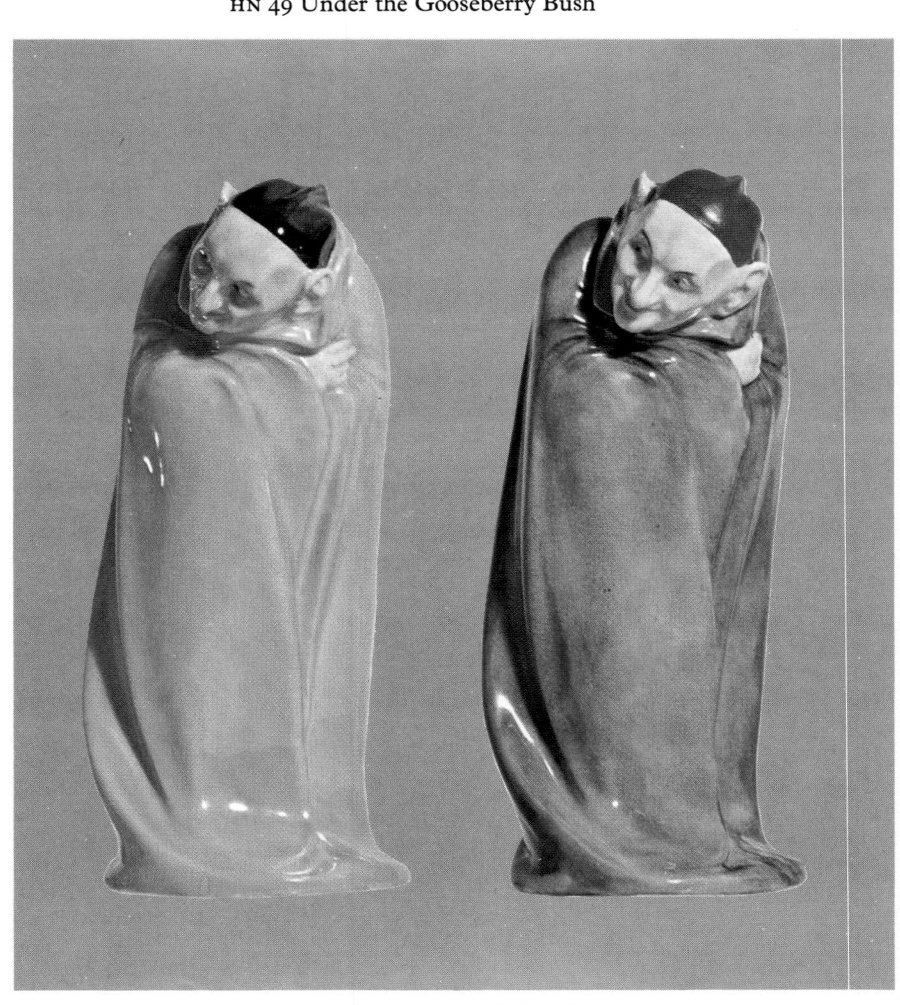

HN 50 & HN 51 A Spook

HN 1218 A Spook
Introduced: 1926
Withdrawn: By 1938
As HN 51, but multicoloured costume, blue cap

HN 52 Lady of the Fan
See page 87

HN 53 Lady of the Fan
See page 87

HN 54 Lady Ermine
Designer: C. J. Noke
Size: $8\frac{1}{2}$ in (21.5 cm)
Introduced: 1916
Withdrawn: By 1938
Also known as *Lady with Ermine Muff* and *The Ermine Muff*

HN 332 Lady Ermine
Introduced: 1918
Withdrawn: By 1938
As HN 54, but red coat and hat, green and yellow patterned skirt

HN 671 Lady Ermine
Introduced: 1924
Withdrawn: By 1938
As HN 54, but green coat, yellow skirt

HN 55 A Jester (second version, model 171)
See page 85

HN 56 The Land of Nod
Designer: H. Tittensor
Size: $9\frac{3}{4}$ in (24.7 cm)
Introduced: 1916
Withdrawn: By 1938
As HN 56A, but ivory nightshirt
The title of the figure comes from a poem by R. L. Stevenson included in *A Child's Garden of Verses*, published in 1885:

'Every night I go abroad
Afar into the Land of Nod
All by myself I go
With none to tell me what to do . . .
All alone beside the streams
And up the mountainside of dreams . . .'

HN 56A The Land of Nod
Introduced: 1916
Withdrawn: By 1938

HN 56B The Land of Nod
Introduced: 1916
Withdrawn: By 1938
As HN 56A, but pale grey nightshirt and red candlestick

HN 54 Lady Ermine

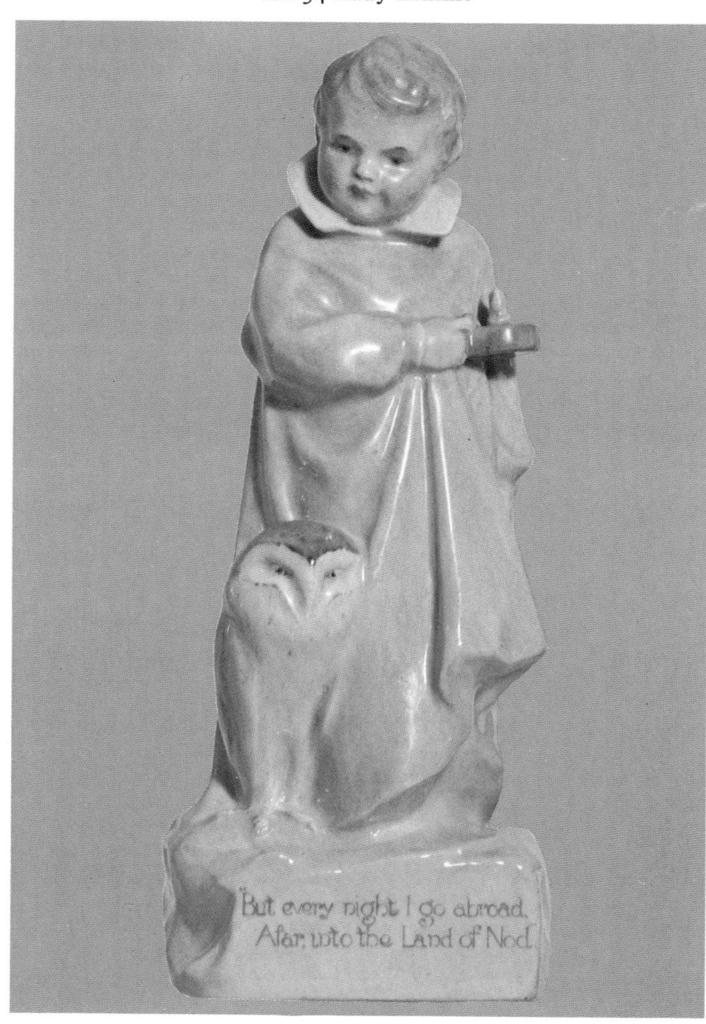

HN 56A The Land of Nod

HN 327 The Curtsey (illustration from the figure design book)

The Curtsey (colour version not recorded in the figure design book)

HN 57 The Curtsey
Designer: E. W. Light
Size: 11 in (27.9 cm)
Introduced: 1916
Withdrawn: By 1938
As HN 327, but orange lustre dress
This figure was designed to be a pair with *The Flounced Skirt*, and in some cases the two were issued with complementary colour schemes

HN 57B The Curtsey
Introduced: 1916
Withdrawn: By 1938
As HN 327, but lilac dress

HN 66A The Curtsey
Introduced: 1916
Withdrawn: By 1938
As HN 327, but lilac dress. It is possible that this is a renumbered version of HN 57B, but neither is illustrated in the figure design book

HN 327 The Curtsey
Introduced: 1918
Withdrawn: By 1938

HN 334 The Curtsey
Introduced: 1918
Withdrawn: By 1938
As HN 327, but lilac dress with brown patterning and green trim

HN 363 The Curtsey
Introduced: 1919
Withdrawn: By 1938
As HN 327, but lilac and peach costume

HN 371 The Curtsey
Introduced: 1920
Withdrawn: By 1938
As HN 327, but yellow dress

HN 518 The Curtsey
Introduced: 1921
Withdrawn: By 1938
As HN 327, but lilac skirt with orange spots

HN 547 The Curtsey
Introduced: 1922
Withdrawn: By 1938
As HN 327, but blue bodice, green and yellow skirt

HN 629 The Curtsey
Introduced: 1924
Withdrawn: By 1938
As HN 327, but green dress with black trimmings

HN 670 The Curtsey
Introduced: 1924
Withdrawn: By 1938
As HN 327, but pink and yellow spotted dress

HN 57A The Flounced Skirt
Designer: E. W. Light
Size: $9\frac{3}{4}$ in (24.7 cm)
Introduced: 1916
Withdrawn: By 1938
As HN 333, but orange lustre dress
Also known as *The Bow*

HN 333 The Flounced Skirt

HN 59 Upon Her Cheeks She Wept HN 64 Shy Anne HN 62A A Child's Grace

HN 66 The Flounced Skirt
Introduced: 1916
Withdrawn: By 1938
As HN 333, but lilac dress

HN 77 The Flounced Skirt
Introduced: 1917
Withdrawn: By 1938
As HN 333, but lemon yellow dress with black trimmings

HN 78 The Flounced Skirt
Introduced: 1917
Withdrawn: By 1938
As HN 333, but flowered yellow lustre dress

HN 333 The Flounced Skirt
Introduced: 1918
Withdrawn: By 1938

HN 58 A Spook
See page 88

HN 59 Upon her Cheeks she Wept
Designer: L. Perugini
Size: 9 in (22.8 cm)
Introduced: 1916
Withdrawn: By 1938
This, and the two other figures designed by Perugini, *Shy Anne* and *A Child's Grace*, are quite distinctive in style, differing noticeably from the series as a whole. According to a note in the figure design book, these were modelled from plasters supplied by Perugini.

The title of this figure is taken from *Upon Electra's Tears*, a poem by Robert Herrick, 1591–1674, part of which is printed on the base:

'Upon her cheeks she wept,
And from these showers
Sprang up a sweet nativity of flowers.'

Laurence Perugini, a sculptor and modeller, was the son of the painter Kate Perugini, a daughter of Charles Dickens. He exhibited regularly, at the Royal Academy and elsewhere, and lived much of his life at Rye, in Sussex, where he was a popular member of the community, giving free painting lessons to local children on Saturday mornings.

HN 511 Upon her Cheeks she Wept
Introduced: 1921
Withdrawn: By 1938
As HN 59, but lilac dress with large spots

HN 522 Upon her Cheeks she Wept
Introduced: 1921
Withdrawn: By 1938
As HN 59, but lilac dress with small spots

HN 60 Shy Anne
Designer: L. Perugini
Size: $7\frac{3}{4}$ in (19.6 cm)
Introduced: 1916
Withdrawn: By 1938
As HN 64, but flowered blue dress

HN 568 Shy Anne

HN 64 Shy Anne
Introduced: 1916
Withdrawn: By 1938
For illustration, see previous page

HN 65 Shy Anne
Introduced: 1916
Withdrawn: By 1938
As HN 64, but spotted blue dress with dark blue hem

HN 568 Shy Anne
Introduced: 1923
Withdrawn: By 1938

HN 61 Katharine
Designer: C. J. Noke
Size: 5¾ in (14.6 cm)
Introduced: 1916
Withdrawn: By 1938

HN 74 Katharine
Introduced: 1917
Withdrawn: By 1938
As HN 61, but pale blue dress with green spots

HN 341 Katharine
Introduced: 1919
Withdrawn: By 1938
As HN 61, but red dress

HN 471 Katharine
Introduced: 1921
Withdrawn: By 1938
As HN 61, but spotted blouse and dress

HN 615 Katharine
Introduced: 1924
Withdrawn: By 1938
As HN 61, but pink skirt with green spots

HN 793 Katharine
Introduced: 1926
Withdrawn: By 1938
As HN 61, but lilac dress with green spots

HN 62 A Child's Grace
Designer: L. Perugini
Size: 6¾ in (17.1 cm)
Introduced: 1916
Withdrawn: By 1938
As HN 62A, but with additional black patterning over the green coat. Printed on the base is the poem, *Another Grace*, by Robert Herrick:

'Here, a little child, I stand,
Heaving up my either hand,
Cold as paddocks tho' they be,
Here I lift them up to Thee,
For a benison to fall
On our meat and on our all
Amen

(In this context, paddocks means frogs)

HN 62A A Child's Grace
Introduced: 1916
Withdrawn: By 1938
For illustration, see previous page

HN 61 Katharine

HN 70 Pretty Lady

HN 763 Pretty Lady

HN 510 A Child's Grace
Introduced: 1921
Withdrawn: By 1938
As HN 62A, but chequered dress, green base

HN 63 The Little Land
Designer: H. Tittensor
Introduced: 1916
Withdrawn: By 1938
As HN 67, but green and yellow costume
The title of this figure is taken from a poem by R. L. Stevenson, *The Little Land:*

'When at home alone I sit,
And am very tired of it,
I have just to shut my eyes
To go sailing through the skies.
To go sailing far away
To the pleasant land of play,
To the fairy land afar
Where the little people are . . .'

HN 67 The Little Land
Introduced: 1916
Withdrawn: By 1938

HN 64 Shy Anne
See page 92

HN 67 The Little Land
(illustration from the figure design book)

HN 65 Shy Anne
See page 92

HN 66 The Flounced Skirt
See page 91

HN 67 The Little Land
See above

HN 68 Lady with Rose
See page 87

HN 69 Pretty Lady
Designer: H. Tittensor
Size: 9½ in (24.1 cm)
Introduced: 1916
Withdrawn: By 1938
As HN 70, but flowered blue dress

HN 70 Pretty Lady
Introduced: 1916
Withdrawn: By 1938

HN 302 Pretty Lady
Introduced: 1918
Withdrawn: By 1938
As HN 70, but patterned lilac dress

HN 72 An Orange Vendor

HN 1966 An Orange Vendor

HN 330 Pretty Lady
Introduced: 1918
Withdrawn: By 1938
As HN 70, but patterned blue dress

HN 361 Pretty Lady
Introduced: 1919
Withdrawn: By 1938
As HN 70, but blue-green dress

HN 384 Pretty Lady
Introduced: 1920
Withdrawn: By 1938
As HN 70, but red dress with striped skirt

HN 565 Pretty Lady
Introduced: 1923
Withdrawn: By 1938
As HN 70, but orange dress, white sleeves with green spots

HN 700 Pretty Lady
Introduced: 1925
Withdrawn: By 1938
As HN 70, but yellow dress with black spots

HN 763 Pretty Lady
Introduced: 1925
Withdrawn: By 1938
For illustration, see previous page

HN 783 Pretty Lady
Introduced: 1926
Withdrawn: By 1938
As HN 70, but blue dress

HN 71 A Jester (first version, model 170)
See page 84

HN 72 An Orange Vendor
Designer: C. J. Noke
Size: $6\frac{1}{4}$ in (15.8 cm)
Introduced: 1917
Withdrawn: By 1938

HN 508 An Orange Vendor
Introduced: 1921
Withdrawn: By 1938
An HN 72, but purple coat

HN 521 An Orange Vendor
Introduced: 1921
Withdrawn: By 1938
As HN 72, but pale blue costume, black collar, purple hood

HN 1966 An Orange Vendor
Introduced: 1941
Withdrawn: 1949
This model was made in earthenware

HN 73 A Lady of the Elizabethan Period
See page 80

HN 74 Katharine
See page 92

HN 75 Blue Beard (first version)
Designer: E. W. Light
Introduced: 1917
Withdrawn: By 1938
Blue Beard, a man of great wealth, but disfigured by a blue beard, had several wives who disappeared mysteriously. He then married Fatima and, shortly after the wedding, went away leaving strict instructions that she should not enter a particular room. Overcome by curiosity she opened the door and found in the room the bodies of all the former wives. Blue Beard then returned and ordered her death, but just in time her brothers saved her and killed Blue Beard.
The figure may have been inspired by the costumes and sets designed by Bakst for Diaghilev's Russian Ballet, which had a great influence on the styles and fashions of the period.
Of particular relevance was the Russian Ballet's version of *Scheherazade*, first performed in Paris on June 24th 1910, which music by Rimsky-Korsakov.
The story, loosely based on *The Thousand and One Arabian Nights*, and set among the passions of the harem, was a rich mixture of Russian and Eastern styles and traditions. It helped to create the fashion for orientalism that swept across Europe, reaching even Stoke-on-Trent. Several other figures owe a direct debt to the styles of the Russian Ballet.
A similar Blue Beard figure was also produced by Royal Worcester, in 1931.

HN 410 Blue Beard (first version)
Introduced: 1920
Withdrawn: By 1938
As HN 75, but blue costume

HN 75 Blue Beard (illustration from the figure design book)

Above
Cover for *Comoedia Illustré*, 1910, showing a costume for *Schéhérazade*, designed by Léon Bakst

Left
HN 76 The Carpet Vendor (second version, illustration from the figure design book)

HN 76 The Carpet Vendor (second version, model 163)
Designer: C. J. Noke
Introduced: 1917
Withdrawn: By 1938

HN 350 The Carpet Vendor (second version, model 163)
Introduced: 1919
Withdrawn: By 1938
As HN 76, but blue costume, green and brown floral carpet

HN 77 The Flounced Skirt
See page 91

HN 78 The Flounced Skirt
See page 91

HN 79 Shylock
Designer: C. J. Noke
Introduced: 1917
Withdrawn: By 1938
As HN 317, but multicoloured cloak, yellow sleeves.
Shylock, the Jewish usurer in the *Merchant of Venice*, is one of the best known of Shakespeare's characters. His claim to his 'pound of flesh' and his subsequent defeat by the skilled advocacy of Portia have made him into one of the great villains of the theatre.
Sir Henry Irving played Shylock opposite Ellen Terry's Portia in his last performance, on 19th July 1903, while another famous interpretation of the part was that of Herbert Beerbohm Tree, at His Majesty's Theatre in 1908.

HN 317 Shylock

HN 359 Fisherwomen (illustration from the figure design book)

HN 81 A Shepherd (first version, illustration from the figure design book)

HN 82 The Afternoon Call (illustration from the figure design book)

HN 83 The Lady Anne (illustration from the figure design book)

HN 317 Shylock
Introduced: 1918
Withdrawn: By 1938
For illustration, see previous page

HN 80 Fisherwomen
Introduced: 1917
Withdrawn: By 1938
As HN 359, but central figure with pink shawl.
This group is also known as *Waiting for the Boats*, or *Looking for the Boats*. It may have been based on the many popular Victorian paintings with this theme.

HN 349 Fisherwomen
Introduced: 1919
Withdrawn: By 1968
As HN 359, but central figure with yellow shawl.

HN 359 Fisherwomen
Introduced: 1919
Withdrawn: By 1938

HN 631 Fisherwomen
Introduced: 1924
Witbdrawn: By 1938
As HN 359, but central figure with green shawl.

HN 81 A Shepherd (first version)
Designer: C. J. Noke
Introduced: 1918
Withdrawn: By 1938
This figure was made in earthenware.

HN 617 A Shepherd (first version)
Introduced: 1924
Withdrawn: By 1938
As HN 81, but china body and purple-blue trousers and coat.

HN 632 A Shepherd (first version)
Introduced: 1924
Withdrawn: By 1938
As HN 81, but china body and white smock, blue trousers.

HN 82 The Afternoon Call
Introduced: 1918
Withdrawn: By 1938
This figure is also known as *Making a Call*

HN 83 The Lady Anne
Designer: E. W. Light
Introduced: 1918
Withdrawn: By 1938
As HN 87, but yellow dress
This figure does not appear to be based on any particular historical character; it may relate to Lady Anne Neville, wife of Richard III, for in Shakespeare's play *Richard III* she is titled 'The Lady Anne'.

HN 87 The Lady Anne
Introduced: 1918
Withdrawn: By 1938

HN 93 The Lady Anne
Introduced: 1918
Withdrawn: By 1938
As HN 87, but blue dress

HN 316 A Mandarin (first version, illustration from the figure design book)

HN 318 A Mandarin (first version). The decoration of this model is more elaborate than the recorded design

HN 84 A Mandarin (first version, model 189)
Designer: C. J. Noke
Size: $10\frac{1}{4}$ in (26 cm)
Introduced: 1918
Withdrawn: By 1938
As HN 318, but mauve shirt, green cloak
Also known as *A Chinese Mandarin* and *The Mikado*, this figure is one of a series of Chinese characters probably based on contemporary musical comedies, the most famous of which was Gilbert & Sullivan's *Mikado*.

HN 316 A Mandarin (first version, model 189)
Introduced: 1918
Withdrawn: By 1938

HN 318 A Mandarin (first version, model 189)
Introduced: 1918
Withdrawn: By 1938

HN 382 A Mandarin (first version, model 189)
Introduced: 1920
Withdrawn: By 1938
As HN 318, but blue and yellow costume

HN 611 A Mandarin (first version, model 189)
Introduced: 1924
Withdrawn: By 1938
As HN 318, but yellow patterned tunic

HN 746 A Mandarin (first version, model 189)
Introduced: 1925
Withdrawn: By 1938
As HN 318, but black costume with green dragons

HN 787 A Mandarin (first version, model 189)
Introduced: 1926
Withdrawn: By 1938
As HN 318, but pink and orange tunic decorated with black flowers

HN 791 A Mandarin (first version, model 189)
Introduced: 1926
Withdrawn: By 1938
As HN 318, but yellow tunic with green and red markings

HN 91 Jack Point

HN 2080 Jack Point

HN 85 Jack Point
Designer: C. J. Noke
Size: 16¼ in (41.2 cm)
Introduced: 1918
Withdrawn: By 1938
As HN 91, but red chequered costume, green base
One of the most famous theatrical jesters, Jack Point is a central character in Gilbert & Sullivan's *Yeoman of the Guard*, first performed in 1888. Jack, the traditionally tragic part played by a comic character, loses his sweetheart by a mixture of folly and misfortune, and laments her loss with the familiar refrain:
'Misery me, lack a day dee!
He sipped no sup, he craved no crumb,
As he sighed for the love of a lady.'

HN 91 Jack Point
Introduced: 1918
Withdrawn: By 1938

HN 99 Jack Point
Introduced: 1918
Withdrawn: By 1938
As HN 91, but heraldic tunic

HN 2080 Jack Point
Size: 17 in (43.1 cm)
Introduced: 1952
Still in production

HN 86 Out for a Walk (illustration from the figure design book)

HN 86 Out for a Walk
Designer: H. Tittensor
Introduced: 1918
Withdrawn: By 1936
As HN 443, but pink and grey dress

HN 443 Out for a Walk
Introduced: 1921
Withdrawn: By 1936

HN 748 Out for a Walk
Introduced: 1925
Withdrawn: By 1936
As HN 443, but dark multicoloured dress, white muff

HN 87 The Lady Anne
See page 96

HN 88 Spooks
Designer: C. J. Noke
Size: 7¼ in (18.4 cm)
Introduced: 1918
Withdrawn: By 1936
Also known as *Double Spook*

HN 89 Spooks
Introduced: 1918
Withdrawn: By 1936
As HN 88, but red caps

HN 372 Spooks
Introduced: 1920
Withdrawn: By 1936
As HN 88, but patterned green costume, brown caps

HN 88 Spooks

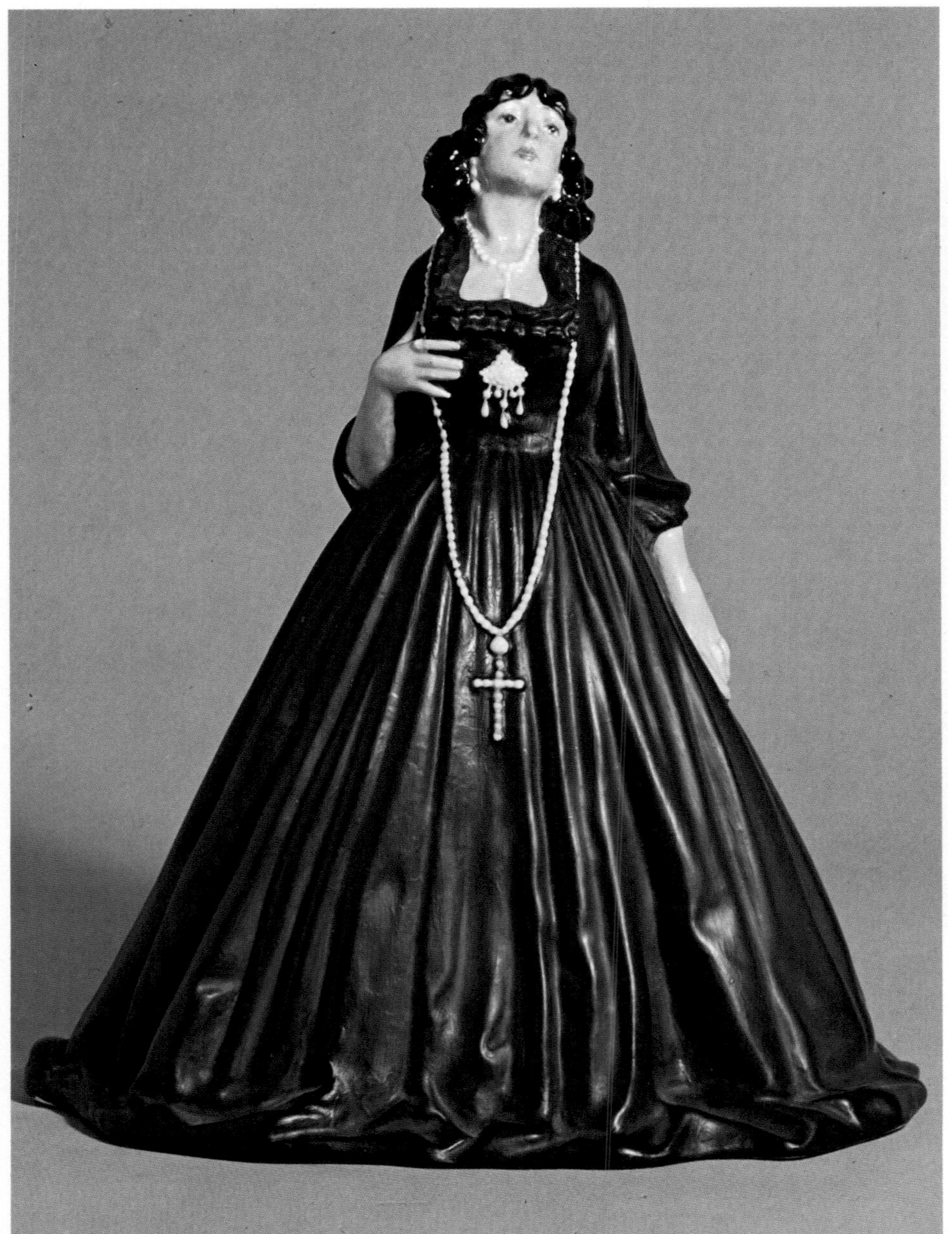

HN 90 Doris Keene as Cavallini (first version)

Model of Doris Keene designed by John Broad at the Doulton Lambeth factory

HN 90 Doris Keene as Cavallini (first version, model 205)
Designer: C. J. Noke
Size: 11 in (27.9 cm)
Introduced: 1918
Withdrawn: By 1936
Doris Keene, a beautiful American actress, came to England in 1915 to star in the play, *Romance*, a story about an opera singer in love with a young clergyman. The play was a great success, running to 1049 performances. Doris Keene became very popular, and featured in a great variety of glamour, or pin-up, postcards, sometimes in rather 'risqué' poses having stripped off the famous crinoline.
This figure should not be confused with the porcelain model of Doris Keene designed for production at the Doulton Lambeth factory by John Broad in about 1919.

HN 467 Doris Keene as Cavallini (first version, model 205)
Introduced: 1921
Withdrawn: By 1936
As HN 90, but gold jewellery

HN 91 Jack Point
See page 99

HN 92 The Welsh Girl
See page 79

HN 93 The Lady Anne
See page 96

HN 94 The Young Knight
Size: $9\frac{1}{2}$ in (24.1 cm)
Introduced: 1918
Withdrawn: By 1936

HN 94 The Young Knight (illustration from the shape record book)

HN 96 Doris Keene as Cavallini (second version)

HN 95 Europa and the Bull

HN 95 Europa and the Bull
Designer: H. Tittensor
Size: 9¾ in (24.7 cm)
Introduced: 1918
Withdrawn: By 1938
Naturalistically painted
A similar figure, modelled by Phoebe Stabler, is illustrated in the Poole Pottery catalogue of 1922–23

HN 96 Doris Keene as Cavallini (second version, model 220)
Designer: C. J. Noke
Size: 10½ in (26.6 cm)
Introduced: 1918
Withdrawn: By 1938
Also known as *Romance*

HN 345 Doris Keene as Cavallini (second version, model 220)
Introduced: 1919
Withdrawn: 1949
As HN 96, but dark fur collar, striped muff

HN 97 The Mermaid

HN 97 The Mermaid
Designer: H. Tittensor
Size: 7 in (17.7 cm)
Introduced: 1918
Withdrawn: By 1936
The mermaid, half woman, half fish, is a well-established creature of popular folk lore. This figure may be based on Hans Andersen's story, *The Little Mermaid*. Versions exist with both fair and brown hair.

HN 300 The Mermaid
Introduced: 1918
Withdrawn: By 1936
As HN 97, but red berries in her hair, darker base

HN 98 Guy Fawkes
Designer: C. J. Noke
Size: $10\frac{1}{2}$ in (26.6 cm)
Introduced: 1918
Withdrawn: By 1949
Guy Fawkes was one of the conspirators involved in the Catholic plot to blow up the Houses of Parliament on November 5, 1605 while the King, the Lords and the Commons were assembled. Fawkes was chosen to carry out the plot, devised by Robert Catesby, but he was discovered in the vaults while placing the charges. All the conspirators were subsequently arrested and executed. The event is commemorated on November 5 every year, with firework displays and bonfires, on which effigies of Guy Fawkes are burnt

HN 347 Guy Fawkes
Introduced: 1919
Withdrawn: By 1938
As HN 98, but brown cloak

HN 445 Guy Fawkes
Introduced: 1921
Withdrawn: By 1938
As HN 98, but green cloak

HN 99 Jack Point
See page 99

HN 100–HN 299 Animal and bird models
For further details see Appendix

HN 300 The Mermaid
See above

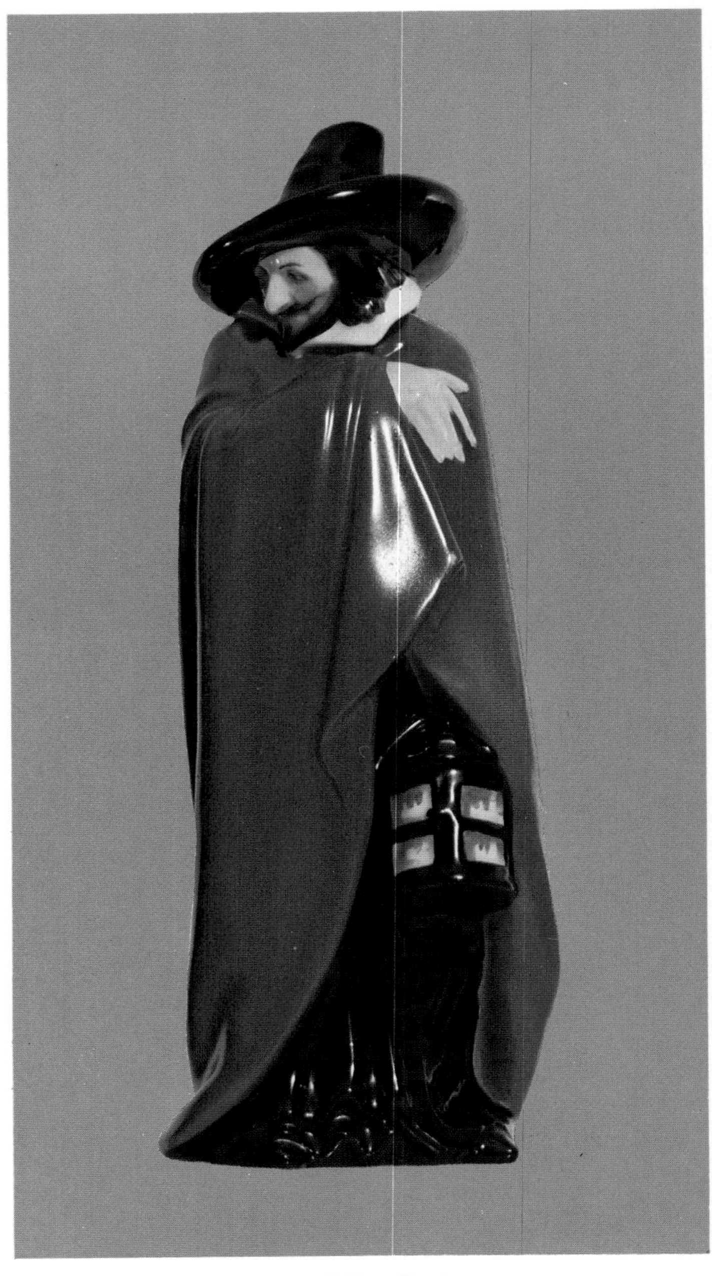

HN 98 Guy Fawkes

HN 301 Moorish Piper Minstrel
Designer: C. J. Noke
Size: 13½ in (34.2 cm)
Introduced: 1918
Withdrawn: By 1938
Made as a pair to HN 34, *Moorish Minstrel*
See illustration on page 76

HN 328 Moorish Piper Minstrel
Introduced: 1918
Withdrawn: By 1938
As HN 301, but green and brown striped robe

HN 416 Moorish Piper Minstrel
Introduced: 1920
Withdrawn: By 1938
As HN 301, but green and yellow striped robe

HN 302 Pretty Lady
See page 93

HN 303 Motherhood
See page 72

HN 304 Lady with Rose
See page 87

HN 305 A Scribe
Designer: C. J. Noke
Size: 6 in (15.2 cm)
Introduced: 1918
Withdrawn: By 1936

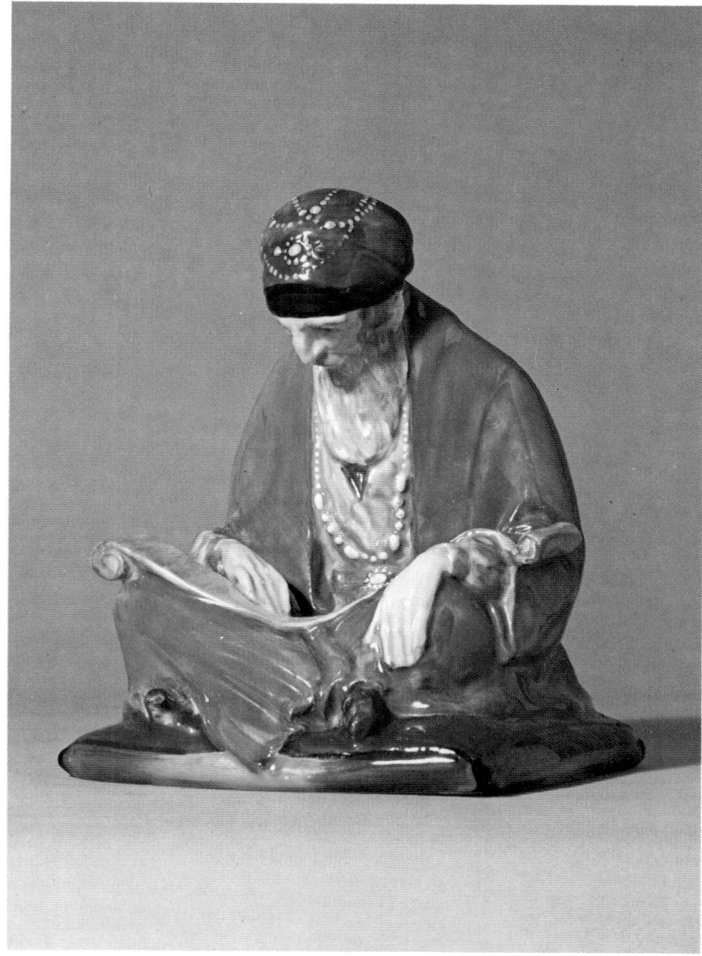

HN 305 A Scribe

HN 324 A Scribe
Introduced: 1918
Withdrawn: By 1938

HN 1235 A Scribe
Introduced: 1927
Withdrawn: By 1938
As HN 305, but brown coat, blue hat

HN 306 Milking Time
See page 66

HN 307 The Sentimental Pierrot
See page 78

HN 308 A Jester (second version, model 171)
See page 85

HN 309 A Lady of the Elizabethan Period (second version, model 232)
See page 80

HN 310 Dunce
See page 67

HN 324 A Scribe

HN 311 ***Dancing Figure***
Size: $17\frac{3}{4}$ in (45 cm)
Introduced: 1918
Withdrawn: By 1938
This figure is closely copied from one of a series of lady musicians and dancers made in biscuit porcelain by the Sèvres factory in about 1903, from designs by A. Leonard.

HN 311 *Dancing Figure* (illustration from the figure design book)

Elaborate trial version of HN 311, not put into production

HN 312–315 The Seasons (first version, Spring, model 215; Summer, model 219; Autumn, model 222; Winter, model 223)
Size: $7\frac{1}{2}$ in (19 cm)
Introduced: 1918
Withdrawn: By 1938
Although this set of figures is in the style of Phoebe Stabler, there is no record that she actually designed them.

HN 312 Spring

HN 313 Summer

HN 314 Autumn

HN 315 Winter

The Seasons have always been a favourite among ceramic modellers, and so this group follows the tradition established by Meissen, Chelsea, Derby, Sèvres and many Staffordshire potters such as Ralph Wood.

HN 472–475 The Seasons (first version, Spring, model 215; Summer, model 219; Autumn, model 222; Winter, model 223)
Introduced: 1921
Withdrawn: By 1938
As HN 312–315, but patterned robes

HN 316 A Mandarin (first version, model 189)
See page 97

HN 317 Shylock
See page 96

HN 318 A Mandarin (first version, model 189)
See page 97

HN 319 ***A Gnome***
Designer: H. Tittensor
Size: $6\frac{1}{4}$ in (15.8 cm)
Introduced: 1918
Withdrawn: By 1938
As HN 380, but pale blue costume

HN 380 *A Gnome*
Introduced: 1920
Withdrawn: By 1938

HN 381 *A Gnome*
Introduced: 1920
Withdrawn: By 1938

HN 320 A Jester (first version, model 170)
See page 84

HN 321 Digger (New Zealand)
Designer: E. W. Light
Size: 11¼ in (28.5 cm)
Introduced: 1918
Withdrawn: By 1938
The word 'digger' was applied generally during the late nineteenth century to anyone searching for gold, or working in the goldfields, particularly in Australia and California. During the First World War, the term became accepted slang for Australian and New Zealand soldiers fighting in the Anzac brigades.
A series of similar soldier figures were modelled in stoneware at the Doulton Lambeth factory by Leslie Harradine in *c.*1910

HN 380 & HN 381 *A Gnome*

Figure of a soldier modelled by L. Harradine at the Doulton Lambeth factory

HN 322 Digger (Australian)

HN 323 Blighty

HN 321 Digger (New Zealand)

HN 322 Digger (Australian)
Designer: E. W. Light
Size: 11¼ in (28.5 cm)
Introduced: 1918
Withdrawn: By 1938
For illustration, see previous page

HN 353 Digger (Australian)
Introduced: 1919
Withdrawn: By 1938
As HN 322, but painted naturalistically

HN 323 Blighty
Designed: E. W. Light
Size: 11½ in (29.2 cm)
Introduced: 1918
Withdrawn: By 1938
For illustration, see previous page
Blighty was army slang for Britain, in the sense of returning home after foreign service. Hence 'a blighty one' was a wound that secured a return to Britain during the First World War.
Take me back to dear old blighty was a hit of 1917, sung by Florrie Ford.

HN 324 A Scribe
See page 103

HN 325 Pussy
See page 70

HN 326 Madonna of the Square
See page 68

HN 327 The Curtsey
See page 90

HN 328 Moorish Piper Minstrel
See page 103

HN 329 The Gainsborough Hat
See page 86

HN 330 Pretty Lady
See page 93

HN 331 A Lady of the Georgian Period
See page 81

HN 332 Lady Ermine
See page 89

HN 333 The Flounced Skirt
See page 91

HN 334 The Curtsey
See page 90

HN 335 Lady of the Fan
See page 87

HN 336 Lady with Rose
See page 87

HN 337 The Parson's Daughter
Designer: H. Tittensor
Size: 10 in (25.4 cm)
Introduced: 1919
Withdrawn: By 1938
As HN 564, but lilac dress with brown floral pattern
Traditionally, the parson's daughter had a life of dedication, with a position in society to be maintained despite considerable poverty. Thus, some versions of this figure show the girl with a patchwork skirt.
The title may be taken from a painting by George Romney, in the National Gallery, London, called *The Parson's Daughter*, which shows a beautiful, but simply dressed girl.
This figure is an adapted version of HN 69, *Pretty Lady*, the lower half being identical.

HN 338 The Parson's Daughter
Introduced: 1919
Withdrawn: By 1938
As HN 564, but patterned blue dress, red bonnet and shawl

HN 441 The Parson's Daughter
Introduced: 1921
Withdrawn: By 1938
As HN 564, but yellow dress with orange spots

HN 564 The Parson's Daughter
Introduced: 1923
Withdrawn: By 1949

HN 790 The Parson's Daughter
Introduced: 1926
Withdrawn: By 1938
As HN 564, but patchwork skirt, dark multicoloured shawl

HN 1242 The Parson's Daughter
Introduced: 1927
Withdrawn: By 1938
As HN 564, but patchwork skirt, lilac shawl with yellow lining

HN 1356 The Parson's Daughter
Introduced: 1929
Withdrawn: By 1938

HN 2018 The Parson's Daughter
Introduced: 1949
Withdrawn: 1953
As HN 564, but darker patchwork skirt, purple hat and cloak

HN 339 In Grandma's Days
See page 82

HN 340 In Grandma's Days
See page 83

HN 341 Katharine
See page 92

HN 564 & HN 1356 The Parson's Daughter

HN 342 The Lavender Woman
See page 72

HN 343 An Arab
See page 74

HN 344 Henry Irving as Cardinal Wolsey
Designer: C. J. Noke
Size: $13\frac{1}{4}$ in (33.6 cm)
Introduced: 1919
Withdrawn: 1949
Sir Henry Irving was actor manager of the Lyceum Theatre in London from 1878 to 1902, and during this period he was largely responsible for reviving popular interest in Shakespeare. His success in a number of Shakespearian parts was aided by his remarkable partnership with the actress Ellen Terry. The part of Cardinal Wolsey in Shakespeare's *Henry VIII* was a particular success for Irving. The play traces Wolsey's decline from a magnificent rival and friend of Henry to a position of disgrace and rejection, caused by his failure to persuade the Pope to agree to Henry's divorce from Catherine of Aragon (played in the production by Ellen Terry).

Early versions of Irving and Ellen Terry, made at Burslem during the 1890s

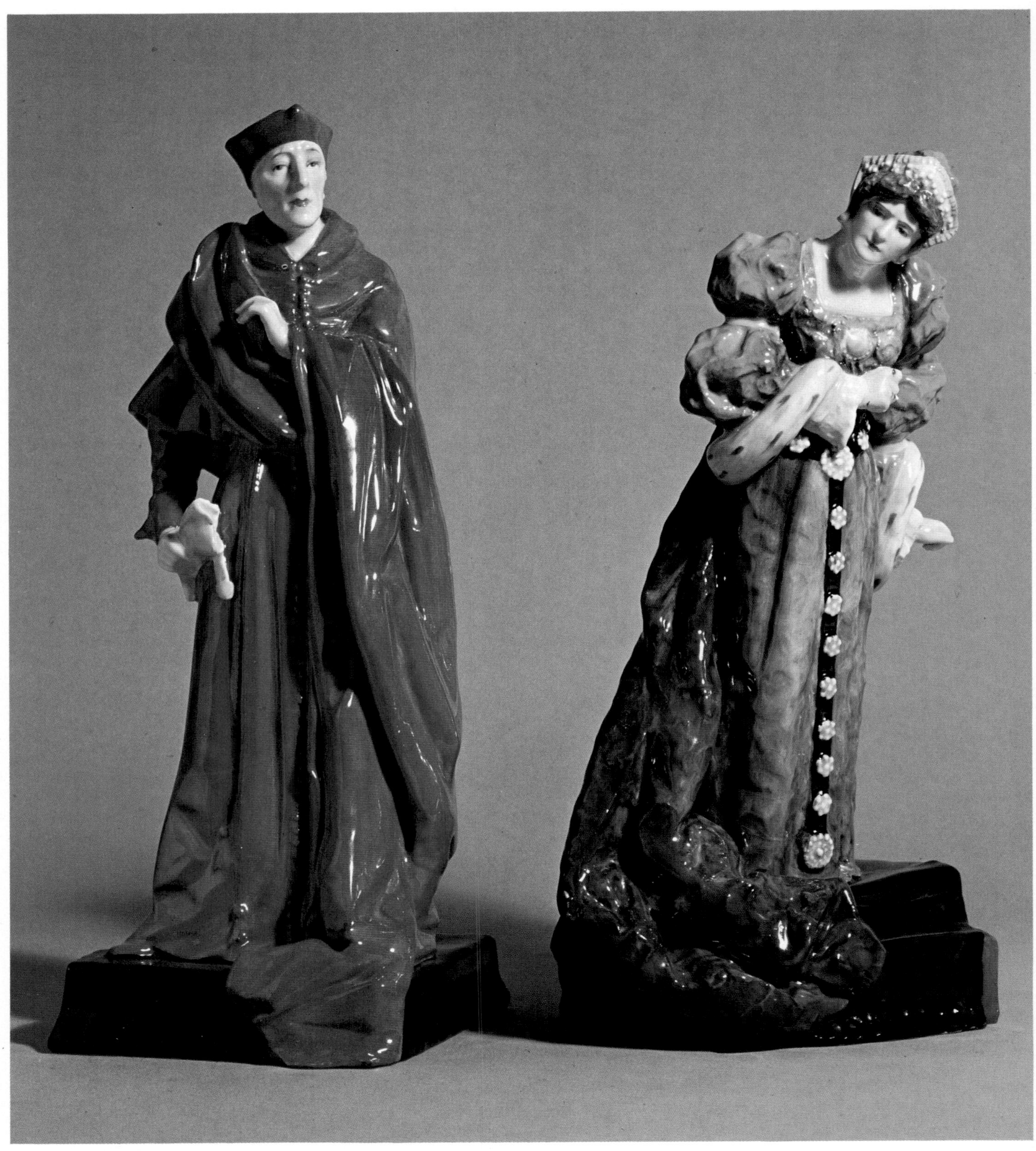

HN 344 Henry Irving as Cardinal Wolsey

HN 379 Ellen Terry as Queen Catherine

This figure, and its pair, HN 379, *Ellen Terry as Queen Catherine*, were among the few figures produced at Burslem during the 1890s, and then later re-issued in the HN series. In this case, the early versions were smaller.

HN 345 Doris Keene as Cavallini (second version, model 220)
See page 101

HN 346 Tony Weller (first version, model 254)
Designer: C. J. Noke
Size: $10\frac{1}{2}$ in (26.6 cm)
Introduced: 1919
Withdrawn: By 1938
As HN 684, but green coat, blue rug, brown base
Tony Weller, a stage-coach driver and father of Sam, is a character in Charles Dickens' *Pickwick Papers*. 'A stout, red-faced, elderly man', greatly addicted to both smoking

HN 684 Tony Weller (first version)

HN 779 A Geisha (first version)

and drinking, he retired from coach driving after his wife's death to a public house near Shooter's Hill in south London. He had a great aversion to widows, 'Be wery careful o' vidders all your life.' Doulton produced a great variety of wares decorated with Dickens characters and scenes, many of which were first made for the centenary of Dickens' birth in 1912. This is the first Dickens figure, although a generally similar whisky flask in the shape of a coachman had been produced in 1912.

HN 368 Tony Weller (first version, model 254)
Introduced: 1920
Withdrawn: By 1938
As HN 684, but blue coat, brown blanket

HN 684 Tony Weller (first version, model 254)
Introduced: 1924
Withdrawn: By 1938

HN 347 Guy Fawkes
See page 102

HN 348 The Carpet Vendor (first version, model 163A)
See page 78

HN 349 Fisherwomen
See page 96

HN 350 The Carpet Vendor (second version, model 163)
See page 95

HN 351 Picardy Peasant (female)
See page 67

HN 352 The Gainsborough Hat
See page 86

HN 353 Digger (Australian)
See page 106

A Geisha and A Mandarin, reproduced from an early advertisement

HN 354 A Geisha (first version, model 238)
Designer: H. Tittensor
Size: 10¾ in (27.3 cm)
Introduced: 1919
Withdrawn: By 1938
As HN 779, but yellow kimono, pink cuffs, blue flowered waistband
This figure, one of a series of Japanese-style models, reflects the contemporary Japanese craze in London which was launched partly by the musical, *The Geisha*, first performed in 1896.
Also known as *The Japanese Lady*.

HN 376 A Geisha (first version, model 238)
Introduced: 1920
Withdrawn: By 1938
As HN 779, but blue and yellow mottled kimono

HN 387 A Geisha (first version, model 238)
Introduced: 1920
Withdrawn: By 1938
As HN 779, but blue kimono, yellow cuffs

HN 634 A Geisha (first version, model 238)
Introduced: 1924
Withdrawn: By 1938
As HN 779, but black and white kimono

HN 741 A Geisha (first version, model 238)
Introduced: 1925
Withdrawn: 1938
As HN 779, but dark multicoloured kimono, black trim

HN 779 A Geisha (first version, model 238)
Introduced: 1926
Withdrawn: By 1938
For illustration, see previous page

HN 1321 A Geisha (first version, model 238)
Introduced: 1929
Withdrawn: By 1938
As HN 779, but green kimono

HN 1322 A Geisha (first version, model 238)
Introduced: 1929
Withdrawn: By 1938
As HN 779, but pink kimono, blue markings

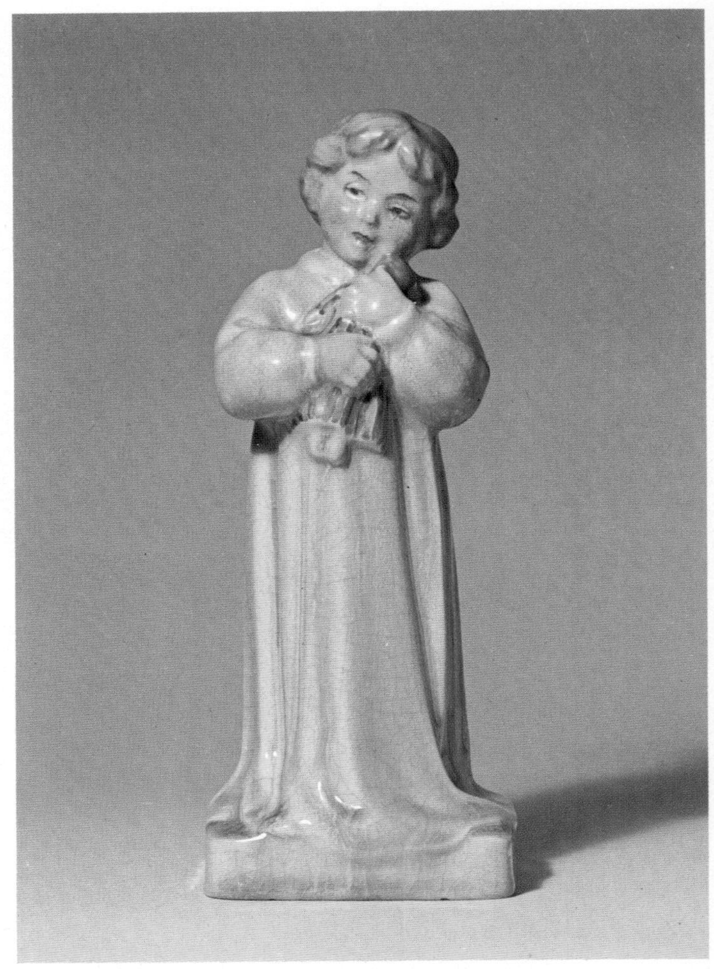

HN 355 Dolly

HN 355 Dolly
Designer: C. J. Noke
Size: 7¾ in (19.6 cm)
Introduced: 1919
Withdrawn: By 1938
This figure was designed to be a pair to HN 1, *Darling*

HN 356 Sir Thomas Lovell
Size: 7¾ in (19.6 cm)
Introduced: 1919
Withdrawn: By 1938
Although this figure is known as *Sir Thomas Lovell*, it bears a close resemblence to a portrait of Edward VI, painted in 1547. Lovell, Chancellor of the Exchequer, died in 1524, and the costume and style of the figure are later. Edward, the boy king, died aged 15 in 1553.

HN 357 Dunce
See page 67

HN 356 Sir Thomas Lovell
(illustration not in scale)

HN 2134 An Old King

HN 358 An Old King
Designer: C. J. Noke
Size: 9¾ in (24.7 cm)
Introduced: 1919
Withdrawn: By 1938
As HN 2134, but green shirt, purple robe
The identity of the king is not known, but it may be based on Edward the Confessor as depicted in the Bayeux Tapestry

HN 623 An Old King
Introduced: 1924
Withdrawn: By 1938
As 2134, but grey, red and green robes

HN 1801 An Old King
Introduced: 1937
Withdrawn: 1954
No details available

HN 2134 An Old King
Introduced: 1954
Still in production

HN 359 Fisherwomen
See page 96

HN 360 No details available

HN 361 Pretty Lady
See page 94

HN 362 In Grandma's Days
See page 83

HN 363 The Curtsey
See page 90

HN 364 A Moorish Minstrel
See page 77

HN 365 Double Jester (illustration from the figure design book)

Early version of Double Jester, made at Burslem during the 1890s

HN 365 Double Jester (model 269)
Designer: C. J. Noke
Introduced: 1920
Withdrawn: By 1938
This figure is one of a number made at Burslem during the 1890s in small quantities, and then later remodelled to fit the HN series

A Mandarin (second version)

HN 366 A Mandarin (second version, model 260)
Designer: C. J. Noke
Size: 8¼ in (20.7 cm)
Introduced: 1920
Withdrawn: By 1938
Yellow and blue costume

HN 455 A Mandarin (second version, model 260)
Introduced: 1921
Withdrawn: By 1938
Green costume

HN 641 A Mandarin (second version model 260)
Introduced: 1924
Withdrawn: By 1938
Onyx style colouring

HN 367 A Jester (first version, model 170)
See page 84

HN 368 Tony Weller (first version, model 254)
See page 108

HN 369 Cavalier (first version, illustration from the figure design book)

HN 369 Cavalier (first version, model 268)
Introduced: 1920
Withdrawn: By 1938
Although known as *A Cavalier*, this figure appears to be based on a painting of King Charles I.
Cavaliers, originally horse-soldiers, came to be popularly associated with those who fought on the Royalist side during the Civil War, 1642–46. Hence, it came to mean a gentleman trained to arms, 'a gay sprightly military man.'

HN 370 Henry VIII (first version, illustration from the figure design book)

Detail from Holbein's cartoon of Henry VIII

HN 375 Lady and Blackamoor (second version)

HN 370 Henry VIII (first version, model 271)
Designer: C. J. Noke
Introduced: 1920
Withdrawn: By 1938
Modelled on a well-known cartoon of Henry by Hans Holbein. A similar figure was also produced by Royal Worcester, modelled by Gertner and based on the same drawing.

HN 673 Henry VIII (first version, model 271)
Introduced: 1924
Withdrawn: By 1938
As HN 370, but brown and lilac robes

HN 371 The Curtsey
See page 90

HN 372 Spooks
See page 99

HN 373 *Boy on a Crocodile*

HN 373 *Boy on a Crocodile*
Designer: C. J. Noke
Size: 14½ in (36.8 cm) long
Introduced: 1920
Withdrawn: By 1938

HN 374 Lady and Blackamoor (first version, model 267)
Designer: H. Tittensor
Introduced: 1920
Withdrawn: By 1938
As HN 375, but blue bodice, patterned blue and green dress

HN 375 Lady and Blackamoor (Second version, model 273)
Designer: H. Tittensor
Introduced: 1920
Withdrawn: By 1938
This version was also made in two pieces as a covered box, but otherwise is generally similar to the first version.

HN 377 Lady and Blackamoor (second version, model 273)
Introduced: 1920
Withdrawn: By 1938
As HN 375, but pink and green dress

HN 470 Lady and Blackamoor (second version, model 273)
Introduced: 1921
Withdrawn: By 1938
As HN 375, but green and lilac dress

HN 376 A Geisha (first version, model 238)
See page 110

HN 377 Lady and Blackamoor (second version, model 273)
See above

HN 378 An Arab
See page 74

HN 2067 St George (first version)

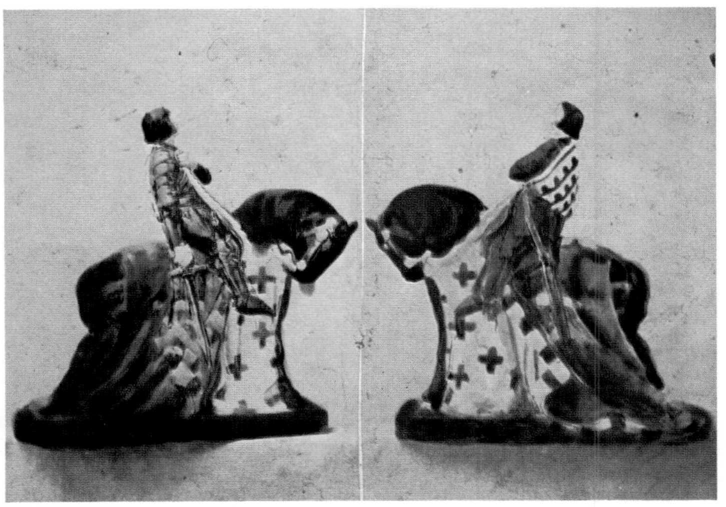

HN 386 St George (first version, illustration from the figure design book)

Original model of St George by Stanley Thorogood, dated 1915

HN 379 Ellen Terry as Queen Catherine
Designer: C. J. Noke
Size: 12½ in (31.7 cm)
Introduced: 1920
Withdrawn: By 1949
See illustration page 108
Henry Irving engaged Ellen Terry as his leading lady at the Lyceum Theatre in 1878, and then developed her career and reputation by giving her important roles in a series of revivals of Shakespeare plays. She played the wronged Queen Catherine in *Henry VIII* opposite Irving's Cardinal Wolsey.

HN 380 *A Gnome*
See page 105

HN 381 *A Gnome*
See page 105

HN 382 A Mandarin (first version, model 189)
See page 97

HN 383 The Gainsborough Hat
See page 86

HN 384 Pretty Lady
See page 94

HN 385 St George (first version, model 191)
Designer: Stanley Thorogood A.R.C.A.
Size: 16 in (40.6 cm)
Introduced: 1920
Withdrawn: By 1938
As HN 386, but blue-green multicoloured costume.
The figure was first modelled by Thorogood in 1915, when he moved to Stoke to become Superintendent of Art Instruction for the Borough, a post he held until 1919. The figure was later remodelled and simplified for production at Burslem in the HN series.
St. George, the patron Saint of England, is a largely legendary figure, popularly associated with the slaying of the Dragon.

HN 386 St George (first version, model 191)
Introduced: 1920
Withdrawn: By 1938

HN 1800 St George (first version, model 191)
Introduced: 1934
Withdrawn: 1950
No details available

Hn 2067 St George (first version, model 191)
Introduced: 1950
Withdrawn: 1976

HN 387 A Geisha (first version, model 238)
See page 110

HN 388 In Grandma's Days
See page 83

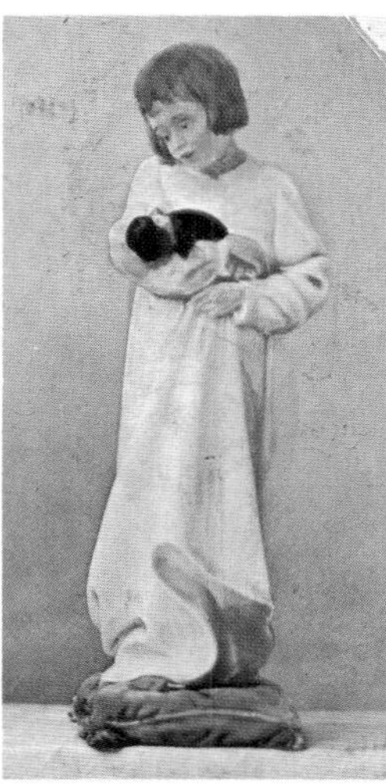

HN 469 The Little Mother (first version, illustration from the figure design book)

HN 389 The Little Mother (first version, model 279)
Designer: H. Tittensor
Introduced: 1920
Withdrawn: By 1938
As HN 469, but pink dress, fair hair

HN 390 The Little Mother (first version, model 279)
Introduced: 1920
Withdrawn: By 1938
As HN 469, but pink dress, dark hair

HN 469 The Little Mother (first version, model 279)
Introduced: 1921
Withdrawn: By 1938

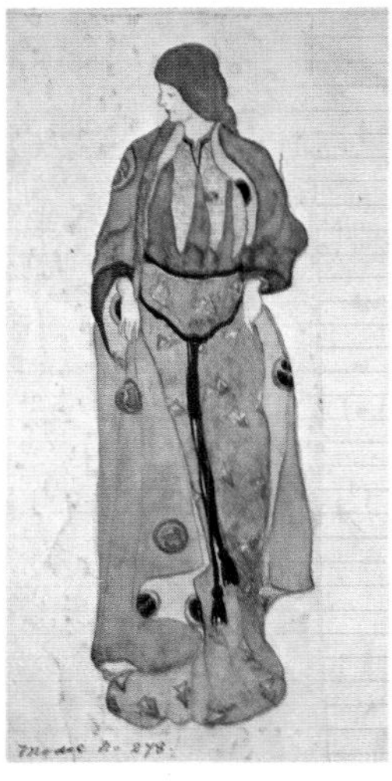

HN 391 A Princess (illustration from the figure design book)

HN 391 A Princess
Introduced: 1920
Withdrawn: By 1938
This figure, and several others that follow, including *Lady Without Bouquet*, show the strong influence of the costumes designed by Léon Bakst for Diaghilev's Russian Ballet

HN 392 A Princess
Introduced: 1920
Withdrawn: By 1938
As HN 391, but multicoloured costume, striped skirt

HN 420 A Princess
Introduced: 1920
Withdrawn: By 1938
As HN 391, but pink and green striped skirt, blue cloak

HN 430 A Princess
Introduced: 1921
Withdrawn: By 1938
As HN 391, but green flowered dress, blue-green striped cloak

HN 431 A Princess
Introduced: 1921
Withdrawn: By 1938
As HN 391, but pink dress, blue-green cloak

HN 633 A Princess
Introduced: 1924
Withdrawn: By 1938
As HN 391, but black and white dress

HN 393 ***Lady Without Bouquet***
Designer: G. Lambert
Size: 9 in (22.8 cm)
Introduced: 1920
Withdrawn: By 1938

HN 394 ***Lady Without Bouquet***
Introduced: 1920
Withdrawn: By 1938
As HN 393, but blue and yellow costume

HN 393 *Lady without Bouquet* (illustration from the figure design book)

Fashion drawing by Léon Bakst, a style that appears to have influenced the Doulton designers

HN 395 Contentment
Designer: L. Harradine
Size: $7\frac{1}{4}$ in (18.4 cm)
Introduced: 1920
Withdrawn: By 1938
As HN 421, but yellow skirt with pink stripes, blue patterned blouse

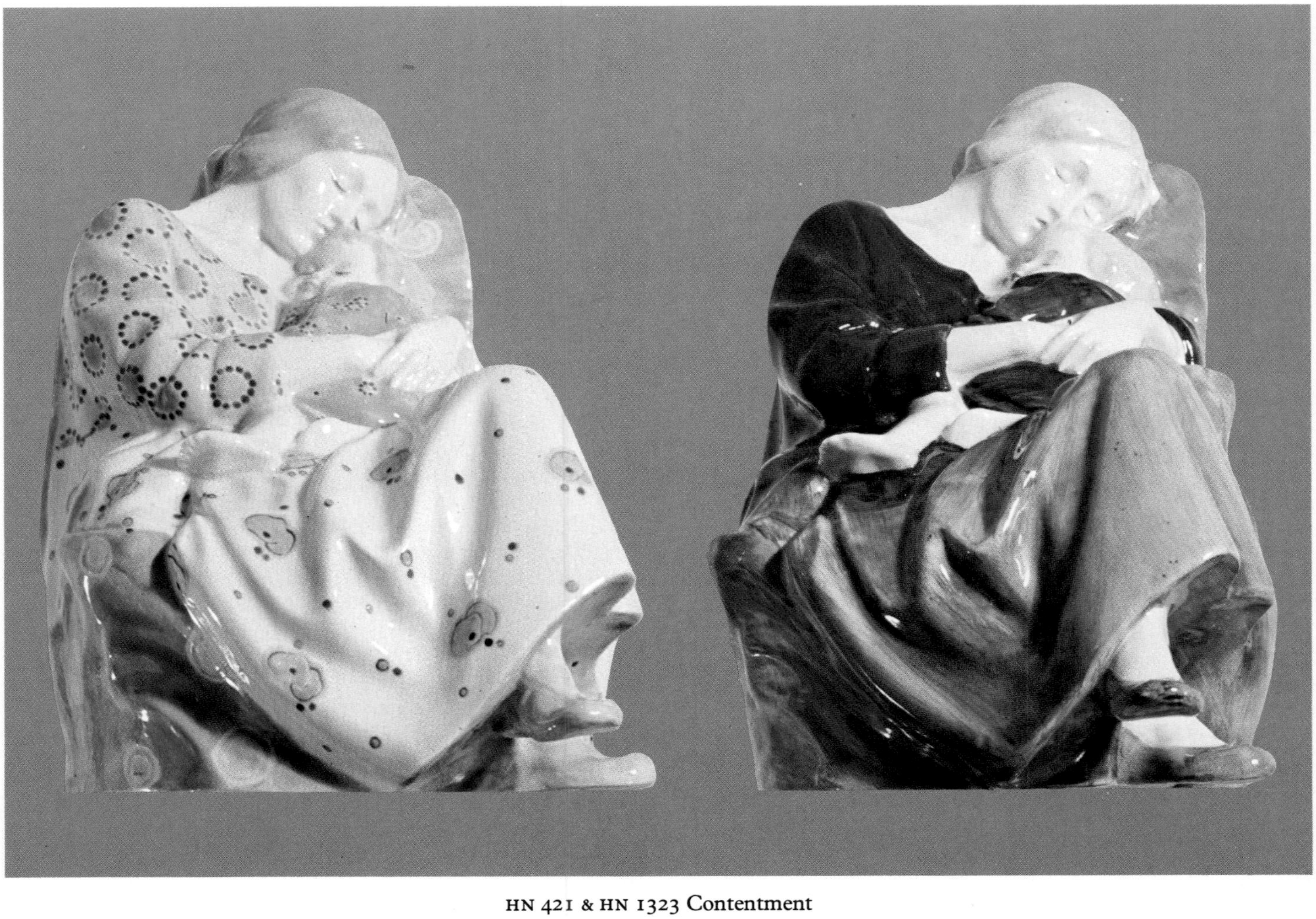

HN 421 & HN 1323 Contentment

HN 396 Contentment
Introduced: 1920
Withdrawn: By 1938
As HN 421, but yellow and pink striped chair

HN 421 Contentment
Introduced: 1920
Withdrawn: By 1938

HN 468 Contentment
Introduced: 1921
Withdrawn: By 1938
As HN 421, but green spotted dress

HN 572 Contentment
Introduced: 1923
Withdrawn: By 1938
As HN 421, but spotted cream skirt, spotted pink blouse

HN 685 Contentment
Introduced: 1923
Withdrawn: By 1938
As HN 421, but black and white floral dress

HN 686 Contentment
Introduced: 1924
Withdrawn: By 1938
As HN 421, but black and white striped chair

HN 1323 Contentment
Introduced: 1929
Withdrawn: By 1938

HN 397 Puff and Powder
Designer: L. Harradine
Introduced: 1920
Withdrawn: By 1938
As HN 398, but yellow skirt, brown bodice

HN 398 Puff and Powder
Introduced: 1920
Withdrawn: By 1938

HN 400 Puff and Powder
Introduced: 1920
Withdrawn: By 1938
As HN 398, but green and blue bodice, yellow skirt

HN 432 Puff and Powder
Introduced: 1921
Withdrawn: By 1938
As HN 398, but lilac skirt with orange spots

HN 433 Puff and Powder
Introduced: 1921
Withdrawn: By 1938
As HN 398, but yellow skirt with blue spots

HN 399 Japanese Fan
Designer: H. Tittensor
Introduced: 1920
Withdrawn: By 1938
This model was also made as a lidded bowl

HN 405 Japanese Fan
Introduced: 1920
Withdrawn: By 1938
As HN 399, but pale yellow costume

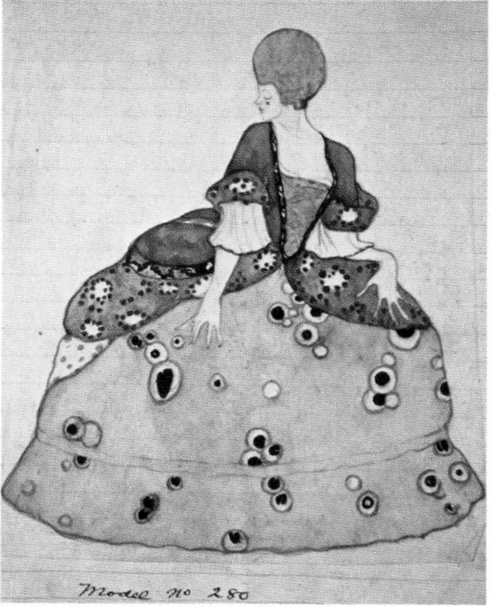

HN 398 Puff and Powder (illustration from the figure design book)

Puff and Powder, reproduced from an early advertisement

HN 439 Japanese Fan
Introduced: 1921
Withdrawn: By 1938
As HN 399, but blue costume, green spots

HN 440 Japanese Fan
Introduced: 1921
Withdrawn: By 1938
As HN 399, but yellow costume with orange spots

HN 400 Puff and Powder
See above

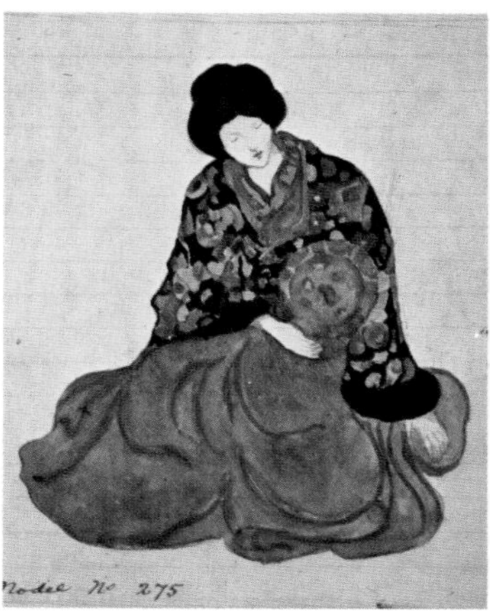

HN 399 Japanese Fan (illustration from the figure design book)

Japanese Fan (colour version not recorded in the figure design book)

HN 401 Marie (first version, model 281)
Designer: L. Harradine
Introduced: 1920
Withdrawn: By 1938

HN 434 Marie (first version, model 281)
Introduced: 1921
Withdrawn: By 1938
As HN 401, but yellow skirt with orange stripes

HN 502 Marie (first version, model 281)
Introduced: 1921
Withdrawn: By 1938
As HN 401, but white dress, red and blue bodice

HN 504 Marie (first version, model 281)
Introduced: 1921
Withdrawn: By 1938
As HN 401, but green and blue dress, red spots

HN 505 Marie (first version, model 281)
Introduced: 1921
Withdrawn: By 1938
As HN 401, but spotted blue bodice, green and lilac skirt

HN 506 Marie (first version, model 281)
Introduced: 1921
Withdrawn: By 1938
As HN 401, but blue and green striped bodice, spotted lilac skirt

HN 402 Betty (first version, model 282)
Designer: L. Harradine
Introduced: 1920
Withdrawn: By 1938

HN 403 Betty (first version, model 282)
Introduced: 1920
Withdrawn: By 1938
As HN 402, but green skirt, blue, yellow, white border

HN 435 Betty (first version, model 282)
Introduced: 1921
Withdrawn: By 1938
As HN 402, but blue skirt with yellow spots

HN 438 Betty (first version, model 282)
Introduced: 1921
Withdrawn: By 1938
As HN 402, but green skirt

HN 477 Betty (first version, model 282)
Introduced: 1921
Withdrawn: By 1938
As HN 402, but spotted green skirt

HN 478 Betty (first version, model 282)
Introduced: 1921
Withdrawn: By 1938
As HN 402, but white spotted skirt

HN 401 Marie (first version, illustration from the figure design book)

HN 402 Betty (first version, illustration from the figure design book)

HN 404 King Charles
Designer: C. J. Noke and H. Tittensor
Size: $16\frac{3}{4}$ in (42.5 cm)
Introduced: 1920
Withdrawn: 1951
As HN 2084, but pink base
Also known as *Charles I*
Charles I reigned between 1625 and 1649, and was beheaded in Whitehall after the victory of the Cromwellian forces in the Civil War.
The model was partly based on a painting after Van Dyck

HN 2084 King Charles
Introduced: 1952
Still in production

HN 405 Japanese Fan
See page 117

HN 406 The Bouquet
Designer: G. Lambert
Size: 9 in (22.8 cm)
Introduced: 1920
Withdrawn: By 1938
As HN 428, but details of colour not recorded
Also known as *The Nosegay*

HN 414 The Bouquet
Introduced: 1920
Withdrawn: By 1938
As HN 428, but pink and yellow shawl

HN 422 The Bouquet
Introduced: 1920
Withdrawn: By 1938
As HN 428, but yellow and pink striped skirt

HN 428 The Bouquet
Introduced: 1921
Withdrawn: By 1938
For illustration, see page 120

HN 2084 King Charles

HN 428 The Bouquet HN 429 The Bouquet HN 567 The Bouquet

HN 429 The Bouquet
Introduced: 1921
Withdrawn: By 1938

HN 567 The Bouquet
Introduced: 1923
Withdrawn: By 1938

HN 794 The Bouquet
Introduced: 1926
Withdrawn: By 1938
As HN 428, but blue shawl with red and green spots

HN 407 Omar Khayyam and the Belovéd
Designer: C. J. Noke
Size: 10 in (25.4 cm)
Introduced: 1920
Withdrawn: By 1938
As HN 419, but colours unrecorded
The Rubaiyat of Omar Khayyam was translated from the Persian by Edward Fitzgerald and published in 1859. The theme of the poem, to enjoy life while it lasts, and its great popularity partly explained the European fascination with the Middle East during the late 19th and early 20th centuries. Many plays and books were published that told of love between European women and Arab men, and *The Rubaiyat* itself was filmed in 1923, starring Ramon Novarro, In fact, in the poem the word Belovéd occurs only in the following lines:
'Ah, my belovéd, fill the cup that clears
Today of past regrets and future fears.'

HN 419 Omar Khayyam and the Belovéd
Introduced: 1920
Withdrawn: By 1938

HN 459 Omar Khayyam and the Belovéd
Introduced: 1921
Withdrawn: By 1938
As HN 419, but multicoloured costumes

HN 598 Omar Khayyam and the Belovéd
Introduced: 1924
Withdrawn: By 1938
As HN 419, but lady in striped pink cloak, striped blue dress

HN 408 Omar Khayyam (first version, model 284)
Designer: C. J. Noke
Size: 6 in (15.2 cm)
Introduced: 1920
Withdrawn: By 1938

HN 408 Omar Khayyam (first version)

HN 419 Omar Khayyam and the Belovéd

HN 409 Omar Khayyam (first version, model 284)
Introduced: 1938
Withdrawn: By 1938
As HN 408, but black robe, yellow trousers

HN 410 Blue Beard (first version)
See page 95

HN 411 A Lady of the Elizabethan Period (first version, model 165)
See page 80

HN 412 A Jester (first version, model 170)
See page 84

HN 413 The Crinoline
See page 68

HN 414 The Bouquet
See page 118

HN 415 A Moorish Minstrel
See page 77

HN 416 A Moorish Piper Minstrel
See page 103

HN 417 One of the Forty (first version, model 289)
Designer: H. Tittensor
Size: 5 in (12.7 cm)
Introduced: 1920
Withdrawn: By 1938
As HN 528, but green and blue robes
Ali Baba and the Forty Thieves, a traditional oriental tale, was adapted for the operetta *Chu Chin Chow*, first performed at His Majesty's Theatre in 1916. A popular success with over 2,000 performances, the operetta had a considerable impact on contemporary fashion. It was later filmed, in 1934.
The Forty Thieves, living in their jars in the magic cave, protected by the secret password, *open sesame*, played an important part in the story.
Other figures were also based on *Chu Chin Chow*, for example *The Cobbler*, and there were in fact considerably more than forty different thief models.

HN 490 One of the Forty (first version, model 289)
Introduced: 1921
Withdrawn: By 1938
As HN 528, but blue and brown chequered coat

HN 495 One of the Forty (first version, model 289)
Introduced: 1921
Withdrawn: By 1938
As HN 528, but blue hat and waistband

HN 501 One of the Forty (first version, model 289)
Introduced: 1921
Withdrawn: By 1938
As HN 528, but green striped coat

Above left
One of the Forty (first version)
Above right
HN 528 One of the Forty (first version, illustration from the figure design book)
Right
HN 494 One of the Forty (second version, illustration from the figure design book)

HN 423 One of the Forty (third-eighth versions, illustration from the figure design book)

HN 423 One of the Forty (third-eighth versions, all produced in a variety of colours)

HN 528 One of the Forty (first version, model 289)
Introduced: 1921
Withdrawn: By 1938

HN 648 One of the Forty (first version, model 289)
Introduced: 1924
Withdrawn: By 1938
As HN 528, but blue, black and white robes

HN 677 One of the Forty (first version, model 289)
Introduced: 1924
Withdrawn: By 1938
As HN 528, but orange, green and red striped coat

HN 1351 One of the Forty (first version, model 289)
Introduced: 1920
Withdrawn: By 1949
As HN 528, but no colour details available

HN 1352 One of the Forty (first version, model 289)
Introduced: 1929
Withdrawn: By 1949
As HN 528, but multicoloured robes

HN 418 One of the Forty (second version, model 298)
Designer: H. Tittensor
Introduced: 1920
Withdrawn: By 1938
As HN 494, but striped green robes

HN 494 One of the Forty (second version, model 298)
Introduced: 1921
Withdrawn: By 1938

HN 498 One of the Forty (second version, model 298)
Introduced: 1921
Withdrawn: By 1938
As HN 494, but dark striped coat, pale striped trousers

HN 647 One of the Forty (second version, model 298)
Introduced: 1924
Withdrawn: By 1938
As HN 494, but blue, black and white robes

HN 666 One of the Forty (second version, model 298)
Introduced: 1924
Withdrawn: By 1938
As HN 494, but chequered yellow robes

HN 704 One of the Forty (second version, model 298)
Introduced: 1925
Withdrawn: By 1938
As HN 494, but chequered red robe

HN 1353 One of the Forty (second version, model 298)
Introduced: 1929
Withdrawn: By 1949
As HN 494, but multicoloured robes

HN 423 One of the Forty (third-eighth versions, models 291, 295, 296, 299, 300, 301)
Designer: H. Tittensor
Size: $2\frac{3}{4}$–3 in (6.9–7.6 cm)
Introduced: 1921
Withdrawn: By 1938
All these small models were produced in a variety of colour finishes

HN 427 One of the Forty (ninth version)
Designer: H. Tittensor
Introduced: 1921
Withdrawn: By 1938

HN 480 One of the Forty (tenth version, model 328)
Designer: H. Tittensor
Size: $6\frac{3}{4}$ in (17.1 cm)
Introduced: 1921
Withdrawn: By 1938

HN 493 One of the Forty (tenth version, model 328)
Introduced: 1921
Withdrawn: By 1938
As HN 480, but blue hat and waistband

HN 497 One of the Forty (tenth version, model 328)
Introduced: 1921
Withdrawn: By 1938
As HN 480, but brown hat, chequered trousers

HN 499 One of the Forty (tenth version, model 328)
Introduced: 1921
Withdrawn: By 1938
As HN 480, but cream costume, green hat

HN 664 One of the Forty (tenth version, model 328)
Introduced: 1924
Withdrawn: By 1938
As HN 480, but patterned yellow robes

HN 714 One of the Forty (tenth version, model 328)
Introduced: 1925
Withdrawn: By 1938
As HN 480, but patterned red robes

HN 481 One of the Forty (eleventh version, model 319)
Designer: H. Tittensor
Introduced: 1921
Withdrawn: By 1938
As HN 491, but dark spotted robes

HN 483 One of the Forty (eleventh version, model 319)
Introduced: 1921
Withdrawn: By 1938
As HN 491, but brown hat, green striped robes

HN 491 One of the Forty (eleventh version, model 319)
Introduced: 1921
Withdrawn: By 1938

HN 646 One of the Forty (eleventh version, model 319)
Introduced: 1924
Withdrawn: By 1938
As HN 491, but blue black and white robes

HN 667 One of the Forty (eleventh version, model 319)
Introduced: 1924
Withdrawn: By 1938
As HN 491, but chequered yellow robe

HN 712 One of the Forty (eleventh version, model 319)
Introduced: 1925
Withdrawn: By 1938
As HN 491, but chequered red robes

HN 480 One of the Forty (tenth version)

HN 427 One of the Forty (ninth version, illustration from the figure design book)

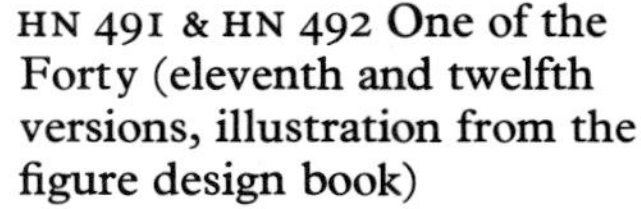

HN 491 & HN 492 One of the Forty (eleventh and twelfth versions, illustration from the figure design book)

HN 1336 One of the Forty (eleventh version, model 319)
Introduced: 1929
Withdrawn: By 1938
As HN 491, but mottled red, orange and blue robes

HN 1350 One of the Forty (eleventh version, model 319)
Introduced: 1929
Withdrawn: By 1949
As HN 491, but multicoloured robes

HN 482 One of the Forty (twelfth version, model 327)
Designer: H. Tittensor
Size: 6 in (15.2 cm)
Introduced: 1921
Withdrawn: By 1938
As HN 492, but spotted waistband

HN 484 One of the Forty (twelfth version, model 327)
Introduced: 1921
Withdrawn: 1938
As HN 492, but mottled green robes

HN 492 One of the Forty (twelfth version, model 327)
Introduced: 1921
Withdrawn: By 1938
For illustration, see previous page

HN 645 One of the Forty (twelfth version, model 327)
Introduced: 1924
Withdrawn: By 1938
As HN 492, but blue, black and white robes

HN 663 One of the Forty (twelfth version, model 327)
Introduced: 1924
Withdrawn: By 1938
As HN 492, but chequered yellow robes

HN 713 One of the Forty (twelfth version, model 327)
Introduced: 1925
Withdrawn: By 1938
As HN 492, but chequered red robes

HN 496 One of the Forty (thirteenth version, model 313)
Designer: H. Tittensor
Size: 7¾ in (19.6 cm)
Introduced: 1921
Withdrawn: By 1938
As HN 665, but yellow hat and vase

HN 500 One of the Forty (thirteenth version, model 313)
Introduced: 1921
Withdrawn: By 1938
As HN 665, but chequered coat and red hat

HN 649 One of the Forty (thirteenth version, model 313)
Introduced: 1924
Withdrawn: By 1938
As HN 665, but blue, black and white robes

HN 665 One of the Forty (thirteenth version, model 313)
Introduced: 1924
Withdrawn: By 1938

HN 1354 One of the Forty (thirteenth version, model 313)
Introduced: 1929
Withdrawn: By 1949
As HN 665, but multicoloured robes

HN 419 Omar Khayyam and the Beloved
See page 120

HN 420 A Princess
See page 115

HN 421 Contentment
See page 117

HN 422 The Bouquet
See page 118

HN 423 One of the Forty
See above

HN 424 Sleep
See page 72

HN 425 The Goosegirl
Designer: L. Harradine
Introduced: 1921
Withdrawn: By 1938
As HN 560, but blue skirt, striped blue blouse
This figure is based on the fairy tale by the Grimm brothers, in which a Princess is forced to change places with her maid and become a goosegirl, while the maid marries the Prince. She is eventually rescued from this plight by the spirit of her horse, Falada, is restored to her rightful position, and lives happily ever after with the Prince.

HN 436 The Goosegirl
Introduced: 1921
Withdrawn: By 1938
As HN 560, but green skirt with blue spots, spotted blouse

HN 437 The Goosegirl
Introduced: 1921
Withdrawn: By 1938
As HN 560, but chequered brown and blue dress

HN 448 The Goosegirl
Introduced: 1921
Withdrawn: By 1938
As HN 560, but blue striped blouse, blue hat

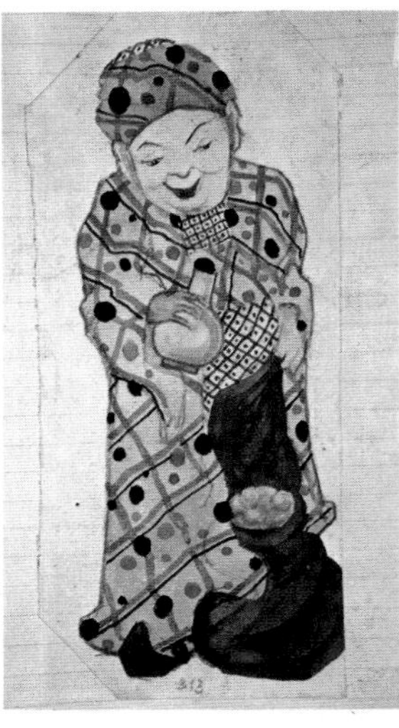

HN 665 One of the Forty (thirteenth version)

HN 560 The Goosegirl (illustration from the figure design book)

HN 559 The Goosegirl
Introduced: 1923
Withdrawn: By 1938
As HN 560, but spotted pink dress

HN 560 The Goosegirl
Introduced: 1923
Withdrawn: By 1938

HN 426 A Jester (first version, model 170)
See page 84

HN 427 One of the Forty
See page 123

HN 428 The Bouquet
See page 119

HN 429 The Bouquet
See page 120

HN 430 A Princess
See page 116

HN 431 A Princess
See page 116

HN 432 Puff and Powder
See page 117

HN 433 Puff and Powder
See page 117

HN 434 Marie (first version, model 281)
See page 118

HN 435 Betty (first version, model 282)
See page 118

HN 436 The Goosegirl
See previous page

HN 437 The Goosegirl
See previous page

HN 438 Betty (first version, model 282)
See page 118

HN 439 Japanese Fan
See page 117

HN 440 Japanese Fan
See page 117

HN 441 The Parson's Daughter
See page 106

HN 442 In Grandma's Days
See page 83

HN 443 Out for a Walk
See page 99

HN 444 A Lady of the Georgian Period
See page 81

HN 445 Guy Fawkes
See page 102

HN 446 A Jester (first version, model 170)
See page 84

HN 447 Lady with Shawl
Designer: L. Harradine
Size: 13¼ in (34.2 cm)
Introduced: 1921
Withdrawn: By 1938
This unusually elegant figure was inspired directly by contemporary fashion illustrations.
For illustration, see next page

HN 458 Lady with Shawl
Introduced: 1921
Withdrawn: By 1938
As HN 447, but multicoloured shawl, pink dress

HN 626 Lady with Shawl
Introduced: 1924
Withdrawn: By 1938
As HN 447, but yellow shawl with pink spots, white dress with green spots

HN 678 Lady with Shawl
Introduced: 1924
Withdrawn: By 1938
As HN 447, but black and white shawl, yellow and white dress

HN 679 Lady with Shawl
Introduced: 1924
Withdrawn: By 1938
As HN 447, but black, yellow, and blue shawl, black and white dress

HN 448 The Goosegirl
See page 124

HN 449 Fruit Gathering
Designer: L. Harradine
Introduced: 1921
Withdrawn: By 1938
As HN 561, but blue striped blouse, blue skirt
Designed to be a pair to HN 425, *The Goosegirl*

HN 476 Fruit Gathering
Introduced: 1921
Withdrawn: By 1938
As HN 561, but green check blouse, blue check skirt

HN 447 Lady with Shawl

HN 561 Fruit Gathering (illustration from the figure design book)

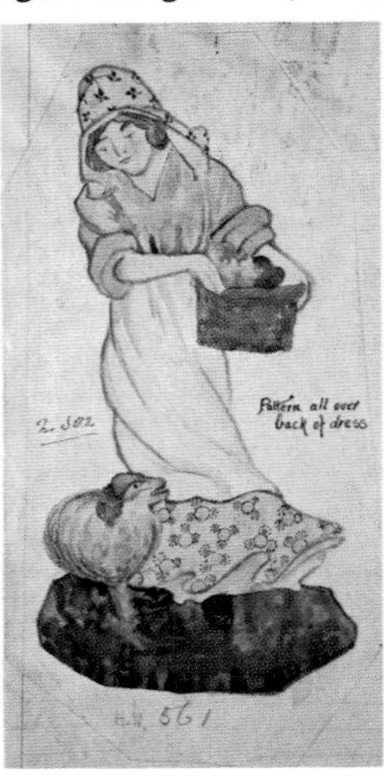

HN 503 Fruit Gathering
Introduced: 1921
Withdrawn: By 1938
As HN 561, but brown and blue chequered dress

HN 561 Fruit Gathering
Introduced: 1923
Withdrawn: By 1938

HN 562 Fruit Gathering
Introduced: 1923
Withdrawn: By 1938
As HN 561, but pink blouse, spotted skirt

HN 706 Fruit Gathering
Introduced: 1925
Withdrawn: By 1938
As HN 561, but purple blouse, yellow skirt

HN 707 Fruit Gathering
Introduced: 1925
Withdrawn: By 1938
As HN 561, but red blouse, spotted skirt

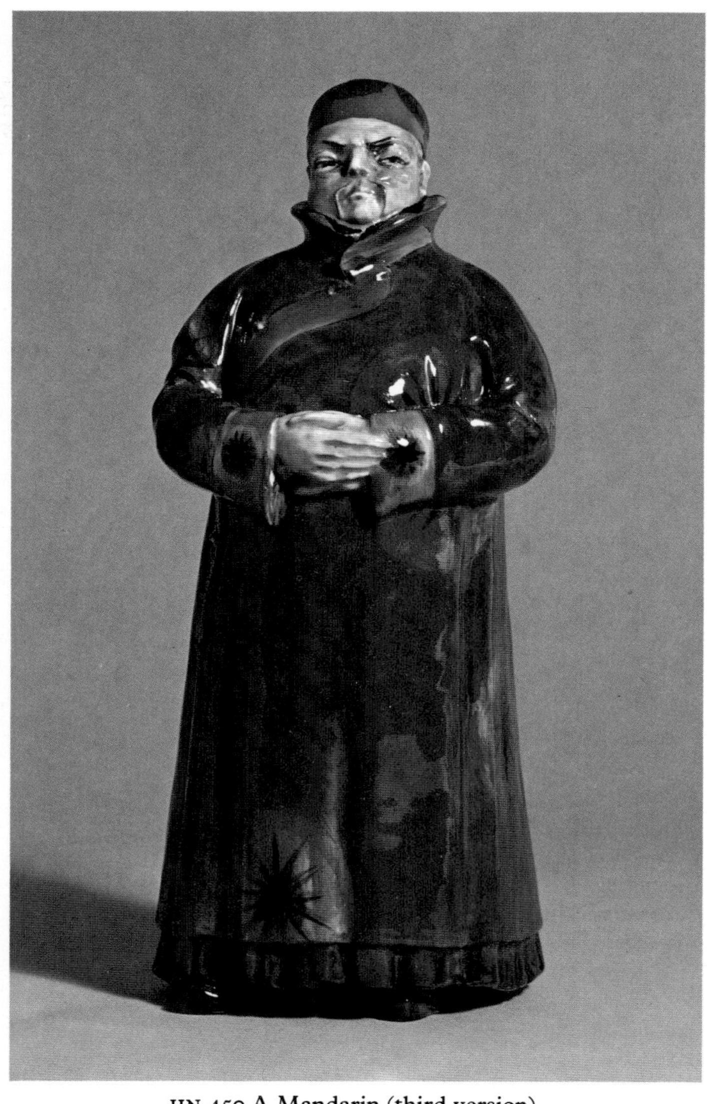

HN 450 A Mandarin (third version)

HN 451 *An Old Man* (illustration from the figure design book)

HN 450 A Mandarin (third version, model 346)
Designer: C. J. Noke
Introduced: 1921
Withdrawn: By 1938

HN 460 A Mandarin (third version, model 346)
Introduced: 1921
Withdrawn: By 1938
As HN 450, but blue costume

HN 461 A Mandarin (third version, model 346)
Introduced: 1921
Withdrawn: By 1938
As HN 450, but red costume

HN 601 A Mandarin (third version, model 346)
Introduced: 1924
Withdrawn: By 1938
As HN 450, but blue costume

HN 451 *An Old Man* (model 305)
Introduced: 1921
Withdrawn: By 1938

HN 452 No details available

HN 453 The Gainsborough Hat
See page 87

HN 454 The Smiling Buddha
Designer: C. J. Noke
Size: $6\frac{1}{4}$ in (15.8 cm)
Introduced: 1921
Withdrawn: By 1938
Like many of the oriental style figures, this model was also produced with flambé glazes, and in the *Sung* range.

HN 455 A Mandarin (second version, model 260)
See page 112

HN 456 The Welsh Girl
See page 79

HN 454 The Smiling Buddha

HN 457 *Crouching Nude*

Woman Holding Child

HN 457 ***Crouching Nude***
Size: 5½ in (13.9 cm)
Introduced: 1921
Withdrawn: By 1938

HN 458 Lady with Shawl
See page 125

HN 459 Omar Khayyam and the Beloved
See page 120

HN 460 A Mandarin (third version, model 346)
See page 127

HN 461 A Mandarin (third version, model 346)
See page 127

HN 462 ***Woman Holding Child***
Size: 9¼ in (23.4 cm)
Introduced: 1921
Withdrawn: By 1938
Green dress, white apron and blanket
A similar figure was designed by L. Harradine for quantity production at the Doulton Lambeth factory in about 1912. A closely related figure in terracotta, entitled *Motherhood*, was also made by the Chelsea sculptor and potter Reginald Wells in about 1920; an example of this figure is in the Doulton collection.

HN 570 *Woman Holding Child*
Introduced: 1923
Withdrawn: By 1938
Pink and green striped skirt, pink and red striped blanket

HN 703 *Woman Holding Child*
Introduced: 1925
Withdrawn: By 1938
Purple cloak, black and red chequered skirt

HN 743 *Woman Holding Child*
Introduced: 1925
Withdrawn: By 1938
Blue and yellow striped apron

HN 463 Polly Peachum (first version, model 320)
Designer: L. Harradine
Size: 6½ in (16.5 cm)
Introduced: 1921
Withdrawn: By 1949
The Beggar's Opera, a pastoral with a London setting, written by John Gay, was first performed in 1728. It concerns the escapades of a lighthearted highwayman, Captain MacHeath, who falls in love with both Polly Peachum and Lucy Lockett, one the daughter of an innkeeper, the other of the warden of Newgate prison

'How happy would I be with either,
were t'other dear charmer away'

The opera was revived at the Lyric Hammersmith, in 1920, a production designed by Claud Lovatt Fraser (1890–1921). The sets and costumes inaugurated a new

The Beggar's Opera: *top*, HN 464 Captain MacHeath, HN 2175 The Beggar (second version), HN 526 The Beggar (first version), HN 527 The Highwayman
bottom, HN 695 Lucy Lockett (second version), HN 549 Polly Peachum (second version), HN 489 Polly Peachum (second version), HN 465 Polly Peachum (first version)

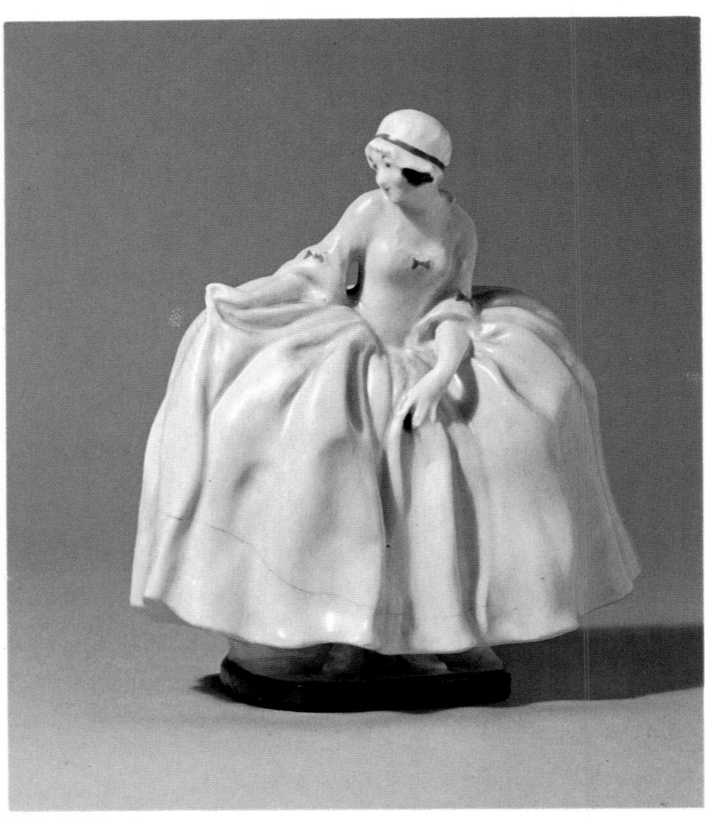

HN 463 Polly Peachum (first version)

Wax model of Lucy Lockett, made by Agatha Walker in 1921

Poster for *The Beggar's Opera*, designed by C. Lovat Fraser for the 1920 revival

era in stage design and greatly influenced contemporary fashion.

The five characters in the Doulton *Beggar's Opera* set, *Polly Peachum, Captain MacHeath, Lucy Lockett, The Highwayman* (a member of the MacHeath gang) and *The Beggar* (the supposed author of the play) were taken directly from the Lovatt Fraser designs. Similar figures were also produced by sculptors Gwendolen Parnell and Agatha Walker; the latter's set, made in 1921, are particularly close to the Doulton versions.

The Beggar's Opera was revived again in 1927, and was then used by Kurt Weill and Berthold Brecht as the basis for *The Threepenny Opera*, first performed in Berlin in 1928 and in New York in 1933.

HN 465 Polly Peachum (first version, model 320)
Introduced: 1921
Withdrawn: By 1949
As HN 463, but with red dress

HN 550 Polly Peachum (first version, model 320)
Introduced: 1922
Withdrawn: By 1949

HN 589 Polly Peachum (first version, model 320)
Introduced: 1924
Withdrawn: By 1949
As HN 463, but pink dress, yellow underskirt

HN 614 Polly Peachum (first version, model 320)
Introduced: 1924
Withdrawn: By 1949
As HN 463, but pale pink dress, blue bows

HN 680 Polly Peachum (first version, model 320)
Introduced: 1924
Withdrawn: By 1949
As HN 463, but white dress with black, yellow and blue spots

HN 693 Polly Peachum (first version, model 320)
Introduced: 1925
Withdrawn: By 1949
As HN 463, but deep rose pink dress with green bows

HN 464 Captain MacHeath
Designer: L. Harradine
Size: 7 in (17.7 cm)
Introduced: 1921
Withdrawn: By 1949
A character from *The Beggar's Opera*. For further details, see HN 463

HN 590 Captain MacHeath
Introduced: 1924
Withdrawn: By 1949
As HN 464, but with a yellow cravat

HN 1256 Captain MacHeath
Introduced: 1927
Withdrawn: By 1949
As HN 590, but earthenware

HN 747 Tulips

HN 465 Polly Peachum (first version, model 320)
See above

HN 466 Tulips
Size: 9½ in (24.1 cm)
Introduced: 1921
Withdrawn: By 1938
As HN 747, but green dress

HN 488 Tulips
Introduced: 1921
Withdrawn: By 1938
As HN 747, but ivory dress

HN 672 Tulips
Introduced: 1924
Withdrawn: By 1938
As HN 747, but green shawl, cream dress

HN 747 Tulips
Introduced: 1925
Withdrawn: By 1938

HN 1334 Tulips
Introduced: 1929
Withdrawn: By 1938
As HN 747, but blue and pink shawl, green dress

HN 467 Doris Keane as Cavallini (first version, model 205)
See page 100

HN 468 Contentment
See page 117

HN 469 The Little Mother (first version, model 279)
See page 115

HN 470 Lady and Blackamoor (second version, model 273)
See page 113

HN 471 Katharine
See page 92

HN 472–475 The Seasons (first version, Spring, model 215; Summer, model 219; Autumn, model 222; Winter, model 223)
See page 104

HN 476 Fruit Gathering
See page 125

HN 477 Betty (first version, model 282)
See page 118

HN 478 Betty (first version, model 282)
See page 118

HN 479 The Balloon Seller
Designer: L. Harradine
Size: 9 in (22.8 cm)
Introduced: 1921
Withdrawn: By 1938
As HN 583, but blue dress, white spots
Also known as *The Balloon Woman*
This, the first of a long and popular series of Doulton balloon sellers and other street characters, was inspired by a Chelsea figure, *The Balloon Woman*, made by Charles Vyse in 1920.
Apart from their connection with Vyse, figures of this type show also the influence of the painter Augustus John.

HN 486 The Balloon Seller
Introduced: 1921
Withdrawn: By 1938
As HN 583, but blue dress, no hat

HN 548 The Balloon Seller
Introduced: 1922
Withdrawn: By 1938
As HN 583, but black shawl, blue dress

HN 583 The Balloon Seller
Introduced: 1923
Withdrawn: By 1949
For illustration, see next page

HN 583 The Balloon Seller

The Balloon Woman, modelled by Charles Vyse, introduced in 1920

The Tulip Woman, modelled by Charles Vyse, introduced in 1921

HN 697 The Balloon Seller
Introduced: 1925
Withdrawn: By 1938
As HN 583, but striped red shawl, blue dress

HN 480 One of the Forty
See page 123

HN 481 One of the Forty
See page 123

HN 482 One of the Forty
See page 124

HN 483 One of the Forty
See page 123

HN 484 One of the Forty
See page 124

HN 485 Lucy Lockett (first version)
Designer: L. Harradine
Size: 6 in (15.2 cm)
Introduced: 1921
Withdrawn: By 1949
A character from *The Beggar's Opera*. For further details see HN 463, *Polly Peachum*

HN 524 Lucy Lockett (first version)
Introduced: 1921
Withdrawn: By 1949
As HN 485, but yellow dress

HN 486 The Balloon Seller
See previous page

HN 485 Lucy Lockett (first version, illustration from the figure design book)

HN 487 Pavlova

Contemporary photograph of Pavlova, as *The Dying Swan*

HN 487 Pavlova
Size: 4¼ in (11.4 cm)
Introduced: 1921
Withdrawn: By 1938
Also known as *Swan Song*.
Anna Pavlova, (1882–1931), a great Russian Ballerina, first came to Europe in 1908. Her fame, skill and artistry prompted Diaghilev to say of her: 'She is the greatest ballerina in the world . . . she doesn't dance, but floats.' Her most famous role, as The Dying Swan in *La Cygne* by Saint-Caens was created for her by the choreographer, Fokine, a performance that set new standards in ballet. This figure was reissued after Pavlova's death in 1931.

HN 676 Pavlova
Introduced: 1924
Withdrawn: By 1938
As HN 487, but green base

HN 488 Tulips
See page 131

HN 489 Polly Peachum (second version, model 316)
Designer: L. Harradine
Size: 4¼ in (11.4 cm)
Introduced: 1921
Withdrawn: By 1938
For illustration, see page 129
Also known as *Polly Peachum—Curtsey*, or simply as *Curtsey*
A character from *The Beggar's Opera*. For further details, see HN 463.

HN 549 Polly Peachum (second version, model 316)
Introduced: 1922
Withdrawn: By 1949
For illustration, see page 129

HN 620 Polly Peachum (second version, model 316)
Introduced: 1924
Withdrawn: By 1938
As HN 489, but pink dress, cream underskirt

HN 694 Polly Peachum (second version, model 316)
Introduced: 1925
Withdrawn: By 1949
As HN 489, but deep rose pink dress, green bows

HN 734 Polly Peachum (second version, model 316)
Introduced: 1925
Withdrawn: By 1949
As HN 489, but black bodice, white skirt, black spots

HN 490 One of the Forty
See page 121

HN 491 One of the Forty
See page 123

HN 492 One of the Forty
See page 124

HN 493 One of the Forty
See page 123

HN 494 One of the Forty
See page 122

HN 495 One of the Forty
See page 121

HN 496 One of the Forty
See page 124

HN 497 One of the Forty
See page 123

HN 498 One of the Forty
See page 122

HN 499 One of the Forty
See page 123

HN 500 One of the Forty
See page 124

HN 501 One of the Forty
See page 121

HN 502 Marie (first version, model 281)
See page 118

HN 503 Fruit Gathering
See page 126

HN 504 Marie (first version, model 281)
See page 118

HN 505 Marie (first version, model 281)
See page 118

HN 506 Marie (first version, model 281)
See page 118

HN 507 Pussy
See page 70

HN 508 The Orange Vendor
See page 94

HN 509 Lady of the Fan
See page 89

HN 510 A Child's Grace
See page 93

HN 511 'Upon her Cheeks she Wept'
See page 91

HN 512 A Spook
See page 88

HN 513 Picardy Peasant (female)
See page 67

HN 514 The Welsh Girl
See page 79

HN 515 Lady with Rose
See page 88

HN 516 The Welsh Girl
See page 79

HN 517 Lady with Rose
See page 88

HN 518 The Curtsey
See page 90

HN 519 The Welsh Girl
See page 79

HN 520 The Welsh Girl
See page 79

HN 521 The Orange Vendor
See page 94

HN 522 'Upon her Cheeks she Wept'
See page 91

HN 523 Sentinel (illustration from the figure design book)

HN 523 Sentinel
Size: $17\frac{1}{2}$ in (44.4 cm)
Introduced: 1921
Withdrawn: By 1938
This figure was apparently made for the Sentinel Waggon Works, Shrewsbury, and is a replica of a figure on the factory gate. The figure carries the Coat of Arms of Shrewsbury on the shield.
Sentinel, famous for its railway locomotives, steam lorries and other vehicles, is now part of Rolls-Royce.

HN 524 Lucy Lockett (first version)
See page 132

HN 525 The Flower Seller's Children
Designer: L. Harradine
Size: $8\frac{1}{4}$ in (21.4 cm)
Introduced: 1921
Withdrawn: By 1949
As HN 1206, but boy in green costume, girl in blue costume.
This popular street seller group may have been inspired by the many flower sellers who used to gather on the steps below Alfred Gilbert's *Eros* statue in London's Piccadilly Traditionally, Harradine is supposed to have come across this scene while walking in London late one night, which he sketched there and then on the cuff of his evening shirt.

HN 551 The Flower Seller's Children
Introduced: 1922
Withdrawn: By 1949
As HN 1206, but boy in blue costume, girl in chequered orange and yellow costume

HN 1206 The Flower Seller's Children
Introduced: 1926
Withdrawn: By 1949

HN 1342 The Flower Seller's Children
Introduced: 1929
Still in Production

HN 1206 The Flower Seller's Children

HN 1342 The Flower Seller's Children

HN 1406 The Flower Seller's Children
Introduced: 1930
Withdrawn: By 1938
As HN 1206, but girl in yellow costume, dark blue cloth over the basket

HN 526 The Beggar (first version, model 348)
Designer: L. Harradine
Size: 6½ in (16.5 cm)
Introduced: 1921
Withdrawn: By 1949
For illustration, see page 129
A character from *The Beggar's Opera*. For further details, see HN 463, *Polly Peachum*

HN 591 The Beggar (first version, model 348)
Introduced: 1924
Withdrawn: By 1949
As HN 526, but different glaze finish

HN 527 The Highwayman
Designer: L. Harradine
Size: 6½ in (16.5 cm)
Introduced: 1921
Withdrawn: By 1949
For illustration, see page 129
A character from *The Beggar's Opera*. For further details, see HN 463, *Polly Peachum*

HN 592 The Highwayman
Introduced: 1924
Withdrawn: By 1949
As HN 527, but different glaze finish

HN 1257 The Highwayman
Introduced: 1927
Withdrawn: By 1949
As HN 592, but earthenware

HN 528 One of the Forty
See page 122

HN 529 Mr Pickwick (first version, miniature)
Designer: L. Harradine
Size: 3¾ in (9.5 cm)
Introduced: 1922
Renumbered as a miniature: 1932
First produced in 1922, the series of miniature Dickens figures have remained in production until the present day, with a few additions. In 1932 they were removed from the HN series, and then reappeared in the miniatures series, where they remained until 1949 when the series was given up. They were then re-introduced, in slightly larger sizes, but were sold without any identification numbers. In this form the series is still in production.
Samuel Pickwick was the lovable and delightfully innocent hero of *Pickwick Papers*, whose cheerful acceptance of misfortunes and indignities determined the humour of the book.

HN 530 The Fat Boy (first version, miniature)
Designer: L. Harradine
Size: 3½ in (8.9 cm)
Introduced: 1922
Renumbered as a miniature: 1932
Joe, Mr Wardle's page at Manor Farm in *Pickwick Papers*, was described as: 'a fat, red faced boy, in a state of somnolency'. Permanently asleep, Joe only shows signs of life when food is present.

HN 531 Sam Weller
Designer: L. Harradine
Size: 4 in (10.1 cm)
Introduced: 1922
Renumbered as a miniature: 1932
Sam Weller, the companion of Mr Pickwick, was known for his imperturbable humour and his droll figures of speech

HN 532 Mr Micawber (first version, miniature)
Designer: L. Harradine
Size: 3½ in (8.9 cm)
Introduced: 1922
Renumbered as a miniature: 1932
Wilkins Micawber, the genial agent in *David Copperfield*, was described as: 'a stoutish, middle-aged person in a brown surtout and black tights and shoes, with no more hair upon his head than there is upon an egg.' Constantly in debt, Mr Micawber lives in hope of 'something turning up'.

HN 533 Sairey Gamp (first version, miniature)
Designer: L. Harradine
Size: 4 in (10.1 cm)
Introduced: 1922
Renumbered as a miniature: 1932
Sairey Gamp, the fat old nurse in *Martin Chuzzlewit*, was renowned for her husky voice, her moist eye, her enjoyment of spirits and her equal relish for 'a laying-in or a laying-out'.

HN 534 Fagin
Designer: L. Harradine
Size: 4 in (10.1 cm)
Introduced: 1922
Renumbered as a miniature: 1932
Fagin, the grim master thief in *Oliver Twist*, failed in his attempts to lure Oliver to a life of crime, and instead paved his own way to the scaffold.

HN 535 Pecksniff (first version, miniature)
Designer: L. Harradine
Size: 3¾ in (9.5 cm)
Introduced: 1922
Renumbered as a miniature: 1932
Pecksniff, whose name is synonymous with hypocrisy, was the senile, smooth-tongued, crawling knave in *Martin Chuzzlewit*.

HN 536 Stiggins
Designer: L. Harradine
Size: 3¾ in (9.5 cm)
Introduced: 1922
Renumbered as a miniature: 1932
The Rev Mr Stiggins from *Pickwick Papers*, was a leading light at the Brick Lane Temperance meetings until exposed by Tony Weller: 'he was a prim-faced, red-nosed man, with a long, thin countenance and a semi-rattlesnake sort of eye.'

Miniature Dickens figures: *top*, Tony Weller, Sam Weller, Fat Boy, Mr Micawber, Mr Pickwick, Sairey Gamp
centre, Captain Cuttle, Pecksniff, Fagin, Uriah Heep, Stiggins, Bill Sykes
bottom, Bumble, Little Nell, Jingle, Tiny Tim, Artful Dodger, Buz Fuz
This illustration includes the two M series models added to the range in 1939, Bumble and Captain Cuttle, that were not included in the HN series

HN 537 Bill Sykes
Designer: L. Harradine
Size: 3¾ in (9.5 cm)
Introduced: 1922
Renumbered as a miniature: 1932
For illustration of this and of the following small Dickens figures, see previous page
Bill Sykes, the brutal ruffian in *Oliver Twist*, was utterly devoid of any redeeming trait. However, despite his constant ill-treatment of them, he is loved by Nancy and his dog. By murdering Nancy he causes his own dreadful death.

HN 538 Buz Fuz
Designer: L. Harradine
Size: 3¾ in (9.5 cm)
Introduced: 1922
Renumbered as a miniature: 1932
Sergeant Buz Fuz, a pugnacious bully in *Pickwick Papers*, was the leading counsel for Mrs Bardell in her breach of promise case against Mr Pickwick.

HN 539 Tiny Tim
Designer: L. Harradine
Size: 3½ in (8.9 cm)
Introduced: 1922
Renumbered as a miniature: 1932
Tiny Tim was the crippled son of Bob Cratchit, the ill-used clerk of Mr Scrooge in *A Christmas Carol*

HN 540 Little Nell
Designer: L. Harradine
Size: 4 in (10.1 cm)
Introduced: 1922
Renumbered as a miniature: 1932
Little Nell was a gentle, pure-spirited child who moved quietly through the pages of *The Old Curiosity Shop* towards her eventual and inevitable death.

HN 541 Alfred Jingle
Designer: L. Harradine
Size: 3¾ in (9.4 cm)
Introduced: 1922
Renumbered as a miniature: 1932
Alfred Jingle, the irresponsible strolling actor in *Pickwick Papers*, befriends the Pickwickians, then embarrasses them by eloping with Rachel Wardle, goes to prison, and is ultimately rescued by Mr Pickwick.

HN 542 The Cobbler (first version, model 362)
Designer: C. J. Noke
Size: 7½ in (19 cm)
Introduced: 1922
Withdrawn: By 1939
Baba Mustapha, the cobbler in *Ali Baba and the Forty Thieves* (and in the operetta *Chu Chin Chow*) has to sew together the quartered body of Kassim, Ali Baba's brother, after his murder at the hands of the thieves. In the operetta, the cobbler sings a doleful, but popular song:
'I sit and cobble at slippers and shoon
From the rise of the sun to the set of the moon.'

HN 543 The Cobbler (first version, model 362)
Introduced: 1922
Withdrawn: By 1938
As HN 542, but special firing

HN 682 The Cobbler (first version, model 362)
Introduced: 1924
Withdrawn: By 1938
As HN 542, but red shirt, green robe

HN 544 Tony Weller (second version, miniature)
Designer: L. Harradine
Size: 3½ in (8.9 cm)
Introduced: 1922
Renumbered as a miniature: 1932
For further details, see HN 346

HN 545 Uriah Heep (first version, miniature)
Designer: L. Harradine
Size: 4 in (10.1 cm)
Introduced: 1922
Renumbered as a miniature: 1932
The red-headed Uriah Heep was the 'umble, fawning, slimy clerk and later partner of Mr Wickfield in *David Copperfield*

HN 546 The Artful Dodger
Designer: L. Harradine
Size: 3¾ in (9.4 cm)
Introduced: 1922
Renumbered as a miniature: 1932
John Dawkins, the Artful Dodger in *Oliver Twist*, was the smartest of all Fagin's promising pupils, yet, when the time came, he met his downfall with dignity.

HN 547 The Curtsey
See page 90

HN 548 The Balloon Seller
See page 131

HN 549 Polly Peachum (second version, model 316)
See page 133

HN 550 Polly Peachum (first version, model 320)
See page 130

HN 551 The Flower Seller's Children
See page 134

HN 552 A Jester (first version, model 170)
See page 84

HN 553 Pecksniff (second version, model 385)
Designer: L. Harradine
Size: 7 in (17.7 cm)
Introduced: 1923
Withdrawn: 1939
For further details, see HN 535
For illustration, see page 140

HN 542 The Cobbler (first version)

HN 1283 The Cobbler (second version)

HN 1706 The Cobbler (third version)

HN 1705 The Cobbler (third version)

HN 557 Mr Micawber (second version) HN 555 The Fat Boy (second version) HN 556 Mr Pickwick (second version)

HN 553 Pecksniff (second version) HN 558 Sairey Gamp (second version) HN 554 Uriah Heep (second version)

HN 1891 Pecksniff (second version, model 385)
Introduced: 1938
Withdrawn: 1952
As HN 553, but very minor colour changes

HN 554 Uriah Heep (second version, model 384)
Designed: L. Harradine
Size: 7¼ in (18.4 cm)
Introduced: 1923
Withdrawn: 1939
For further details, see HN 545

HN 1892 Uriah Heep (second version, model 384)
Introduced: 1938
Withdrawn: 1952
As HN 554, but very minor colour changes

HN 555 The Fat Boy (second version model 381)
Designer: L. Harradine
Size: 7 in (17.7 cm)
Introduced: 1923
Withdrawn: 1939
For further details, see HN 530

HN 1893 The Fat Boy (second version, model 381)
Introduced: 1938
Withdrawn: 1952
As HN 555, but very minor colour changes

HN 556 Mr Pickwick (second version, model 379)
Designer: L. Harradine
Size: 7 in (17.7 cm)
Introduced: 1923
Withdrawn: 1939
For further details, see HN 529

HN 1894 Mr Pickwick (second version, model 379)
Introduced: 1938
Withdrawn: 1952
As HN 556, but very minor colour changes

HN 557 Mr Micawber (second version, model 380)
Designer: L. Harradine
Size: 7 in (17.7 cm)
Introduced: 1923
Withdrawn: 1939
For further details, see HN 532

HN 1895 Mr Micawber (second version, model 380)
Introduced: 1938
Withdrawn: 1952
As HN 557, but very minor colour changes

HN 558 Sairey Gamp (second version, model 382)
Designer: L. Harradine
Size: 7 in (17.7 cm)
Introduced: 1923
Withdrawn: 1939
For further details, see HN 533

HN 1896 Sairey Gamp (second version, model 382)
Introduced: 1938
Withdrawn: 1952
As HN 558, but very minor colour changes

Saltglazed stoneware versions of two Dickens figures, from the set made at the Doulton Lambeth factory by L. Harradine on which the HN models were based

HN 559 The Goosegirl
See page 124

HN 560 The Goosegirl
See page 125

HN 561 Fruit Gathering
See page 126

HN 562 Fruit Gathering
See page 126

HN 563 *Man in Tudor Costume*
Introduced: 1923
Withdrawn: By 1938

HN 563 *Man in Tudor Costume* (illustration from the figure design book)

HN 564 The Parson's Daughter
See page 106

HN 565 Pretty Lady
See page 94

HN 566 The Crinoline
See page 68

HN 567 The Bouquet
See page 120

HN 568 Shy Anne
See page 92

HN 569 The Lavender Woman
See page 72

HN 570 *Woman Holding Child*
See page 128

HN 571 Falstaff (first version, model 401)
Designer: C. J. Noke
Size: 7 in (17.7 cm)
Introduced: 1923
Withdrawn: By 1938

One of the most popular of Shakespeare's characters, Falstaff, the great companion of Henry, Prince of Wales, was a traditional lovable rogue, a fat and good-humoured old knight, addicted equally to jests, food, drink and good living

HN 575 Falstaff (first version, model 401)
Introduced: 1923
Withdrawn: By 1938
As HN 571, but brown coat, yellow spotted cloth over base

HN 608 Falstaff (first version, model 401)
Introduced: 1924
Withdrawn: By 1938
As HN 571, but red coat, red cloth over base

HN 609 Falstaff (first version, model 401)
Introduced: 1924
Withdrawn: By 1938
As HN 571, but green coat, green cloth over base

HN 619 Falstaff (first version, model 401)
Introduced: 1924
Withdrawn: By 1938
As HN 571, but brown coat with green collar, yellow cloth over base

HN 638 Falstaff (first version, model 401)
Introduced: 1924
Withdrawn: By 1938
As HN 571, but red coat, spotted cream cloth over base

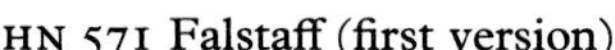
HN 571 Falstaff (first version)

HN 1606 Falstaff (first version)

HN 1216 Falstaff (first version, model 401)
Introduced: 1926
Withdrawn: By 1949
As HN 571, but multicoloured costume

HN 1606 Falstaff (first version, model 401)
Introduced: 1933
Withdrawn: By 1949

HN 572 Contentment
See page 117

HN 573 Madonna of the Square
See page 68

HN 574 No details available

HN 575 Falstaff (first version, model 401)
See above 142

HN 576 Madonna of the Square
See page 68

HN 577 The Chelsea Pair (female)
Designer: L. Harradine
Size: 6 in (15.2 cm)
Introduced: 1923
Withdrawn: By 1938
During the early 1920s there was a revival of interest in the products of the 18th century Chelsea China factory. This was prompted partly by the many potters and sculptors of note then living in the area, who included Gwendolen Parnell, Reginald Wells, Charles Vyse, Harry Parr, Madeline Raper and many others. Several of these were keen to revive the art of figure making and had been working to this end in their Chelsea studios since about 1918. Their models, partly 18th century and partly modern in style, quickly became popular and so complemented the figures being produced at Burslem. There were inevitable links between Doulton and the Chelsea modellers, for example Charles Vyse who established his Chelsea studio in 1919 after leaving Burslem, and so the figures were frequently quite similar. Doulton's responded to this new interest in Chelsea by producing a series of broadly 18th century style figures during the early 1920s, a series launched by *The Chelsea Pair*.
The Chelsea revival reached its climax in an exhibition of Chelsea pottery and porcelain of the 18th, 19th and 20th centuries held at Chelsea Town Hall in June 1924.

HN 578 The Chelsea Pair (female)
Introduced: 1923
Withdrawn: By 1938
As HN 577, but red blouse

HN 579 & HN 577 The Chelsea Pair

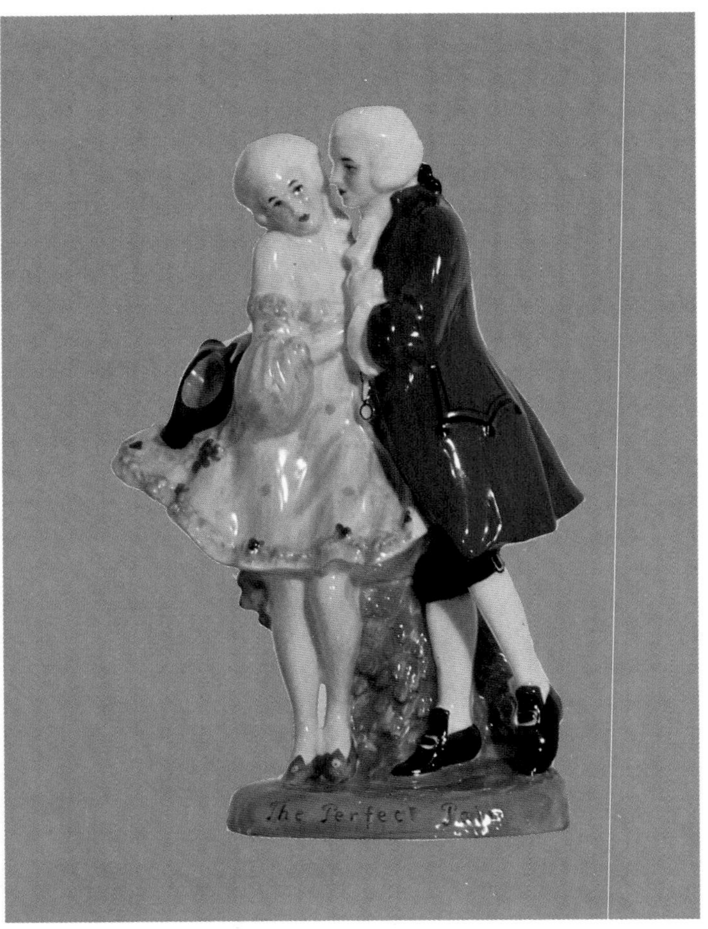

HN 581 The Perfect Pair

Reprinted from EVE THE LADY'S PICTORIAL, May 7th, 1924.

1.—Powder and Puff and "The Perfect Pair" ("Eve" and "The Tatler")

2.—"The Sketch" girl

THE VOGUE OF THE STATUETTE

I HAVE been rebuked for so rarely straying later than the end of the eighteenth century in writing about pottery or porcelain, and my invariable reply has been to demand plaintively: "Show me some pottery produced later than about 1800 which is worth writing about, and which would not look out of place illustrated on these lily-white pages." Believe me, there is a vast amount of rubbish abroad, masquerading as art, which never seems to get smashed, and is eternally being foisted upon an unsuspecting public—tortured shapes meticulously painted with meaningless decoration, gilded and monstrous forms—in short, all the horrors of the junk shop. It was therefore with real interest that I found myself looking at the little figures on this page, and thereby take back some of the hard things I have said in the past about modern methods of pottery manufacture.

3.—The Mikado and Japanese lady.

4.—Pierrette, Parson's daughter, and Harlequinade

5.—Fruit gathering

6.—Motherhood

P.T.O.

Part of an article about Doulton figures, first published in *Eve* magazine in 1924

HN 585 Harlequinade

HN 579 The Chelsea Pair (male)
Designer: L. Harradine
Size: 6 in (15.2 cm)
Introduced: 1923
Withdrawn: By 1938
For illustration, see previous page

HN 580 The Chelsea Pair (male)
Introduced: 1923
Withdrawn: By 1938
As HN 579, but blue flowers in bocage

HN 581 The Perfect Pair
Designer: L. Harradine
Size: 7 in (17.7 cm)
Introduced: 1923
Withdrawn: By 1938
Although this is apparently a Chelsea-style figure, there is a possibility that it was specially made for the magazines *Tatler* and *Eve*, a 'perfect pair' of popular journals then in the same stable.

HN 582 Grossmith's 'Tsang Ihang' Perfume of Tibet
Size: 11½ in (29.2 cm)
Introduced: 1923
Date of withdrawal not known
Although Doulton are known to have produced a number of figures for advertising purposes, very few of these were included in the HN series. Most were simply adaptions of existing models, such as the use of the *London Cry*

An advertisement for Yardley's Old English Lavender, showing the same figure, *c.*1925

Yardley's Old English Lavender, an advertising model adapted from HN 752, *London Cry*

HN 582 Grossmith's 'Tsang Ihang'

figure by Yardleys, but the Grossmith figure appears to have been specially designed.

HN 583 The Balloon Seller
See page 131

HN 584 Lady with Rose
See page 88

HN 585 Harlequinade
Designer: L. Harradine
Size: 7 in (17.7 cm)
Introduced: 1923
Withdrawn: By 1938
The story of Harlequin and Columbine was an important part of the traditional Italian *Commedia dell'Arte*, and had frequently been used by 18th century ceramic modellers. However, the presentation of this old name in rather stylish contemporary dress appears to have been a new development at Burslem.

HN 635 Harlequinade
Introduced: 1924
Withdrawn: By 1938
As HN 585, but gold costume

HN 711 Harlequinade
Introduced: 1925
Withdrawn: By 1938
As HN 585, but black and white costume

HN 780 Harlequinade
Introduced: 1926
Withdrawn: By 1938
As HN 585, but pink dress with blue, black and orange markings

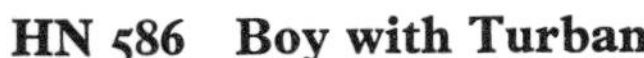

HN 586 & HN 1212 Boy with Turban

HN 588 *Girl with Yellow Frock* (illustration from the figure design book)

HN 586 Boy with Turban
Designer: L. Harradine
Size: $3\frac{3}{4}$ in (9.5 cm)
Introduced: 1923
Withdrawn: By 1938
Also known as *Eastern Boy*, this figure may have been inspired by the continuing interest in oriental tales such as Ali Baba

HN 587 Boy with Turban
Introduced: 1923
Withdrawn: By 1938
As HN 586, but with pink shirt and green trousers

HN 661 Boy with Turban
Introduced: 1924
Withdrawn: By 1938
As HN 586, but blue costume

HN 662 Boy with Turban
Introduced: 1924
Withdrawn: By 1938
As HN 586, but chequered black and white costume

HN 1210 Boy with Turban
Introduced: 1926
Withdrawn: By 1938
As HN 586, but black and red turban

HN 1212 Boy with Turban
Introduced: 1926
Withdrawn: 1938

HN 1213 Boy with Turban
Introduced: 1926
Withdrawn: 1938
As HN 586, but white costume, black squares

HN 1214 Boy with Turban
Introduced: 1926
Withdrawn: By 1938
As HN 586, but white costume, black and green markings

HN 1225 Boy with Turban
Introduced: 1927
Withdrawn: By 1938
As HN 586, but yellow trousers, blue spots

HN 588 *Girl with Yellow Frock*
Introduced: 1923
Withdrawn: By 1938

HN 589 Polly Peachum (first version, model 320)
See page 130

HN 590 Captain MacHeath
See page 130

HN 591 The Beggar
See page 136

HN 592 The Highwayman
See page 136

HN 593 *Nude on Rock*
Size: $6\frac{3}{4}$ in (17.1 cm)
Introduced: 1924
Withdrawn: By 1938

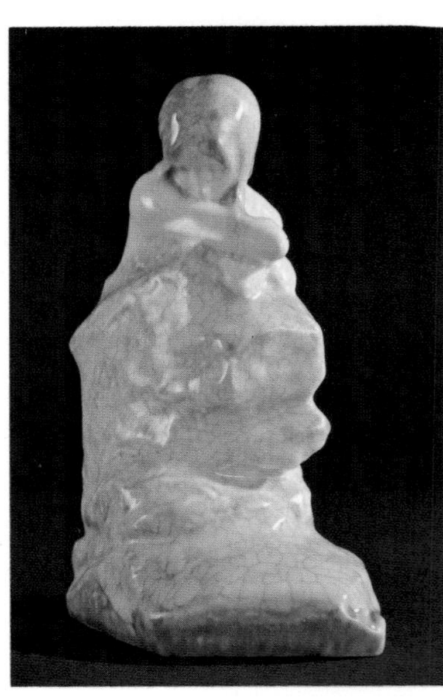

HN 593 *Nude on Rock* (illustration not in scale)

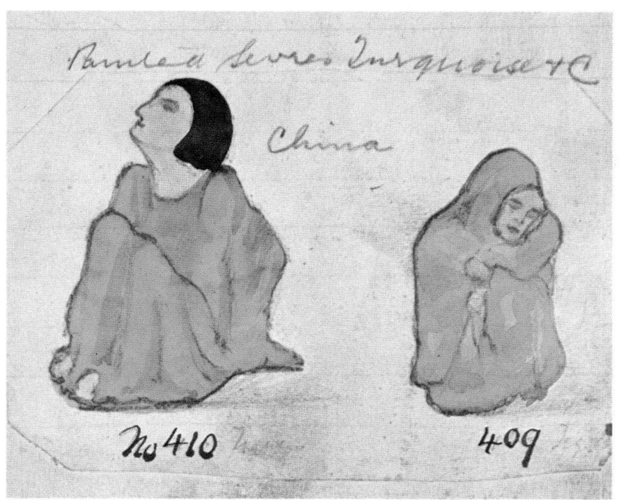

HN 595 *Grief* & HN 596 *Despair*
(illustrations from the figure design book)

HN 594 Madonna of the Square
See page 68

HN 595 *Grief*
Introduced: 1924
Withdrawn: By 1938

HN 596 *Despair*
Introduced: 1924
Withdrawn: By 1938

HN 597 The Bather (first version, model 428)
Designer: L. Harradine
Size: $7\frac{3}{4}$ in (19.6 cm)
Introduced: 1924
Withdrawn: By 1938
As HN 687, but mottled grey robes, blue base
During the early 1920s several quite new styles of figures were introduced. These included stylish models in contemporary dress, inspired by the fashions of the period, and a series of bathing beauties and nudes. Both show the influence of contemporary Art Deco sculpture, especially the bronze and ivory figure of Preiss and Chiparus, and contemporary continental ceramics. This should not be confused with an earlier version of *The Bather*, modelled by John Broad and produced at the Doulton Lambeth factory in about 1914.

HN 687 The Bather (first version, model 428)
Introduced: 1924
Withdrawn: By 1949

HN 781 The Bather (first version, model 428)
Introduced: 1926
Withdrawn: By 1938
As HN 687, but blue and green robe

HN 782 The Bather (first version, model 428)
Introduced: 1926
Withdrawn: By 1938
As HN 687, but mottled purple robe, black lining

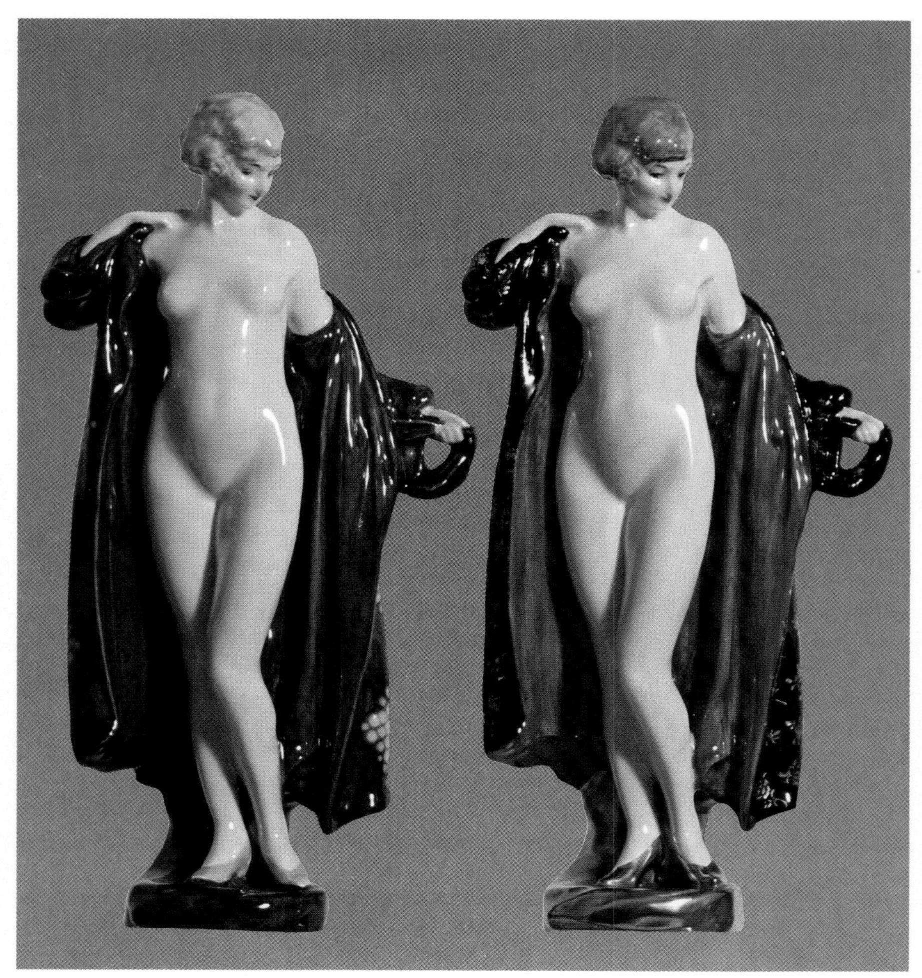

HN 687 & HN 1238 The Bather (first version)

HN 1708 The Bather (first version)

HN 1238 The Bather (first version, model 428)
Introduced: 1927
Withdrawn: By 1938
For illustration, see previous page

HN 1708 The Bather (first version, model 428)
Introduced: 1935
Withdrawn: By 1938
In response to the changes in popular taste, this late version of *The Bather* was produced with the addition of a painted bathing costume!
For illustration, see previous page

HN 598 Omar Khayyam and the Beloved
See page 120

HN 599 Masquerade (male, first version, model 420)
Designer: L. Harradine
Size: 6¾ in (17.1 cm)
Introduced: 1924
Withdrawn: By 1949

HN 600 Masquerade (female, first version, model 417)
Introduced: 1924
Withdrawn: 1949
The Masquerade, or masked ball theme, was a traditional one, and so these figures are a part of the 18th century revival.
A special masquerade was held in Ranelagh Gardens, Chelsea, on 24 May 1759 to celebrate the birthday of the Prince of Wales, and a number of Chelsea figures of

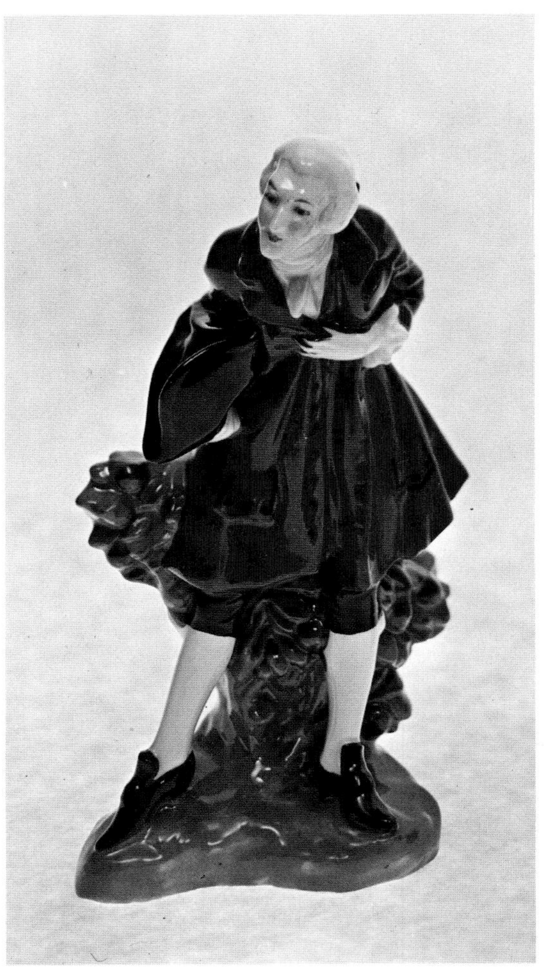

HN 599 Masquerade (male, first version)

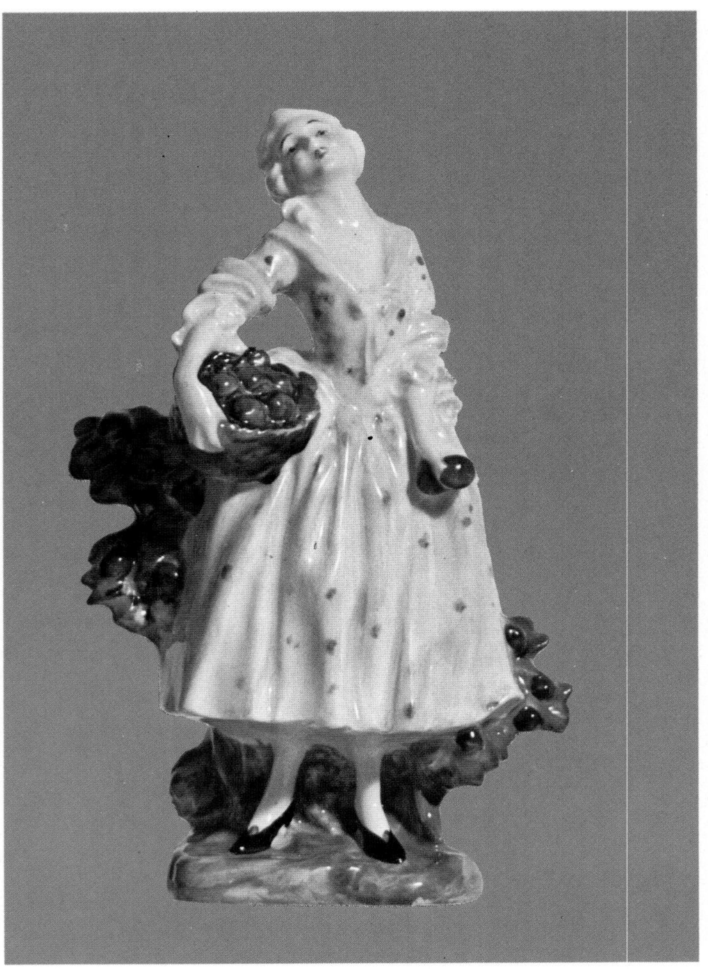

HN 600 Masquerade (female, first version)

HN 637 Masquerade (female, first version)

masqueraders were subsequently produced which may have inspired the Doulton models.
There was also an opera, *Masquerade*, by Carl Nielson, performed in 1906.

HN 636 Masquerade (male, first version, model 420)
Introduced: 1924
Withdrawn: By 1938
As HN 599, but gold costume

HN 637 Masquerade (female, first version, model 417)
Introduced: 1924
Withdrawn: By 1938

HN 674 Masquerade (female, first version, model 417)
Introduced: 1924
Withdrawn: By 1938
As HN 600, but orange and yellow chequered dress

HN 683 Masquerade (male, first version, model 420)
Introduced: 1924
Withdrawn: By 1938
As HN 599, but green coat

HN 601 A Mandarin (third version, model 346)
See page 127

HN 602 No details available

HN 603a Child Study
Designer: L. Harradine
Size: 4¾ in (12 cm)
Introduced: 1924
Withdrawn: By 1938
These figures, which were also produced without the floral decorations, were made primarily to be used as ornaments in floral displays. They were based on models designed about ten years before but not issued at the time. They also show the influence of similar figures modelled by John Broad at the Doulton Lambeth factory.

HN 603b Child Study
Introduced: 1924
Withdrawn: By 1938
As HN 603a, but kingcups round the base

HN 604a Child Study
Designer: L. Harradine
Size: 5¾ in (14.6 cm)
Introduced: 1924
Withdrawn: By 1938
As HN 604b, but primroses round the base

HN 604b Child Study
Introduced: 1924
Withdrawn: 1938

HN 605a Child Study
Introduced: 1924
Withdrawn: By 1938

HN 605b Child Study
Introduced: 1924
Withdrawn: By 1938

HN 606a Child Study
Designer: L. Harradine
Size: 5 in (12.7 cm)
Introduced: 1924
Withdrawn: By 1938

HN 606b Child Study
Introduced: 1924
Withdrawn: By 1938
As HN 606a, but kingcups round the base

HN 607 No details available

HN 605 Child Study (illustration from the figure design book)

HN 603A, HN 604B & HN 606A Child Study

HN 610 Henry Lytton as Jack Point HN 639 Elsie Maynard

HN 2054 Falstaff (second version)

HN 608 Falstaff (first version, model 401)
See page 142

HN 609 Falstaff (first version, model 401)
See page 142

HN 610 Henry Lytton as Jack Point
Designer: C. J. Noke
Size: 6½ in (16.5 cm)
Introduced: 1924
Withdrawn: By 1949
Jack Point, the tragic clown in Gilbert and Sullivan's *Yeoman of the Guard*, was a favourite part of the actor Sir Henry Lytton. In fact, his final performance of all was as Jack Point at the Gaiety Theatre, Dublin, in 1934. Apparently Noke had access to Lytton's actual Jack Point costume while designing this figure.

HN 611 A Mandarin (first version, model 189)
See page 97

HN 612 Poke Bonnet
See page 83

HN 613 Madonna of the Square
See page 68

HN 614 Polly Peachum (first version, model 320)
See page 130

HN 615 Katharine
See page 92

HN 616 A Jester (first version, model 170)
See page 84

HN 617 A Shepherd (first version)
See page 96

HN 618 Falstaff (second version, model 353)
Designer: C. J. Noke
Size: 7 in (17.7 cm)
Introduced: 1924
Withdrawn: By 1938
As HN 2054, but black collar, spotted lilac blanket, green base

HN 2054 Falstaff (second version, model 353)
Introduced: 1950
Still in production

HN 619 Falstaff (first version, model 401)
See page 142

HN 620 Polly Peachum (second version, model 316)
See page 133

HN 621 *Pan on Rock*
Introduced: 1924
Withdrawn: By 1938
This figure of the satyr Pan, the god of flocks and shepherds and the personification of nature, may have been based on a similar model produced by Charles Vyse in 1924.

HN 622 *Pan on Rock*
Introduced: 1924
Withdrawn: By 1938
As HN 621, but black base

HN 623 An Old King
See page 111

HN 624 Lady With Rose
See page 88

HN 625 A Spook
See page 88

HN 626 Lady With Shawl (second version, model 306)
See page 125

HN 627 A Jester (first version, model 170)
See page 85

HN 628 The Crinoline
See page 68

HN 629 The Curtsey
See page 90

HN 630 A Jester (second version, model 171)
See page 85

HN 631 Fisherwomen
See page 96

HN 632 A Shepherd (first version)
See page 96

HN 633 A Princess
See page 116

HN 634 A Geisha (first version, model 238)
See page 110

HN 635 Harlequinade
See page 145

HN 636 Masquerade (male, first version, model 420)
See page 149

HN 621 *Pan on Rock* (illustration from the figure design book)

Leap-Frog, modelled by Charles Vyse, introduced in 1924

HN 637 Masquerade (female, first version, model 417)
See page 149

HN 638 Falstaff (first version, model 401)
See page 142

HN 639 Elsie Maynard
Designer: C. J. Noke
Size: 7 in (17.7 cm)
Introduced: 1924
Withdrawn: By 1949
For illustration, see page
Made as a pair for HN 610, *Henry Lytton as Jack Point*, this figure represents the singer in Gilbert and Sullivan's *Yeoman of the Guard*, Jack Point's partner, who later causes him great distress by marrying Colonel Fairfax. The costumes of this figure and HN 610 are from a D'Oyle Carte production of the time.
For illustration, see opposite

HN 640 Charley's Aunt (first version, model 161)
See page 77

HN 641 A Mandarin (second version, model 260)
See page 112

HN 642 Pierrette (first version, model 445)
Designer: L. Harradine
Size: $7\frac{1}{4}$ in (18.4 cm)
Introduced: 1924
Withdrawn: By 1938
As HN 643, but red dress
Although this figure represents the traditional female clown, the partner of Pierrot, the use of contemporary dress makes it quite original.

HN 643 Pierrette (first version, model 445)
Introduced: 1924
Withdrawn: By 1938
For illustration, see next page

HN 643 & HN 644 Pierrette (first version)

HN 644 Pierrette (first version, model 445)
Introduced: 1924
Withdrawn: By 1938

HN 691 Pierrette (first version, model 445)
Introduced: 1925
Withdrawn: 1938
As HN 643, but gold costume

HN 721 Pierrette (first version, model 445)
Introduced: 1925
Withdrawn: By 1938
As HN 643, but black and white striped skirt

HN 731 Pierette (first version, model 445)
Introduced: 1925
Withdrawn: By 1938
As HN 643, but spotted black and white skirt

HN 732 Pierette (first version, model 445)
Introduced: 1925
Withdrawn: By 1938
As HN 643, black and white dress with petalled border

HN 784 Pierette (first version, model 445)
Introduced: 1926
Withdrawn: By 1938
As HN 643, but jazzy markings, on pink costume with black ruff

HN 645 One of the Forty
See page 124

HN 646 One of the Forty
See page 123

HN 647 One of the Forty
See page 122

HN 648 One of the Forty
See page 122

HN 649 One of the Forty
See page 124

HN 650 Crinoline Lady (miniature)
Size 3 in (7.6 cm)
Introduced: 1924
Withdrawn: By 1938

HN 651 Crinoline Lady (miniature)
Introduced: 1924
Withdrawn: By 1938

HN 650 & HN 651 Crinoline Lady

HN 652 Crinoline Lady (miniature)
Introduced: 1924
Withdrawn: By 1938
As HN 650, but purple dress

HN 653 Crinoline Lady (miniature)
Introduced: 1924
Withdrawn: By 1938
As HN 650, but grey and white striped dress

HN 654 Crinoline Lady (miniature)
Introduced: 1924
Withdrawn: By 1938
As HN 650, but orange and green mottled dress

HN 655 Crinoline Lady (miniature)
Introduced: 1924
Withdrawn: By 1938
As HN 650, but blue dress

HN 656 The Mask
Designer: L. Harradine
Size: $6\frac{3}{4}$ in (17.1 cm)
Introduced: 1924
Withdrawn: By 1938
As HN 657, but blue and purple costume
The use of masks as a means of both identifying and concealing characters was an essential part of classical drama. From this developed the idea of masked balls, or masques, where the identity of those taking part was concealed behind masks.
The presence of Cupid, hidden behind this figure, suggests a more flirtatious use of masks.

HN 657 The Mask
Introduced: 1924
Withdrawn: By 1938

HN 729 The Mask
Introduced: 1925
Withdrawn: By 1938

HN 733 The Mask
Introduced: 1925
Withdrawn: By 1938
As HN 657, but white costume with black squares

HN 785 The Mask
Introduced: 1926
Withdrawn: By 1938
As HN 657, but blue costume, pink striped skirt

HN 1271 The Mask
Introduced: 1928
Withdrawn: By 1938

HN 1271, HN 657 & HN 729 The Mask

HN 659, HN 658 & HN 786 Mam'selle

HN 658 Mam'selle
Designer: L. Harradine
Size: 7 in (17.7 cm)
Introduced: 1924
Withdrawn: By 1938
This figure, with its hidden cupid, is a modern interpretation of the traditional naughtiness of the French mademoiselle

HN 659 Mam'selle
Introduced: 1924
Withdrawn: By 1938

HN 724 Mam'selle
Introduced: 1925
Withdrawn: By 1938
As HN 658, but red hat, yellow trimmed dress

HN 786 Mam'selle
Introduced: 1926
Withdrawn: By 1938

HN 660 The Welsh Girl
See page 79

HN 661 Boy with Turban
See page 146

HN 662 Boy with Turban
See page 146

HN 663 One of the Forty
See page 124

HN 664 One of the Forty
See page 123

HN 665 One of the Forty
See page 124

HN 666 One of the Forty
See page 122

HN 667 One of the Forty
See page 123

HN 668 The Welsh Girl
See page 79

HN 669 The Welsh Girl
See page 79

HN 670 The Curtsey
See page 90

HN 671 Lady Ermine
See page 89

HN 672 Tulips
See page 131

HN 688 A Yeoman of the Guard

HN 689 A Chelsea Pensioner

Miniature Chelsea Pensioner, not recorded in the design books

HN 673 Henry VIII (first version, model 271)
See page 113

HN 674 Masquerade (female, first version, model 417)
See page 149

HN 675 The Gainsborough Hat
See page 87

HN 676 Pavlova
See page 133

HN 677 One of the Forty
See page 122

HN 678 Lady with Shawl
See page 125

HN 679 Lady with Shawl
See page 125

HN 680 Polly Peachum (first version, model 320)
See page 130

HN 681 The Cobbler (second version)
Designer: C. J. Noke
Size: 8½ in (21.5 cm)
Introduced: 1924
Withdrawn: By 1938
As HN 1283, but green costume, red skirt
For further details, see HN 542

HN 1251 The Cobbler (second version)
Introduced: 1927
Withdrawn: By 1938
As HN 1283, but black trousers, red shirt

HN 1283 The Cobbler (second version)
Introduced: 1928
Withdrawn: By 1949
For illustration, see page 139

HN 682 The Cobbler (first version, model 362)
See page 138

HN 683 Masquerade (male, first version, model 420)
See page 149

HN 684 Tony Weller (first version, model 254)
See page 109

HN 685 Contentment
See page 117

HN 686 Contentment
See page 117

HN 687 The Bather (first version, model 428)
See page 147

HN 688 A Yeoman of the Guard
Designer: L. Harradine
Size 5¾ in (14.6 cm)
Introduced: 1924
Withdrawn: By 1938

Commonly known as Beefeaters, the Yeomen of the Guard are the warders of the Tower of London. Although they form the Queen's bodyguard, their roles today are largely nominal and decorative. Founded by Henry VII in 1485 as a personal bodyguard, the Yeomen are now staffed by veterans and retired soldiers. Their costume dates from their founding in the 15th century. Although made as a pair to HN 689, *A Chelsea Pensioner*, this figure could also have been based on the Gilbert and Sullivan opera, *The Yeoman of the Guard*, first produced in 1888.

HN 2122 A Yeoman of the Guard
Introduced: 1954
Withdrawn: 1959
As HN 688, very minor glaze differences

HN 689 A Chelsea Pensioner
Designer: L. Harradine
Size: 5¾ in (14.6 cm)
Introduced: 1924
Withdrawn: By 1938
The Royal Hospital, Chelsea, was founded by Charles II as a home for disabled soldiers. Today, the pensioners of the Hospital still wear their distinctive uniforms, and frequently take part in ceremonial occasions.
For illustration, see previous page

HN 690 A Lady of the Georgian Period
See page 81

HN 691 Pierrette (first version, model 445)
See page 152

HN 692 Sleep
See page 72

HN 693 Polly Peachum (first version, model 320)
See page 130

HN 694 Polly Peachum (second version, model 316)
See page 133

HN 695 Lucy Lockett (second version, model 360)
Designer: L. Harradine
Size: 6 in (15.2 cm)
Introduced: 1925
Withdrawn: By 1949
For illustration, see page 129
A character from *The Beggar's Opera*. For further details, see HN 463, *Polly Peachum*

HN 696 Lucy Lockett (second version, model 360)
Introduced: 1925
Withdrawn: By 1949
As HN 695, but powder blue costume

HN 697 The Balloon Seller
See page 132

HN 698 Polly Peachum (third version, miniature, model 462)
Designer: L. Harradine
Size: 2¼ in (5.7 cm)
Introduced: 1925
Withdrawn: By 1949
Pink dress
See also the other miniature versions included in the M series, some of which are illustrated

HN 699 Polly Peachum (third version, miniature, model 462)
Introduced: 1925
Withdrawn: By 1949
Blue dress

HN 757 Polly Peachum (third version, miniature, model 462)
Introduced: 1925
Withdrawn: By 1949
Red bodice, spotted skirt and holding coloured streamers

HN 758 Polly Peachum (third version, miniature, model 462)
Introduced: 1925
Withdrawn: By 1949
Pink skirt with orange stripes

HN 759 Polly Peachum (third version, miniature, model 462)
Introduced: 1925
Withdrawn: By 1949
Yellow and white skirt with black spots

HN 760 Polly Peachum (third version, miniature, model 462)
Introduced: 1925
Withdrawn: By 1949
Mottled multicoloured skirt

HN 761 Polly Peachum (third version, miniature, model 462)
Introduced: 1925
Withdrawn: By 1949
Blue and purple skirt

HN 762 Polly Peachum (third version, miniature, model 462)
Introduced: 1925
Withdrawn: By 1949
Pink roses on skirt

HN 700 Pretty Lady
See page 94

HN 701 A Welsh Girl
See page 79

HN 702 A Lady of the Georgian Period
See page 81

HN 703 *Woman Holding Child*
See page 128

HN 704 One of the Forty
See page 122

HN 705 The Gainsborough Hat
See page 87

HN 706 Fruit Gathering
See page 126

HN 707 Fruit Gathering
See page 126

HN 708 Shepherdess (first version, miniature, model 469)
Size: 3½ in (8.8 cm)
Introduced: 1925
Withdrawn: By 1948
Red overskirt, yellow and pink striped skirt
No illustrations available of this and HN 709. For style, see the full-size models HN 735 and 751, page 162

HN 709 Shepherd (second version, miniature, model 470)
Size: 3½ in (8.8 cm)
Introduced: 1925
Withdrawn: By 1938
Green jacket, red cloak, black trousers
See also the other miniature versions included in the M series

HN 710 Sleep
See page 72

HN 711 Harlequinade
See page 145

HN 712 One of the Forty
See page 123

HN 713 One of the Forty
See page 124

HN 714 One of the Forty
See page 123

HN 715 Proposal (lady)
Size: 5¾ in (14.6 cm)
Introduced: 1925
Withdrawn: By 1938
Made as a pair to HN 725, *Proposal* (male)
For illustration, see page 159

HN 716 Proposal (lady)
Introduced: 1925
Withdrawn: By 1938

HN 788 Proposal (lady)
Introduced: 1926
Withdrawn: By 1938
As HN 715, but pink dress

HN 717 *Lady Clown*
Designer: L. Harradine
Size: 7½ in (19 cm)
Introduced: 1925
Withdrawn: By 1938
The vogue for clowns and clown costume continued throughout the 1920s, a fashion expressed by this figure, with its party dress. There were a number of plays and musicals which encouraged the fashion, for example, *Clowns in Clover*, first performed in 1927.

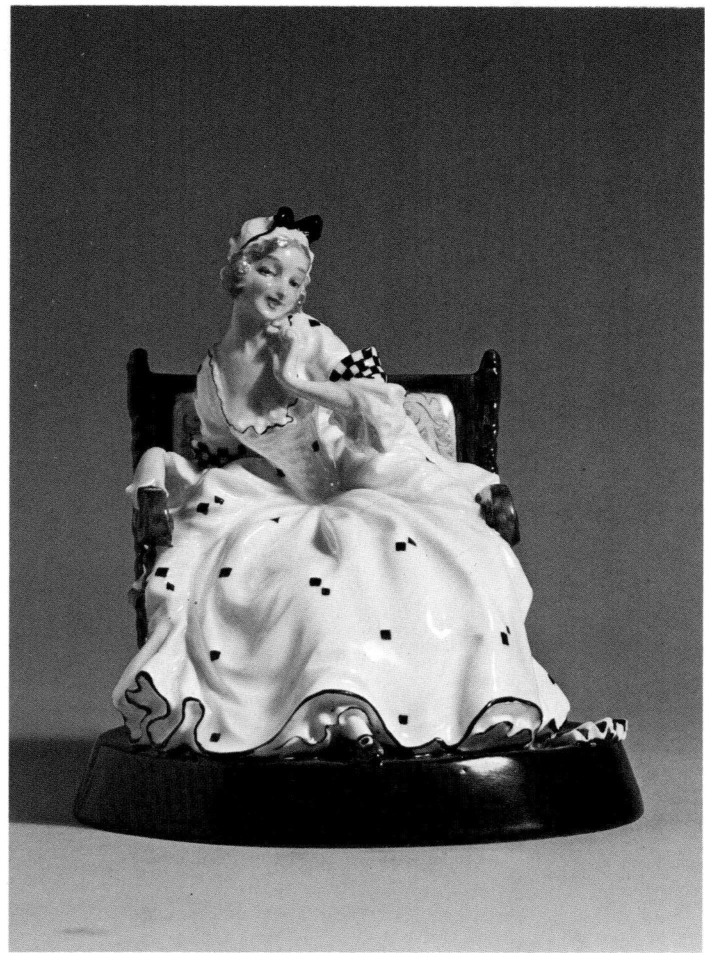

HN 716 Proposal (lady)

HN 717 *Lady Clown*

HN 718 ***Lady Clown***
Introduced: 1925
Withdrawn: By 1938
As HN 717, but white costume, red stripes, black spots

HN 738 *Lady Clown*
Introduced: 1925
Withdrawn: By 1938
As HN 717, but black and white trousers, red spots

HN 770 *Lady Clown*
Introduced: 1925
Withdrawn: By 1938
AS HN 717, but costume painted with green masks and streamers

HN 1263 *Lady Clown*
Introduced: 1927
Withdrawn: By 1938
As HN 717, but particoloured trousers, one leg blue, the other red stripes

HN 719 Butterfly
Designer: L. Harradine
Size: 6½ in (16.5 cm)
Introduced: 1925
Withdrawn: By 1938
Also known as *Butterfly Woman*
This figure is probably based on the fancy costumes popular at the masked balls of the period

HN 720 Butterfly
Introduced: 1925
Withdrawn: By 1938

HN 730 Butterfly
Introduced: 1925
Withdrawn: By 1938
As HN 719, but yellow dress, blue-black wings

HN 1203 Butterfly
Introduced: 1926
Withdrawn: By 1938
As HN 719, but gold wings

HN 1456 Butterfly
Introduced: 1931
Withdrawn: By 1938

HN 721 Pierrette (first version, model 445)
See page 152

HN 722 Mephisto
Designer: L. Harradine
Size: 6½ in (16.5 cm)
Introduced: 1925
Withdrawn: By 1938
As HN 723, but black blouse
Mephisto is the traditional demon king of pantomime, whose appearance is usually heralded by puffs of green smoke and dramatic light effects. In this case, the figure appears to be based more on masquerade costumes, like HN 719, *Butterfly*

HN 723 Mephisto
Introduced: 1925
Withdrawn: By 1938

HN 719, HN 1456 & HN 720 Butterfly

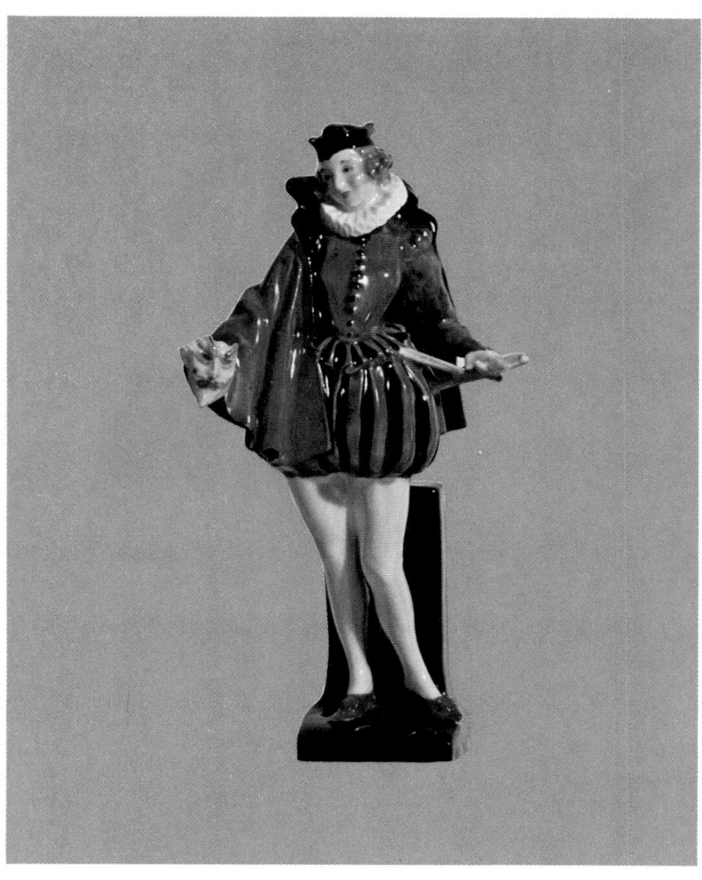

HN 723 Mephisto

HN 724 Mam'selle
See page 154

HN 725 The Proposal (male)
Size: $5\frac{1}{2}$ in (13.9 cm)
Introduced: 1925
Withdrawn: By 1938
Made as a pair to HN 715, *Proposal* (lady)

HN 1209 The Proposal (male)
Introduced: 1926
Withdrawn: By 1938
As HN 725, but blue coat, flowered pink waistcoat

HN 726 A Victorian Lady
Designer: L Harradine
Size: $7\frac{3}{4}$ in (19.6 cm)
Introduced: 1925
Withdrawn: By 1938
For illustration, see next page
Despite its name, this figure is only loosely based on Victorian costume. However, the fifteen different versions, some of which were still in production in 1949, make it one of the most popular of the Doulton ladies.

HN 727 A Victorian Lady
Introduced: 1925
Withdrawn: By 1938
For illustration, see next page

HN 728 A Victorian Lady
Introduced: 1925
Withdrawn: 1952
For illustration, see next page

HN 715 Proposal (lady) & HN 725 Proposal (male)

A Victorian Lady: HN 727 HN 728 HN 1208
HN 726 HN 1345 HN 736

HN 736 A Victorian Lady
Introduced: 1925
Withdrawn: By 1938

HN 739 A Victorian Lady
Introduced: 1925
Withdrawn: By 1938
As HN 726, but mottled red, blue and yellow skirt, yellow scarf

HN 740 A Victorian Lady
Introduced: 1925
Withdrawn: By 1938

HN 742 A Victorian Lady
Introduced: 1925
Withdrawn: By 1938
As HN 726, but black and white chequered shawl, white dress with blue spots

HN 745 A Victorian Lady
Introduced: 1925
Withdrawn: By 1938
As HN 726, but dress patterned with pink roses

HN 1208 A Victorian Lady
Introduced: 1926
Withdrawn: By 1938

HN 1258 A Victorian Lady
Introduced: 1927
Withdrawn: By 1938
As HN 726, but mottled purple shawl, mottled blue dress

A Victorian Lady: HN 1276 HN 1529

HN 740 A Victorian Lady

HN 1276 A Victorian Lady
Introduced: 1928
Withdrawn: By 1938
For illustration, see page 161

HN 1277 A Victorian Lady
Introduced: 1928
Withdrawn: By 1938
As HN 726, but red shawl, yellow and blue tiered dress

HN 1345 A Victorian Lady
Introduced: 1929
Withdrawn: By 1949
For illustration, see page 160

HN 1452 A Victorian Lady
Introduced: 1931
Withdrawn: By 1949
As HN 726, but green dress and shawl

HN 1529 A Victorian Lady
Introduced: 1932
Withdrawn: By 1938
For illustration, see page 161

HN 729 The Mask
See page 153

HN 730 Butterfly
See page 158

HN 731 Pierrette (first version, model 445)
See page 152

HN 732 Pierrette (first version, model 445)
See page 152

HN 733 The Mask
See page 153

HN 734 Polly Peachum (second version, model 316)
See page 133

HN 735 Shepherdess (second version, model 455)
Size: 7 in (17.7 cm)
Introduced: 1925
Withdrawn: By 1938
Also known as *Milkmaid*, this figure was made as a pair to HN 751, *Shepherd*. The two were freely based on 18th century Chelsea figures, although the subject is a traditional one among ceramic modellers.

HN 750 Shepherdess (second version, model 455)
Introduced: 1925
Withdrawn: By 1938
As HN 735, but pink bodice, yellow skirt

HN 736 A Victorian Lady
See page 161

HN 735 Shepherdess HN 751 Shepherd

HN 737 No details available

HN 738 ***Lady Clown***
See page 158

HN 739 **A Victorian Lady**
See page 161

HN 740 **A Victorian Lady**
See page 161

HN 741 **A Geisha** (first version, model 238)
See page 110

HN 742 **A Victorian Lady**
See page 161

HN 743 ***Woman Holding Child***
See page 128

HN 744 **The Lavender Woman**
See page 72

HN 745 **A Victorian Lady**
See page 161

HN 746 **A Mandarin** (first version, model 189)
See page 97

HN 747 **Tulips**
See page 131

HN 748 **Out for a Walk**
See page 99

HN 749 **London Cry, Strawberries**
Designer: L. Harradine
Size: 6¾ in (17.1 cm)
Introduced: 1925
Withdrawn: By 1938
London Cries, the traditional melodic calls of the street vendors, were immortalised in a series of engravings of itinerant street sellers and their wares by Francis Wheatley (1747-1801). This figure, and its pair, HN 752, were based on the Wheatley designs, although models of street vendors had also been produced at the 18th century Chelsea factory.
For illustration, see next page

HN 772 London Cry, Strawberries
Introduced: 1925
Withdrawn: By 1938
For illustration, see next page

HN 750 **Shepherdess** (second version, model 455)
See page 162

HN 751 **Shepherd** (third version, model 453)
Size: 7 in (17.7 cm)
Introduced: 1925
Withdrawn: By 1938
Made as a pair to HN 735, *Shepherdess*
For illustration, see opposite

HN 752 **London Cry, Turnips and Carrots**
Designer: L. Harradine
Size: 6¾ in (17.1 cm)
Introduced: 1925
Withdrawn: By 1938
For illustration, see next page
This figure, a pair to HN 749, was adapted to be used as an advertising model for Yardley's, who had been using a trade mark based on a Wheatley *London Cry* engraving for their Old English Lavender since 1913. This adaption was not included in the HN series, but is illustrated on page 145

HN 771 London Cry, Turnips and Carrots
Introduced: 1925
Withdrawn: By 1938
For illustration, see next page

HN 753 **The Dandy**
Designer: L. Harradine
Size: 6¾ in (17.1 cm)
Introduced: 1925
Withdrawn: By 1938
For illustration, see page 165
Made as a pair to HN 754, *The Belle*

HN 754 **The Belle**
Designer: L. Harradine
Size: 6½ in (16.5 cm)
Introduced: 1925
Withdrawn: By 1938
For illustration, see page 165
This figure in 18th century style was made as a pair to HN 753, *The Dandy*. It should not be confused with HN 2340, *Belle*.

HN 776 The Belle
Introduced: 1925
Withdrawn: By 1938

HN 755 **Mephistopheles and Marguerite**
Designer: C. J. Noke
Size: 7¾ in (19.6 cm)
Introduced: 1925
Withdrawn: By 1949
As HN 775, but lady in orange dress, purple cloak
A larger version of this double figure was made in small quantities at Burslem during the 1890s, inspired perhaps by Ellen Terry and Henry Irving who played in *Faust* at the Lyceum Theatre in 1886.
Based on the play by Goethe, which was adapted as an opera by Gounod, the figure represents the conflict between good and evil.

HN 775 Mephistopheles and Marguerite
Introduced: 1925
Withdrawn: 1949
For illustration, see page 165

HN 771 London Cry, Turnips and Carrots
HN 752 London Cry, Turnips and Carrots

HN 772 London Cry, Strawberries
HN 749 London Cry, Strawberries

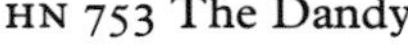

HN 753 The Dandy

HN 754 The Belle

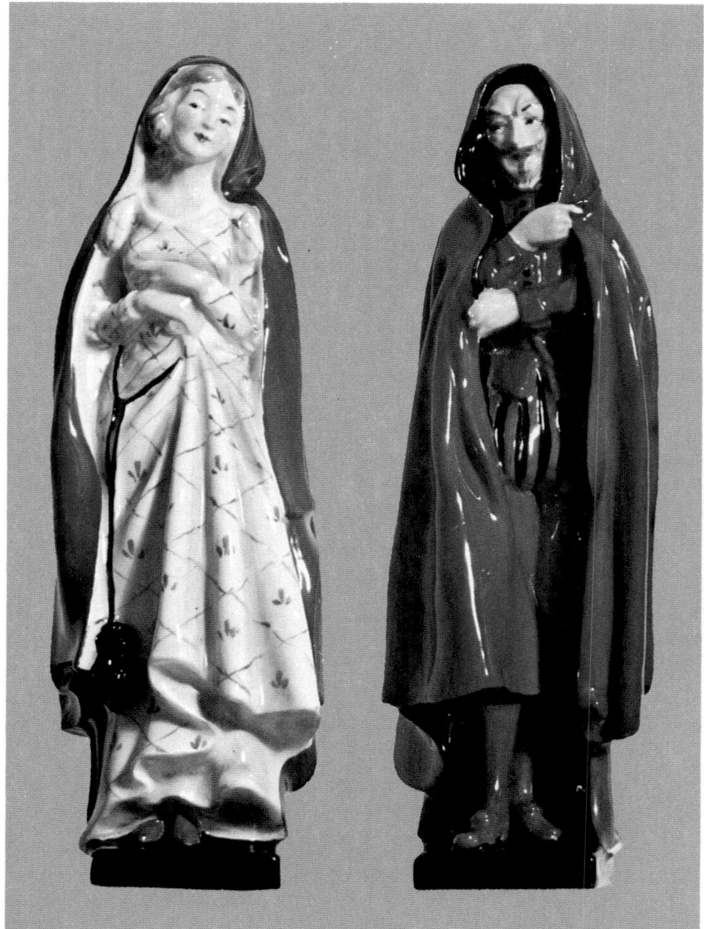

HN 775 Mephistopheles and Marguerite

Three views of an early version of Mephistopheles and Marguerite, made at Burslem during the 1890s

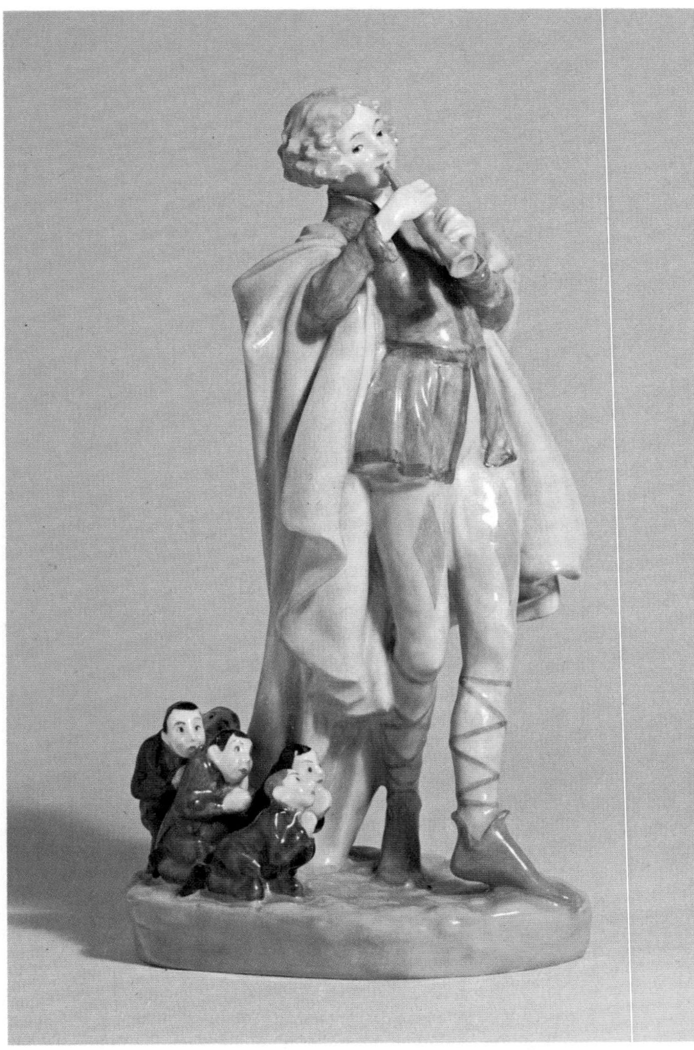

HN 756 The Modern Piper

HN 761 Polly Peachum (third version, miniature, model 462)
See page 156

HN 762 Polly Peachum (third version, miniature, model 462)
See page 156

HN 763 Pretty Lady
See page 94

HN 764 Madonna of the Square
See page 68

HN 765 The Poke Bonnet
See page 83

HN 766 & HN 767
Irish Colleen

HN 756 The Modern Piper
Designer: L. Harradine
Size: 8½ in (21.5 cm)
Introduced: 1925
Withdrawn: By 1938
This female Pied Piper, leading the men astray, probably came from a contemporary revue.

HN 757 Polly Peachum (third version, miniature, model 462)
See page 156

HN 758 Polly Peachum (third version, miniature, model 462)
See page 156

HN 759 Polly Peachum (third version, miniature, model 462)
See page 156

HN 760 Polly Peachum (third version, miniature, model 462)
See page 156

HN 766 Irish Colleen
Designer: L. Harradine
Introduced: 1925
Withdrawn: By 1938
Colleen is an Anglo-Irish word, derived from the Gaelic word *cailin*, meaning a young girl.

HN 767 Irish Colleen
Introduced: 1925
Withdrawn: By 1938

HN 768 Harlequinade Masked
Designer: L. Harradine
Size: 6½ in (16.5 cm)
Introduced: 1925
Withdrawn: By 1938
As HN 1274, but black, red, green, chequered costume

HN 769 Harlequinade Masked
Introduced: 1925
Withdrawn: By 1938
As HN 1274, but blue, red and yellow chequered costume

HN 1274 Harlequinade Masked
Introduced: 1928
Withdrawn: By 1938

HN 1274 Harlequinade Masked

HN 774 The Bather (second version)

HN 1304 Harlequinade Masked
Introduced: 1928
Withdrawn: 1938
As HN 1274, but spotted black costume

HN 770 ***Lady Clown***
See page 158

HN 771 London Cry, Turnips and Carrots
See page 163

HN 772 London Cry, Strawberries
See page 163

HN 773 The Bather (second version, model 486)
Designer: L. Harradine
Size: 7½ in (19 cm)
Introduced: 1925
Withdrawn: By 1938
As HN 774, but pink robe, blue, black markings

HN 774 The Bather (second version, model 486)
Introduced: 1925
Withdrawn: By 1938

HN 1227 The Bather (second version, model 486)
Introduced: 1927
Withdrawn: By 1938
As HN 774, but flowered pink robe

HN 775 Mephistopheles and Marguerite
See page 163

HN 766 The Belle
See page 163

HN 777 Bo-Peep (first version, model 484)
Designer: L. Harradine
Size: 6¾ in (17.1 cm)
Introduced: 1926
Withdrawn: By 1938
Another 18th century style model, this figure is a rather adult version of the nursery rhyme girl who lost her sheep.
For illustration, see next page

HN 1202 Bo-Peep (first version, model 484)
Introduced: 1926
Withdrawn: By 1938
As HN 777, but purple skirt, green, pink, black trim

HN 1327 Bo-Peep (first version, model 484)
Introduced: 1929
Withdrawn: By 1938
As HN 777, but flowered multicoloured costume

HN 1328 Bo-Peep (first version, model 484)
Introduced: 1929
Withdrawn: By 1938
For illustration, see next page

HN 1328 & HN 777 Bo-Peep (first version)

HN 778 Captain (first version)

HN 778 Captain (first version)
Designer: L. Harradine
Size: 7 in (17.7 cm)
Introduced: 1926
Withdrawn: By 1938
Another 18th century style model, the costume of this figure relates more to contemporary pantomime than to military dress.

HN 779 Geisha (first version, model 238)
See page 110

HN 780 Harlequinade
See page 145

HN 781 The Bather (first version, model 428)
See page 147

HN 782 The Bather (first version, model 428)
See page 147

HN 783 Pretty Lady
See page 94

HN 784 Pierrette (first version, model 445)
See page 152

HN 785 The Mask
See page 153

HN 786 Mam'selle
See page 154

HN 787 A Mandarin (first version, model 189)
See page 97

HN 788 Proposal (lady)
See page 157

HN 789 The Flower Seller
Designer: L. Harradine
Size: $8\frac{3}{4}$ in (22.2 cm)
Introduced: 1926
Withdrawn: By 1938
Like so many of the street vendors, this figure seems to have been inspired by the models of Charles Vyse, and the paintings of Augustus John.

HN 790 The Parson's Daughter
See page 106

HN 791 A Mandarin (first version, model 189)
See page 97

HN 789 The Flower Seller

HN 792 The Welsh Girl
See page 79

HN 793 Katharine
See page 92

HN 794 The Bouquet
See page 120

HN 795 Pierrette (second version, miniature, model 498)
Designer: L. Harradine
Size: 3½ in (8.8 cm)
Introduced: 1926
Withdrawn: By 1938
Pink roses on skirt
Also made in colour schemes not recorded in the pattern books

HN 796 Pierrette (second version, miniature, model 498)
Introduced: 1926
Withdrawn: By 1938
White skirt with silver spots

HN 797 The Moorish Minstrel
See page 77

HN 798 Tête-à-Tête (first version, model 487)
Designer: L. Harradine
Size: 5¾ in (14.6 cm)
Introduced: 1926
Withdrawn: By 1938
As HN 799, but mottled pink and pale blue dress

HN 799 Tête-à-Tête (first version, model 487)
Introduced: 1926
Withdrawn: By 1938

HN 799 Tête-à-tête (first version) HN 1236 Tête-à-tête (second version)

HN 1201 Hunts Lady

HN 1204 Angela

HN 800 HN 1200 Animal and Bird Models
For further details see Appendix

HN 1201 Hunts Lady
Designer: L. Harradine
Size: 8¼ in (21 cm)
Introduced: 1926
Withdrawn: By 1938
This elegant figure in smart contemporary dress was made as a pair to HN 1226, *Huntsman*

HN 1202 Bo-Peep (first version, model 484)
See page 167

HN 1203 Butterfly
See page 158

HN 1204 Angela
Designer: L. Harradine
Size: 7¼ in (18.5 cm)
Introduced: 1926
Withdrawn: By 1938
When first issued, this figure was named *Fanny*; however it was changed to *Angela* as the original name was considered by some to be rather risqué.
Versions can be found carrying the original name.

HN 1303 Angela
Introduced: 1928
Withdrawn: By 1938
As 1204, but with blue fan and spotted costume

HN 1205 Miss 1926
Designer: L. Harradine
Introduced: 1926
Withdrawn: Before 1938
With its stylish Eton crop, this figure has more in common with American film revues than with today's Miss Great Britain contest. It is rare for a figure to be so closely associated with a particular period, although the name was changed each year to *Miss 1927*, *Miss 1928* and so on.

HN 1205 Miss 1926 (illustration from the figure design book)

HN 1211 Quality Street

Poster for the first production of Barrie's play *Quality Street*

HN 1207 Miss 1926
As 1205, but with black fur collar

HN 1206 The Flower Seller's Children
See page 134

HN 1207 Miss 1926
See above

HN 1208 A Victorian Lady
See page 161

HN 1209 The Proposal (male)
See page 159

HN 1210 Boy with Turban
See page 146

HN 1211 Quality Street
Size: $7\frac{1}{2}$ in (19 cm)
Introduced: 1926
Withdrawn: By 1938
Quality Street, a 'delightful, sentimental comedy' by J. M. Barrie, was first performed at the Vaudeville Theatre, London, in 1903. The story, set during the Napoleonic Wars, concerned two sisters, Phoebe and Susan Throssel, who ran a girls' school.

HN 1212 Boy with Turban
See page 146

HN 1213 Boy with Turban
See page 146

HN 1214 Boy with Turban
See page 146

HN 1215 The Pied Piper
Designer: L. Harradine
Size: $8\frac{3}{4}$ in (21 cm)
Introduced: 1926
Withdrawn: By 1938
For illustration, see next page
The Pied Piper of Hamelin is the title of a poem by Robert Browning first published in 1845. It was based on the old German legend of the mystery piper who freed the town of a plague of rats in 1284. When his fee was not paid, he charmed away all the children in the town in revenge. The poem refers to his 'Gipsy coat of red and yellow'.

HN 2102 The Pied Piper
Introduced: 1953
Withdrawn: 1976
For illustration, see next page

HN 1216 Falstaff (first version, model 401)
See page 143

HN 1215 The Pied Piper

HN 2102 The Pied Piper

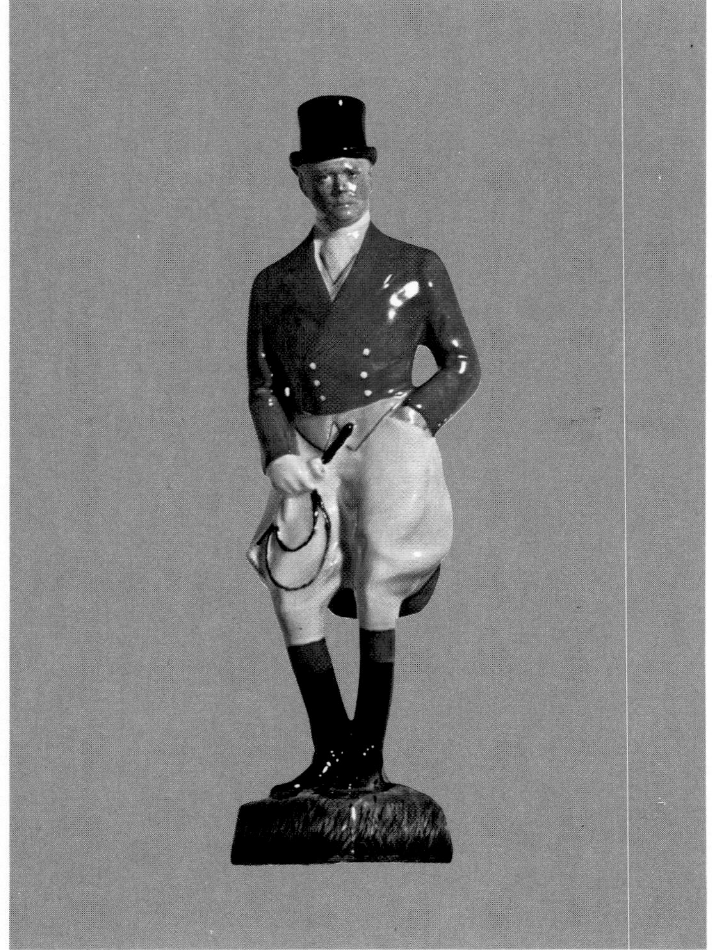

HN 1217 The Prince of Wales

HN 1220 Lido Lady

HN 1217 The Prince of Wales
Designer: L. Harradine
Size: 7¼ in (18.5 cm)
Introduced: 1926
Withdrawn: By 1938
Edward, the eldest son of George V, was invested as Prince of Wales in 1911. Edward was a popular social figure, as suggested by the style of this model, which was based on a painting of Edward by Sir Alfred Munnings, first exhibited in June 1921. On the death of his father he succeeded to the throne, but only reigned briefly as Edward VIII before abdicating in 1936 in order to marry Mrs Simpson. His continuing popularity despite the shock of this event may explain why this figure remained in production long after the abdication.
Edward was a keen horseman, and raced frequently on his tours of the colonies. His interest was started by his father, who reputedly told him as a young man, 'If you can't ride well, I'm afraid people will call you a duffer'.

HN 1218 A Spook
See page 89

HN 1219 Negligée
Designer: L. Harradine
Size: 5 in (12.7 cm)
Introduced: 1927
Withdrawn: By 1938
This figure and HN 1220, *Lido Lady*, were probably taken from Celanese underwear advertisements in glossy ladies' magazines

HN 1228 Negligée
Introduced: 1927
Withdrawn: By 1938

HN 1272 Negligée
Introduced: 1928
Withdrawn: By 1938
As 1219, but mottled red and yellow negligée

HN 1273 Negligée
Introduced: 1928
Withdrawn: By 1938
As 1219, but white negligée

HN 1454 Negligée
Introduced: 1931
Withdrawn: By 1938

HN 1220 Lido Lady
Designer: L. Harradine
Size: 6¾ in (17 cm)
Introduced: 1927
Withdrawn: By 1938
The title of this figure may be taken from a Noel Coward song satirising the contemporary fashion for the lido life-style:
'No more the moon on the still lagoon
Can please the young enchanted . . .
They hitch their star to a cocktail bar
Which is all they really wanted . . .
And all the old Venetians say
They'd like a nice torpedo
To blow the lido away.'

HN 1229 Lido Lady
Introduced: 1927
Withdrawn: By 1938
As 1220, but flowered pink costume

HN 1219 Negligée HN 1228 Negligée HN 1454 Negligée

HN 1222 Lady Jester (first version)

HN 1221 Lady Jester (first version, model 531)
Designer: L. Harradine
Introduced: 1927
Withdrawn: By 1938
As HN 1222, but chequered pink and black skirt

HN 1222 Lady Jester (first version, model 531)
Introduced: 1927
Withdrawn: By 1938

HN 1332 Lady Jester (first version, model 531)
Introduced: 1929
Withdrawn: By 1938
As HN 1222, but red, blue and black scalloped pattern on skirt

HN 1223 A Geisha (second version, model 528)
Designer: C. J. Noke
Size: $6\frac{3}{4}$ in (17.1 cm)
Introduced: 1927
Withdrawn: By 1938

HN 1234 A Geisha (second version, model 528)
Introduced: 1927
Withdrawn: By 1938

HN 1292 A Geisha (second version, model 528)
Introduced: 1928
Withdrawn: By 1938
As HN 1223, but orange kimono, blue/green collar

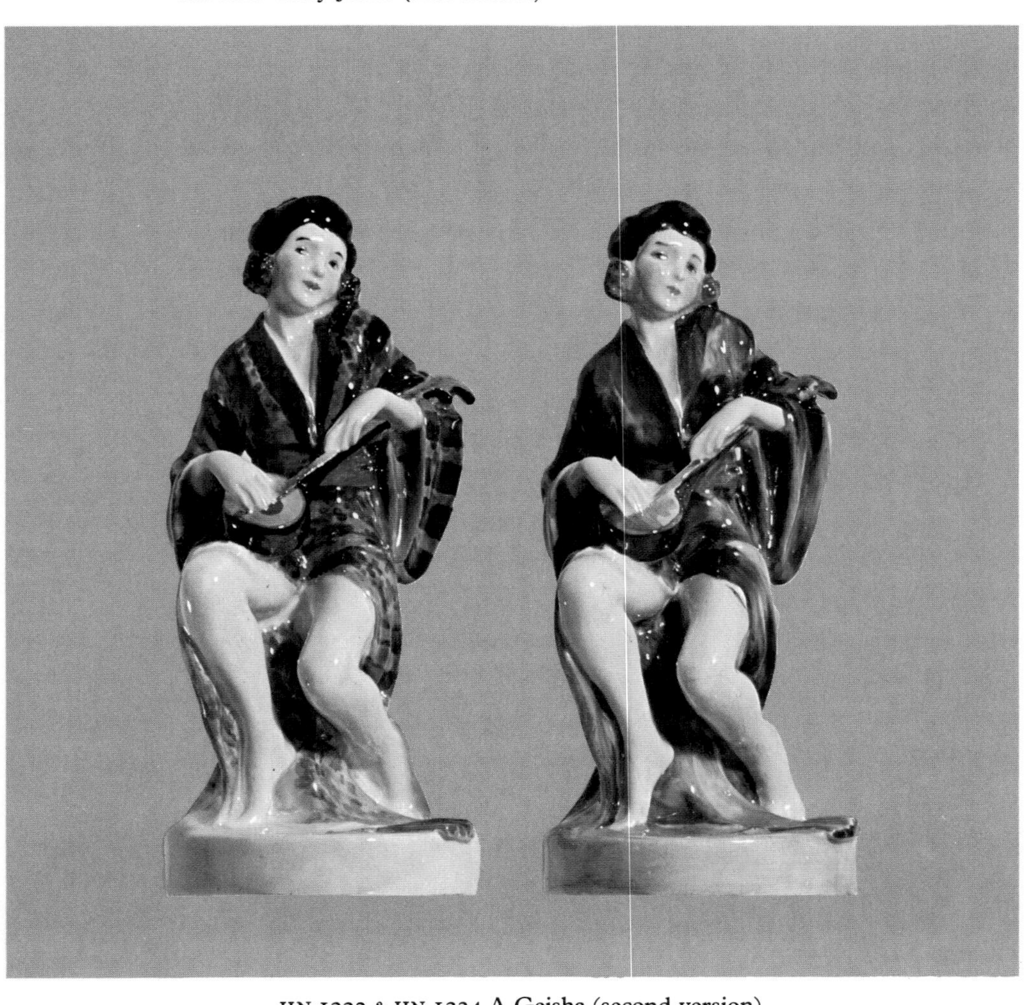

HN 1223 & HN 1234 A Geisha (second version)

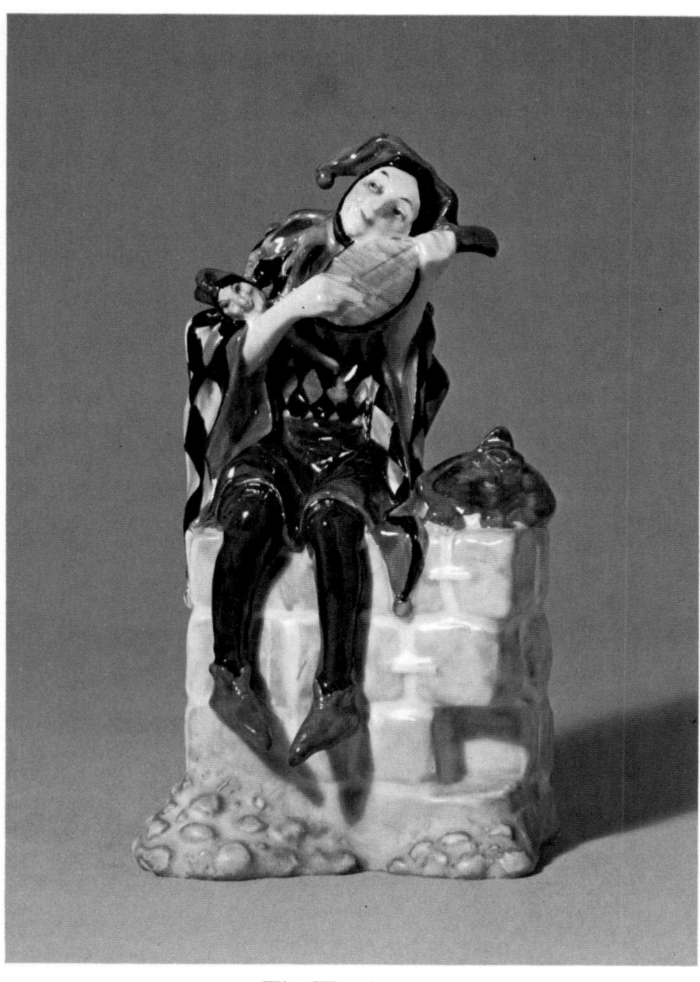

HN 1224 The Wandering Minstrel

HN 1310 A Geisha (second version, model 528)
Introduced: 1929
Withdrawn: By 1938
As HN 1223, but multicoloured spotted kimono

HN 1224 The Wandering Minstrel
Designer: L. Harradine
Size 7 in. (17.7 cm)
Introduced: 1927
Withdrawn: By 1938
In Gilbert and Sullivan's operatta *The Mikado*, first performed in 1885, Nanki-Poo, son of The Mikado of Japan, disguises himself as a minstrel and sings the famous song:
'A wandering minstrel I—
A thing of shreds and patches,
Of ballads, songs and snatches,
And dreamy lullaby.'

HN 1225 Boy with Turban
See page 146

HN 1226 The Huntsman (first version, model 503)
Designer: L. Harradine
Introduced: 1927
Withdrawn: By 1938
Made as a pair to HN 1201, *Hunts Lady*

HN 1226 The Huntsman (first version, illustration from the figure design book)

HN 1227 The Bather (second version, model 485)
See page 167

HN 1228 Negligée
See page 173

HN 1229 Lido Lady
See page 173

HN 1230 Baba
Designer: L. Harradine
Introduced: 1927
Withdrawn: By 1938
As HN 1248, but striped yellow and purple trousers
Ali Baba and his brother Cassim are here represented as young street arabs, before their adventures with the Forty Thieves.

HN 1243 Baba
Introduced: 1927
Withdrawn: 1927
As HN 1248, but orange trousers

HN 1244 Baba
Introduced: 1927
Withdrawn: By 1938
As HN 1248, but yellow and green striped trousers

HN 1245 Baba
Introduced: 1927
Withdrawn: By 1938
As HN 1248, but white trousers, blue-black markings

HN 1248 Baba

HN 1231 Cassim (first version)

HN 1232 Cassim (first version)

HN 1233 & HN 1288 Susanna HN 1249 Circe

HN 1246 Baba
Introduced: 1927
Withdrawn: By 1938
As HN 1248, green trousers

HN 1247 Baba
Introduced: 1928
Withdrawn: By 1938
As HN 1248, but white trousers, black spots

HN 1248 Baba
Introduced: 1927
Withdrawn: By 1938
For illustration, see previous page

HN 1231 Cassim (first version, model 555)
Designer: L. Harradine
Size: 3¾ in (9.5 cm)
Introduced: 1927
Withdrawn: By 1938
Cassim, brother of Ali Baba, was cut into quarters by the Forty Thieves, to be sewn together later by the Cobbler

HN 1232 Cassim (first version, model 555)
Introduced: 1927
Withdrawn: By 1938

HN 1233 Susanna
Designer: L. Harradine
Size: 6 in (15.2 cm)
Introduced: 1927
Withdrawn: By 1938
A larger version of this figure was made, with the title *Circe* (HN 1249). The Book of Daniel in the Bible describes Susanna being surprised in her bath by the Elders: this stylish figure with her bathrobe perhaps represents a modern interpretation of this event!

HN 1288 Susanna
Introduced: 1928
Withdrawn: By 1938

HN 1299 Susanna
Introduced: 1928
Withdrawn: By 1938
As HN 1233, but black, red and blue robe

HN 1234 A Geisha (second version, model 528)
See page 174

HN 1235 A Scribe
See page 103

HN 1236 Tête-à-Tête (second version, model 538)
Designer: C. J. Noke
Size: 3 in (7.6 cm)
Introduced: 1927
Withdrawn: By 1938
For illustration, see HN 798, page 169

HN 1253 Kathleen HN 1252 Kathleen HN 1279 Kathleen

HN 1237 Tête-à-Tête (second version, model 538)
Introduced: 1927
Withdrawn: By 1938
As HN 1236, but pink dress

HN 1238 The Bather (first version, model 428)
See page 148

HN 1239-1241 Animal and Bird models

HN 1242 The Parson's Daughter
See page 106

HN 1243 Baba
See page 175

HN 1244 Baba
See page 175

HN 1245 Baba
See page 175

HN 1246 Baba
See page 176

HN 1247 Baba
See page 176

HN 1248 Baba
See page 176

HN 1249 Circe
Designer: L. Harradine
Size: $7\frac{1}{2}$ in (19.0 cm)
Introduced: 1927
Withdrawn: By 1938
This figure is a larger model of HN 1233, *Susanna*.
Circe, a classical enchantress, lured Ulysses to her Aegean island, and turned his companions into swine. She restored them to their normal form only when Ulysses agreed to become her lover, and stay with her for a year.

HN 1250 Circe
Introduced: 1927
Withdrawn: By 1938
As HN 1249, but orange and black robe

HN 1254 Circe
Introduced: 1927 Withdrawn: By 1938
As HN 1249, but orange and red robe

HN 1255 Circe
Introduced: 1927
Withdrawn: By 1938
As HN 1249, but blue robe

HN 1251 The Cobbler (second version)
See page 155

HN 1252 Kathleen
Designer: L. Harradine
Size: $7\frac{1}{2}$ in (19.0 cm)
Introduced: 1927 Withdrawn: By 1938

HN 1282 The Alchemist

HN 1253 Kathleen
Introduced: 1927
Withdrawn: By 1938
For illustration, see previous page

HN 1275 Kathleen
Introduced: 1928
Withdrawn: By 1938
As HN 1252, but flowered black shawl

HN 1279 Kathleen
Introduced: 1928
Withdrawn: By 1938
For illustration, see previous page

HN 1291 Kathleen
Introduced: 1928
Withdrawn: By 1938
As HN 1252, but red shawl, mottled yellow dress

HN 1357 Kathleen
Introduced: 1929
Withdrawn: By 1938
As HN 1252, but pink, orange and yellow mottled skirt

HN 1512 Kathleen
Introduced: 1932
Withdrawn: By 1938
As HN 1252, but pale lilac dress, blue hat

HN 1254 Circe
See page 177

HN 1255 Circe
See page 177

HN 1256 Captain MacHeath
See page 130

HN 1257 Highwayman
See page 136

HN 1258 A Victorian Lady
See page 161

HN 1259 The Alchemist
Designer: L. Harradine
Size: 11½ in (29.2 cm)
Introduced: 1927
Withdrawn: By 1938
As HN 1282, but mottled robe, red hat

HN 1278 Carnival

HN 1282 The Alchemist
Introduced: 1928
Withdrawn: By 1938

HN 1260 Carnival
Designer: L. Harradine
Size: 8½ in (21.5 cm)
Introduced: 1927
Withdrawn: By 1938
As HN 1278, but pink tights
This figure was particularly influenced by contemporary ballet costume

HN 1278 Carnival
Introduced: 1928
Withdrawn: By 1938

HN 1261 Sea Sprite (first version, model 565)
Designer: L. Harradine
Size: 5¼ in (13.3 cm)
Introduced: 1927
Withdrawn: By 1938

HN 1261 & HN 1543 Sea Sprite (first version)

HN 1262 Spanish Lady
Designer: L. Harradine
Size: 8¼ in (20.9 cm)
Introduced: 1927
Withdrawn: By 1938

HN 1290 Spanish Lady
Introduced: 1928
Withdrawn: By 1938
As 1262, but yellow dress

HN 1262, HN 1293 & HN 1294 Spanish Lady

HN 1265 Lady Fayre

HN 1293 Spanish Lady
Introduced: 1928
Withdrawn: By 1938
For illustration, see previous page

HN 1294 Spanish Lady
Introduced: 1928
Withdrawn: By 1938
For illustration, see previous page

HN 1309 Spanish Lady
Introduced: 1929
Withdrawn: By 1938
As HN 1262, but black bodice, multicoloured skirt

HN 1263 *Lady Clown*
See page 158

HN 1264 Judge and Jury
Designer: J. G. Hughes
Introduced: 1927
Withdrawn: By 1938

HN 1265 Lady Fayre
Designer: L. Harradine
Size: $5\frac{3}{4}$ in (14.6 cm)
Introduced: 1928
Withdrawn: By 1938

HN 1264 Judge and Jury

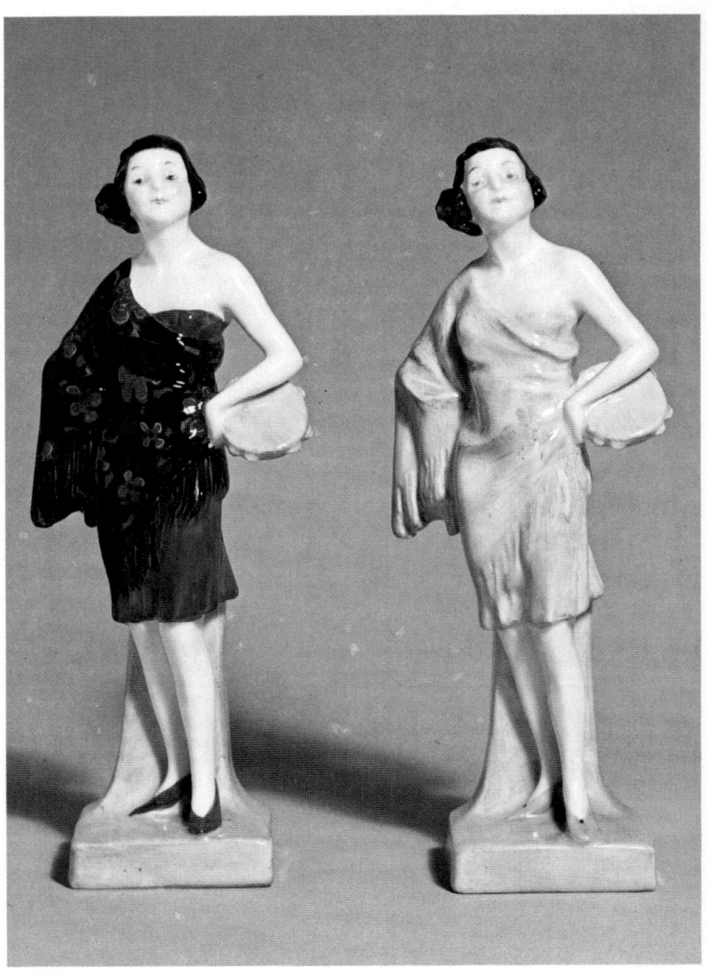

HN 1267 & HN 1300 Carmen (first version)

HN 1557 Lady Fayre
Introduced: 1933
Withdrawn: By 1938
As HN 1265, but pink dress

HN 1266 Ko-Ko
Designer: L. Harradine
Size: 5 in (12.7 cm)
Introduced: 1928
Withdrawn: By 1949
Made as a pair to HN 1268, *Yum-Yum*
In Gilbert and Sullivan's operetta *The Mikado*, Yum-Yum is the ward of Ko-Ko, the Lord High Executioner. Yum-Yum is to marry Ko-Ko, but falls in love with Nanki-Poo, disguised as the Wandering Minstrel.

HN 1286 Ko-Ko
Introduced: 1938
Withdrawn: By 1949

HN 1267 Carmen (first version, model 537)
Designer: L. Harradine
Size: 7 in (17.7 cm)
Introduced: 1928
Withdrawn: By 1938
Despite her fashionable appearance, this figure is named after the tantalising and seductive heroine of Bizet's opera, first performed in 1875.

HN 1300 Carmen (first version, model 537)
Introduced: 1928
Withdrawn: By 1938

HN 1268 Yum-Yum HN 1286 Ko-Ko HN 1266 Ko-Ko HN 1287 Yum-Yum

HN 1268 Yum-Yum
Designer: L. Harradine
Size: 5 in (12.7 cm)
Introduced: 1928
Withdrawn: By 1938
Made as a pair to HN 1266, *Ko-Ko*

HN 1287 Yum-Yum
Introduced: 1928
Withdrawn: By 1939

HN 1269 Scotch Girl
Designer: L. Harradine
Size: $7\frac{1}{2}$ in (19.0 cm)
Introduced: 1928
Withdrawn: By 1938
This figure expresses the popular interest in Scotland and all things 'Scotch' current during the late 1920s and early 1930s. There were revues and musical comedies with Scottish settings and themes, and there was a vogue for Scottish popular songs. Traditional favourites such as *Loch Lomond* featured in the repertoires of Benny Goodman and other Swing bands.

HN 1269 Scotch Girl

HN 1270 The Swimmer

HN 1280 Blue Bird

HN 1270 The Swimmer
Designer: L. Harradine
Size: $7\frac{1}{2}$ in (19.0 cm)
Introduced: 1928
Withdrawn: 1938
This is probably the only Doulton example of the traditional Bathing Belle, a subject popular with other makers of ceramic models of this period.

HN 1326 The Swimmer
Introduced: 1929
Withdrawn: By 1938
As HN 1270, but lilac and orange costume

HN 1329 The Swimmer
Introduced: 1929
Withdrawn: By 1938
As HN 1270, but pink costume

HN 1271 The Mask
See page 153

HN 1272 Negligée
See page 173

HN 1273 Negligée
See page 173

HN 1274 Harlequinade Masked
See page 166

HN 1275 Kathleen
See page 178

HN 1276 A Victorian Lady
See page 162

HN 1277 A Victorian Lady
See page 162

HN 1278 Carnival
See page 179

HN 1279 Kathleen
See page 178

HN 1280 Blue Bird
Designer: L. Harradine
Size: $4\frac{3}{4}$ in (12.0 cm)
Introduced: 1928
Withdrawn: By 1938
In the play *The Blue Bird*, by Maurice Maeterlinck, the two children of a poor woodcutter are sent in search of the Blue Bird of Happiness by the fairy Bérylune. Having failed to discover it, they return home, only to find the bird in their own house, underlining the simple moral that happiness begins at home. The play was performed in London in 1911, and so inspired Sir Malcolm Campbell that he named all his record-breaking cars and boats *Blue Bird*

HN 1281 Scotties

HN 1284 & HN 1285 Lady Jester (second version)

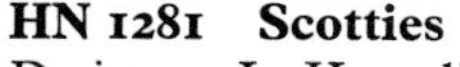

HN 1281 Scotties
Designer: L. Harradine
Size: $5\frac{1}{4}$ in (13.3 cm)
Introduced: 1928
Withdrawn: By 1938
Scotch terriers were a popular fashion accessory during the period when this figure was produced.

HN 1349 Scotties
Introduced: 1929
Withdrawn: By 1949
As HN 1281, but pale multicoloured costume, white dogs

HN 1282 The Alchemist
See page 179

HN 1283 The Cobbler (second version)
See page 155

HN 1284 Lady Jester (second version, model 578)
Designer: L. Harradine
Size: $4\frac{1}{4}$ in (10.7 cm)
Introduced: 1928
Withdrawn: By 1938

HN 1285 Lady Jester (second version, model 578)
Introduced: 1928
Withdrawn: By 1938

HN 1286 Ko-Ko
See page 180

HN 1287 Yum-Yum
See page 181

HN 1288 Susanna
See page 176

HN 1289 Midinette (first version, model 598)
Designer: L. Harradine
Size: 9 in (22.8 cm)
Introduced: 1928
Withdrawn: By 1938
For illustration, see next page
Midinette was a general term for a Parisian shop girl, but referred specifically to a milliner's assistant. She is depicted here in her most usual guise, rushing through the streets at midday (midi) to deliver hats to her customers.

HN 1306 Midinette (first version, model 598)
Introduced: 1928
Withdrawn: By 1938

HN 1290 Spanish Lady
See page 179

HN 1291 Kathleen
See page 178

HN 1289 & HN 1306 Midinette (first version)

HN 1296, HN 1439 & HN 1297 Columbine (first version)

HN 1292 A Geisha (second version, model 528)
See page 174

HN 1293 Spanish Lady
See page 180

HN 1294 Spanish Lady
See page 180

HN 1295 A Jester (first version, model 170)
See page 85

HN 1296 Columbine (first version, model 563)
Designer: L. Harradine
Size: 6 in (15.2 cm)
Introduced: 1928
Withdrawn: By 1938
Columbine, the traditional heroine of the *Commedia dell' Arte*, was frequently modelled in clay, but few versions were as fashionable as this. Curiously, there was no Harlequin made to pair this figure.

HN 1297 Columbine (first version, model 563)
Introduced: 1928
Withdrawn: By 1938

HN 1439 Columbine (first version, model 563)
Introduced: 1930
Withdrawn: By 1938

HN 1298 Sweet and Twenty (first version, model 605)
Designer: L. Harradine
Size: 6 in (15.2 cm)
Introduced: 1928
Withdrawn: 1969
The title of this figure is taken from the song, *O Mistress Mine !*, in Shakespeare's *Twelfth Night*:
'Then come kiss me, sweet and twenty,
Youth's a stuff will not endure.'

HN 1360 Sweet and Twenty (first version, model 605)
Introduced: 1929
Withdrawn: By 1938
For illustration, see next page

HN 1437 Sweet and Twenty (first version, model 605)
Introduced: 1930
Withdrawn: By 1938
As HN 1298, but dark sofa, shaded red dress

HN 1438 Sweet and Twenty (first version, model 605)
Introduced: 1930
Withdrawn: By 1938
As HN 1298, but mottled multicoloured dress

HN 1549 Sweet and Twenty (first version, model 605)
Introduced: 1933
Withdrawn: By 1949
For illustration, see page 187

HN 1563 Sweet and Twenty (first version, model 605)
Introduced: 1933
Withdrawn: By 1938
As HN 1298, but black sofa, pale pink dress

HN 1649 Sweet and Twenty (first version, model 605)
Introduced: 1934
Withdrawn: By 1949
For illustration, see next page

HN 1298 Sweet and Twenty (first version)

HN 1360 Sweet and Twenty (first version)

HN 1589 Sweet and Twenty (second version)

HN 1649 Sweet and Twenty (first version)

HN 1610 Sweet and Twenty (second version)

HN 1549 Sweet and Twenty (first version)

HN 1299 Susanna
See page 176

HN 1300 Carmen (first version, model 537)
See page 180

HN 1301 *Gypsy Woman with Child*
Introduced: 1928
Withdrawn: By 1938
This, and the following figure, seem to have been inspired by the paintings of Augustus John.

HN 1301 *Gypsy Woman with Child* (illustration from the figure design book)

HN 1302 *Gypsy Girl with Flowers*
Introduced: 1928
Withdrawn: By 1938

HN 1302 *Gypsy Girl with Flowers* (illustration from the figure design book)

HN 1303 Angela
See page 170

HN 1304 Harlequinade Masked
See page 167

HN 1305 Siesta
Designer: L. Harradine
Size: 4¾ in (12.0 cm)
Introduced: 1928
Withdrawn: By 1938

HN 1306 Midinette (first version, model 598)
See page 183

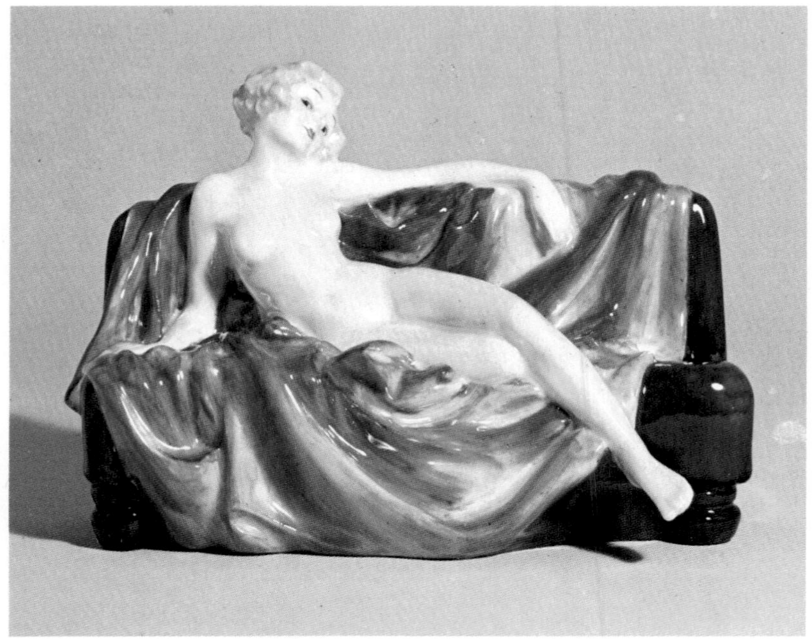
HN 1305 Siesta

HN 1307 An Irishman

HN 1307 An Irishman
Designer: H. Fenton
Size: 6¾ in (17.1 cm)
Introduced: 1928
Withdrawn: By 1938
Harry Fenton first joined Doulton in 1903, as a modeller under C. J. Noke. In 1911 he went to America where he lived until 1929 when he returned to England, and rejoined Doulton shortly afterwards.
He designed a number of figures during the 1930s and 1940s, but was better known as the designer of a number of presentation jugs, loving cups and many of the early character jugs. He died in 1953, and his last model, the character jug, *Johnny Appleseed*, was first produced the same year.

HN 1308 The Moor
See page 76

HN 1309 Spanish Lady
See page 180

HN 1310 A Geisha (second version, model 528)
See page 175

HN 1311 Cassim (second version)
Designer: L. Harradine
Size: 3¾ in (9.5 cm)
Introduced: 1929
Withdrawn: By 1938
Mounted on a lidded pink bowl

HN 1312 Cassim (second version)
Designer: L. Harradine
Introduced: 1929
Withdrawn: By 1938

HN 1312 Cassim (second version, illustration from the figure design book)

HN 1313 & HN 1314 Sonny (illustrations from the figure design book)

HN 1315 Old Balloon Seller

HN 1317 The Snake Charmer

HN 1313 Sonny
Designer: L. Harradine
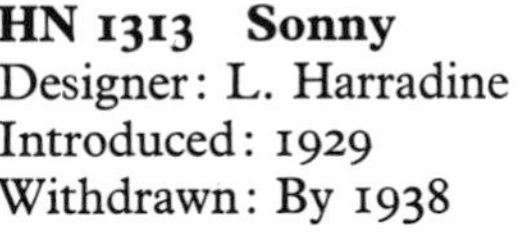
Introduced: 1929
Withdrawn: By 1938
The title of this figure is probably taken from the song, *Sonny Boy*, sung by Al Jolson in the film, *The Singing Fool*, first shown in 1928

HN 1314 Sonny
Introduced: 1929
Withdrawn: By 1938

HN 1315 Old Balloon Seller
Designer: L. Harradine
Size: 7 in (17.7 cm)
Introduced: 1929
Still in production
Probably the best known of all Doulton figures, this model has been in production for nearly fifty years. When it was launched, it was only one among a series of street sellers, but its popularity has outlived all its rivals, turning it into a symbol of the whole Doulton figure range.

HN 1316 Toys
Designer: L. Harradine
Introduced: 1929
Withdrawn: By 1938
This figure, whose origins are uncertain, suggests a satirical approach unusual among Doulton models, shared perhaps only by *The Modern Piper*, HN 756

HN 1317 The Snake Charmer
Size: 4½ in (11.4 cm)
Introduced: 1929
Withdrawn: By 1938

HN 1316 Toys (illustration from the figure design book)

Sweet Anne: HN 1453 HN 1330 HN 1331 HN 1496 HN 1318

HN 1318 Sweet Anne
Designer: L. Harradine
Size: 7 in (17.7 cm)
Introduced: 1929
Withdrawn: By 1949

HN 1330 Sweet Anne
Introduced: 1929
Withdrawn: By 1949

HN 1331 Sweet Anne
Introduced: 1929
Withdrawn: By 1949

HN 1453 Sweet Anne
Introduced: 1931
Withdrawn: By 1949

HN 1496 Sweet Anne
Introduced: 1932
Withdrawn: 1967

HN 1631 Sweet Anne
Introduced: 1934
Withdrawn: By 1938
As HN 1318, but green bonnet, red jacket, pink and yellow skirt

HN 1701 Sweet Anne
Introduced: 1935
Withdrawn: By 1938
As HN 1318, but flowered yellow and pink dress, blue trim

HN 1319 Darling
See page 65

HN 1320 Rosamund (first version, model 618)
Designer: L. Harradine
Introduced: 1929
Withdrawn: By 1938

HN 1321 A Geisha (first version, model 238)
See page 110

HN 1322 A Geisha (first version, model 238)
See page 110

HN 1323 Contentment
See page 117

HN 1324 *Fairy*
Designer: L. Harradine
Introduced: 1929
Withdrawn: By 1938
For illustration, see next page

HN 1374 *Fairy*
Size: 4 in (10.1 cm)
Introduced: 1930
Withdrawn: By 1938
As HN 1532, but yellow flowers

HN 1375 *Fairy*
Introduced: 1930
Withdrawn: By 1938
For illustration, see next page

HN 1376 *Fairy*
Introduced: 1930
Withdrawn: By 1938
As HN 1532, but a smaller version, with no mushroom

HN 1377 *Fairy*, Not issued

HN 1378 *Fairy*
Size: $2\frac{1}{2}$ in (6.3 cm)
Introduced: 1930
Withdrawn: By 1938
As HN 1396, but orange flowers

HN 1379 *Fairy*
Size: $2\frac{1}{2}$ in (6.3 cm)
Introduced: 1930
Withdrawn: By 1938

HN 1320 Rosamund (first version)

HN 1396, HN 1379 & HN 1532 *Fairies*

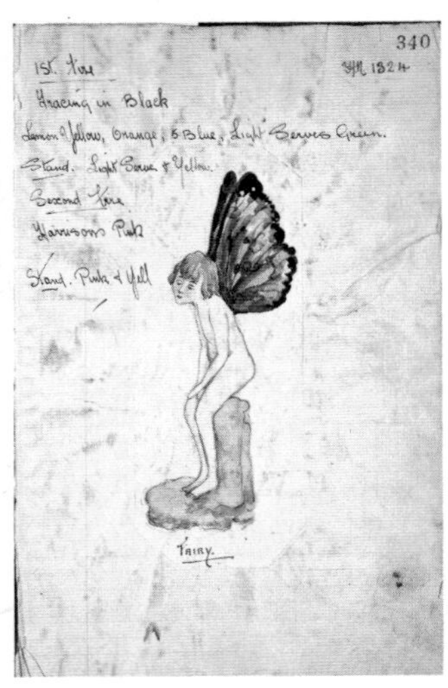

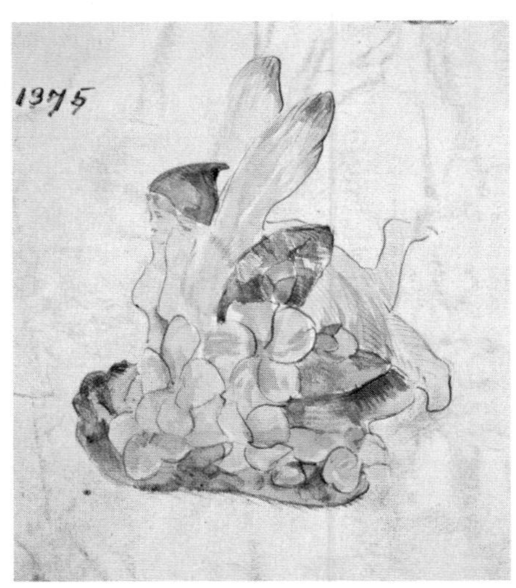

HN 1324, HN 1375 & HN 1393 *Fairies* (illustrations from the figure design book)

HN 1380 *Fairy*
Size: 4 in (10.1 cm)
Introduced: 1930
Withdrawn: By 1938
As HN 1532, but dark mottled mushroom

HN 1381-HN 1386 *Fairies*, Not issued

HN 1393 *Fairy*
Introduced: 1930
Withdrawn: By 1938

HN 1394 *Fairy*
Size: 2½ in (6.3 cm)
Introduced: 1930
Withdrawn: By 1938
As HN 1379, but yellow flowers

HN 1395 *Fairy*
Introduced: 1930
Withdrawn: By 1938
As HN 1375, but blue flowers

HN 1396 *Fairy*
Size: 2½ in (6.3 cm)
Introduced: 1930
Withdrawn: By 1938
For illustration, see previous page

HN 1532 *Fairy*
Size: 4 in (10.1 cm)
Introduced: 1932
Withdrawn: By 1938
For illustration, see previous page

HN 1533 *Fairy*
Introduced: 1932
Withdrawn: By 1938
As HN 1375, but multicoloured flowers

HN 1534 *Fairy*
Size: 2½ in (6.3 cm)
Introduced: 1932
Withdrawn: By 1938
As HN 1379, but large yellow flowers

HN 1535 *Fairy*
Size: 2½ in (6.3 cm)
Introduced: 1932
Withdrawn: By 1938
As HN 1396, but yellow and blue flowers

HN 1536 *Fairy*
Introduced: 1932
Withdrawn: By 1938
As HN 1532, but with light green base

HN 1325 The Orange Seller
Designer: L. Harradine
Size: 7 in (17.7 cm)
Introduced: 1929
Withdrawn: 1949
Made to be a pair with HN 1339, *Covent Garden*

HN 1325 The Orange Seller

HN 1339 Covent Garden

HN 1326 The Swimmer
See page 182

HN 1327 Bo-Peep (first version, model 484)
See page 167

HN 1328 Bo-Peep (first version, model 484)
See page 167

HN 1329 The Swimmer
See page 182

HN 1330 Sweet Anne
See page 191

HN 1331 Sweet Anne
See page 191

HN 1332 Lady Jester (first version, model 531)
See page 174

HN 1333 A Jester (second version, model 171)
See page 85

HN 1334 Tulips
See page 131

HN 1335 Folly
Designer: L. Harradine
Size: 9 in (22.6 cm)
Introduced: 1929
Withdrawn: By 1938

HN 1750 Folly
Introduced: 1936
Withdrawn: By 1949
As HN 1335, but earthenware; also with brown hat, white muff, dark dress

HN 1336 One of the Forty
See page 123

HN 1337 Priscilla
Designer: L. Harradine
Size: 8 in (20.3 cm)
Introduced: 1929
Withdrawn: By 1938

HN 1340 Priscilla
Introduced: 1929
Withdrawn: By 1949

HN 1335 Folly

HN 1337 & HN 1340 Priscilla

HN 1495 & HN 1501 Priscilla

HN 1495 Priscilla
Introduced: 1932
Withdrawn: 1949

HN 1501 Priscilla
Introduced: 1932
Withdrawn: By 1938

HN 1559 Priscilla
Introduced: 1933
Withdrawn: By 1949
As HN 1337, but pink and yellow skirt

HN 1338 The Courtier
Designer: L. Harradine
Size: 4½ in (11.4 cm)
Introduced: 1929
Withdrawn: By 1938

HN 1339 Covent Garden
Designer: L. Harradine
Size: 9 in (22.8 cm)
Introduced: 1929
Withdrawn: By 1938
Made as a pair to HN 1325, *The Orange Seller*
Covent Garden fruit and vegetable market was established in central London in 1634, on the site of a vast garden belonging to the abbey and convent of Westminster. The market continued to operate until 1974, giving a distinctive character to that part of London, which abounded with fruit and flower sellers, many of whom carried their wares in the traditional baskets balanced on the head.
For illustration, see page 192

HN 1340 Priscilla
See page 193

HN 1338 The Courtier

HN 1341 & HN 1446 Marietta

HN 1341 Marietta
Designer: L. Harradine
Size: 8 in (20.3 cm)
Introduced: 1929
Withdrawn: By 1949
In the comic opera *Die Fledermaus*, first performed in 1874, the heroine is called Marietta. Much of the action revolves around a mask ball, with the inevitable cases of mistaken identity. This figure, with its stylish bat costume, may also have been inspired by the musical comedy, *Naughty Marietta*, first performed in 1910.

HN 1446 Marietta
Introduced: 1931
Withdrawn: By 1949

HN 1699 Marietta
Introduced: 1935
Withdrawn: By 1949

HN 1342 The Flower Seller's Children
See page 134

HN 1699 Marietta

HN 1343 Dulcinea

HN 1344 Sunshine Girl

HN 1343 Dulcinea
Designer: L. Harradine
Size: 5¼ in (13.3 cm)
Introduced: 1929
Withdrawn: By 1938
Dulcinea was the lady in Cervantes' *Don Quixote*, for whom the hero attempted to perform his chivalrous deeds. From this, the name became a general term for a sweetheart, mistress or a lady inspiring great devotion.

HN 1419 Dulcinea
Introduced: 1930
Withdrawn: By 1938
As HN 1343, but red and pink dress, green shoes

HN 1344 Sunshine Girl
Designer: L. Harradine
Size: 5 in (12.7 cm)
Introduced: 1929
Withdrawn: By 1938
A development of the bathing beauty idiom, this figure may have been inspired by the musical comedy, *The Sunshine Girl*, first performed at the Gaiety Theatre in 1911. The story revolved around the love affair between a factory girl at the Port Sunlight soap factory, and the factory owner, and included a song in praise of Brighton:
'Take me on the boat to Brighton,
Put me on the pier at Brighton,
That's the place for me,
London by the sea,
Leave me there and I shall be as happy as can be.'

HN 1348 Sunshine Girl
Introduced: 1929
Withdrawn: By 1938
As HN 1344, but black and orange costume

HN 1345 A Victorian Lady
See page 162

HN 1346 Iona
Designer: L. Harradine
Introduced: 1929
Withdrawn: By 1938
This figure is an adaptation of HN 1320, *Rosamund* (first version), with the addition of a dog
The traditional Irish, or Gaelic names of this figure and HN 1347, *Moira*, seem also to be expressed in their costumes.
The name Iona is taken from the church established in the Western Isles of Scotland by St Columba in 563 A.D., the base from which Christianity was spread into Scotland.

HN 1347 Moira
Designer: L. Harradine
Introduced: 1929
Withdrawn: By 1938
This figure is an adaptation of HN 766, *Irish Colleen*, with the addition of a dog

HN 1346 Iona & HN 1347 Moira
(illustrations from the figure design book)

HN 1348 Sunshine Girl
See opposite

HN 1349 Scotties
See page 183

HN 1350 One of the Forty
See page 124

HN 1351 One of the Forty
See page 122

HN 1352 One of the Forty
See page 122

HN 1353 One of the Forty
See page 122

HN 1354 One of the Forty
See page 124

HN 1355 The Mendicant
Designer: L. Harradine
Size: $8\frac{1}{4}$ in (20.9 cm)
Introduced: 1929
Withdrawn: By 1938
As HN 1365, but minor glaze differences
Another Eastern figure, close in style to *The Cobbler*, HN 542, this represents the beggar, a common feature of oriental bazaars, with his tambourine for attracting attention.

HN 1365 The Mendicant
Introduced: 1929
Withdrawn: 1969

HN 1356 The Parson's Daughter
See page 106

HN 1357 Kathleen
See page 178

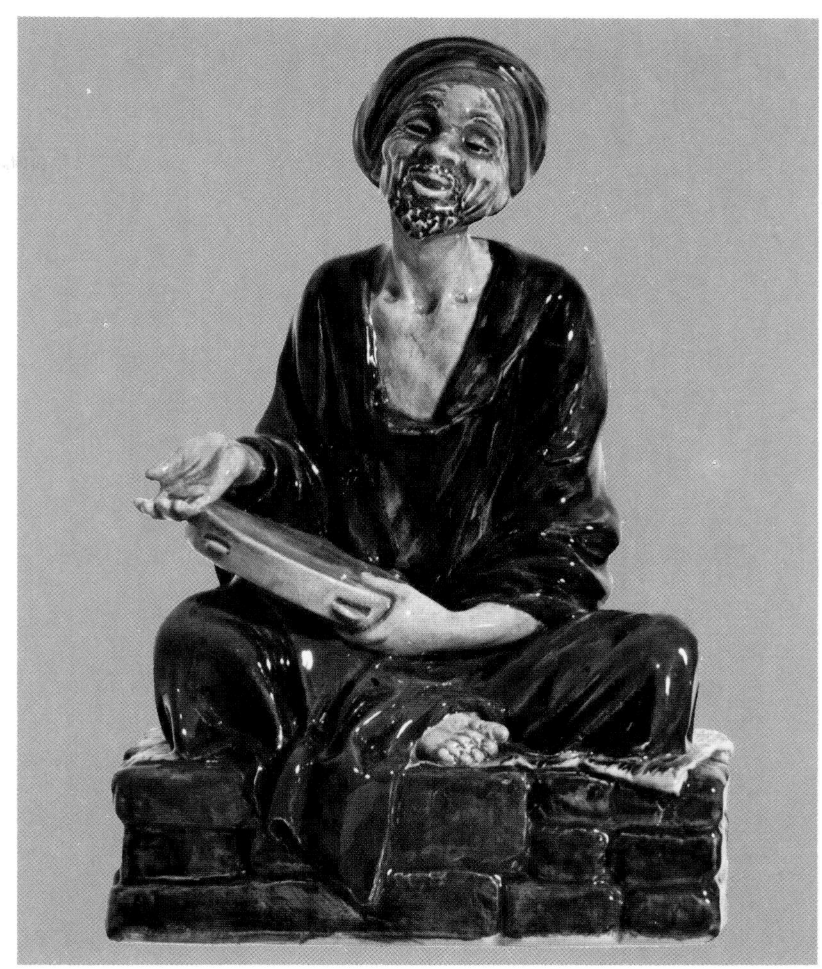

HN 1355 The Mendicant

HN 1358 Rosina
Designer: L. Harradine
Size: $5\frac{1}{4}$ in (13.3 cm)
Introduced: 1929
Withdrawn: By 1938

HN 1364 Rosina
Introduced: 1929
Withdrawn: By 1938

HN 1556 Rosina
Introduced: 1933
Withdrawn: By 1938

HN 1556, HN 1358 & HN 1364 Rosina

HN 1359 Two-A-Penny

HN 1361 Mask Seller

HN 2103 Mask Seller

HN 1362, HN 1412 & HN 1709 Pantalettes

HN 1359 Two-A-Penny
Designer: L. Harradine
Size: 8 in (20.3 cm)
Introduced: 1929
Withdrawn: By 1938

HN 1360 Sweet and Twenty (first version, model 605)
See page 185

HN 1361 Mask Seller
Designer: L. Harradine
Size: 8½ in (21.5 cm)
Introduced: 1929
Withdrawn: By 1938

HN 2103 Mask Seller
Introduced: 1953
Still in production

HN 1362 Pantalettes
Designer: L. Harradine
Size: 8 in (20.3 cm)
Introduced: 1929
Withdrawn: By 1938
Pantalettes, loose drawers or trousers with frills on each leg, were fashionable for young girls between about 1825 and 1855. They were also popularised by a music-hall song, first performed by J. Ashby Sterry in 1887, called *The Song of Schoolgirls*:
'Come the dainty dimpled pets,
With their tresses all in nets,
And their peeping pantalettes just in view.'

HN 1412 Pantalettes
Introduced: 1930
Withdrawn: By 1949

HN 1507 Pantalettes
Introduced: 1932
Withdrawn: By 1949
As HN 1362, but yellow dress

HN 1709 Pantalettes
Introduced: 1935
Withdrawn: By 1938

HN 1363 Doreen
Designer: L. Harradine
Size: 5¼ in (13.3 cm)
Introduced: 1929
Withdrawn: By 1938
As HN 1389, but pink dress

HN 1389 Doreen
Introduced: 1930
Withdrawn: By 1938

HN 1390 Doreen
Introduced: 1929
Withdrawn: By 1938

HN 1364 Rosina
See page 197

HN 1365 The Mendicant
See page 197

HN 1366 The Moor
See page 76

HN 1389 & HN 1390 Doreen

HN 1367 Kitty

HN 1368 & HN 1416 Rose

HN 1367 Kitty
Size: 4 in (10.1 cm)
Introduced: 1930
Withdrawn: By 1938

HN 1368 Rose
Designer: L. Harradine
Size: 4½ in (11.4 cm)
Introduced: 1930
Still in production

HN 1387 Rose
Introduced: 1930
Withdrawn: By 1938
As HN 1368, but flowered blue and pink dress, orange roses

HN 1416 Rose
Introduced: 1930
Withdrawn: By 1949

HN 1506 Rose
Introduced: 1932
Withdrawn: By 1938
As HN 1368, but yellow dress

HN 1654 Rose
Introduced: 1934
Withdrawn: By 1938
As HN 1368, but green bodice, flowered skirt

HN 1369 *Boy on Pig*
Designer: C. J. Noke
Size: 4 in (10.1 cm)
Introduced: 1930
Withdrawn: By 1938
This figure was also produced with a flambé glaze

HN 1370 Marie (second version, model 662)
Designer: L. Harradine
Size: 4½ in (11.4 cm)
Introduced: 1930
Still in production
Made as a pair to HN 1368, *Rose*

HN 1388 Marie (second version, model 662)
Introduced: 1930
Withdrawn: By 1938
As HN 1370, but red and blue flowered dress

HN 1417 Marie (second version, model 662)
Introduced: 1930
Withdrawn: By 1949
As HN 1370, but orange dress

HN 1489 Marie (second version, model 662)
Introduced: 1932
Withdrawn: By 1949

HN 1369 *Boy on Pig*

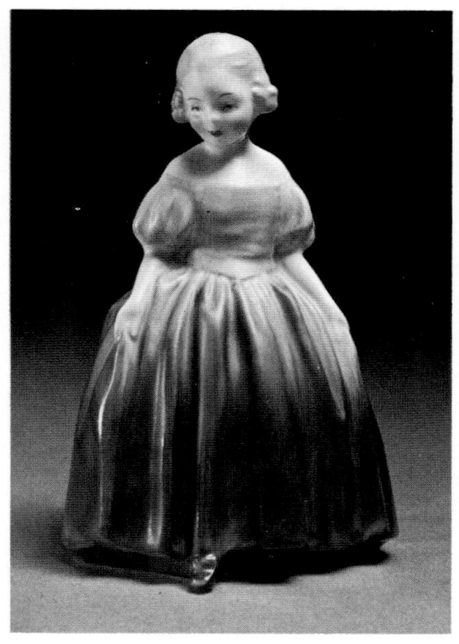
HN 1370 Marie (second version)

HN 1489 Marie (second version)

HN 1376 ***Fairy***
See page 191

HN 1377 ***Fairy***, Not issued

HN 1378 ***Fairy***
See page 191

HN 1379 ***Fairy***
See page 191

HN 1380 ***Fairy***
See page 192

HN 1531 Marie (second version, model 662)
Introduced: 1932
Withdrawn: By 1938
As HN 1370, but yellow/green dress

HN 1635 Marie (second version, model 662)
Introduced: 1934
Withdrawn: By 1949
As HN 1370, but flowered pink skirt

HN 1655 Marie (second version, model 662)
Introduced: 1934
Withdrawn: By 1938
As HN 1370, pink bodice, flowered white skirt

HN 1371 Darling
See page 65

HN 1372 Darling
See page 65

HN 1373 Sweet Lavender
Designer: L. Harradine
Size: 9 in (22.8 cm)
Introduced: 1930
Withdrawn: By 1949
Also known as *Any Old Lavender*, this figure, like so many of the street and market sellers, seems to have been inspired directly by the models of Charles Vyse and the paintings of Augustus John. The title is taken from a traditional London street cry: 'Who'll buy my sweet lavender?'

HN 1373 Sweet Lavender

HN 1374 ***Fairy***
See page 191

HN 1375 ***Fairy***
See page 191

HN 1391 Pierrette (third version)

HN 1392 Paisley Shawl (first version)

HN 1381-HN 1386 ***Fairies,*** Not issued

HN 1387 Rose
See page 200

HN 1388 Marie (second version, model 662)
See page 200

HN 1389 Doreen
See page 199

HN 1390 Doreen
See page 199

HN 1391 Pierrette (third version, model 659)
Designer: L. Harradine
Size: 9 in (22.8 cm)
Introduced: 1930
Withdrawn: By 1938
This large version of *Pierrette* was made in earthenware

HN 1749 Pierrette (third version, model 659)
Introduced: 1936
Withdrawn: By 1949
As HN 643, but pink and blue costume with playing card patterns

HN 1392 Paisley Shawl (first version, model 660)
Designer: L. Harradine
Size: 9 in (22.8 cm)
Introduced: 1930
Withdrawn: By 1949
The Scottish town of Paisley was famous throughout the 19th century for its textiles woven on mechanical looms. The complex scrolling floral patterns associated with Paisley were derived from India via the Middle East. For many years Paisley shawls were prized fashion accessories.

HN 1460 Paisley Shawl (first version, model 660)
Introduced: 1931
Withdrawn: By 1949

HN 1707 Paisley Shawl (first version, model 660)
Introduced: 1935
Withdrawn: By 1949
As HN 1392, but purple shawl, green hat

HN 1739 Paisley Shawl (first version, model 660)
Introduced: 1935
Withdrawn: By 1949

HN 1987 Paisley Shawl (first version, model 660)
Introduced: 1946
Withdrawn: 1959

HN 1460 Paisley Shawl (first version)

HN 1914 Paisley Shawl (second version)

HN 1739 & HN 1987 Paisley Shawl (first version)

HN 1397 Gretchen HN 1398 Derrick HN 1562 Gretchen

HN 1393 ***Fairy***
See page 192

HN 1394 ***Fairy***
See page 192

HN 1395 ***Fairy***
See page 192

HN 1396 ***Fairy***
See page 192

HN 1397 Gretchen
Designer: L. Harradine
Size: 7¾ in (19.6 cm)
Introduced: 1930
Withdrawn: By 1938
During the 1920s and 1930s Dutch themes were popular, a vogue reflected both by musicals and by a number of Doulton figures. The film *Gold Diggers of Broadway*, first shown in 1930, included the song *Tiptoe Through the Tulips*, while other, earlier musical comedy successes included *The Red Mill* and *Miss Hook of Holland.*

HN 1562 Gretchen
Introduced: 1933
Withdrawn: 1938

HN 1398 Derrick
Designer: L. Harradine
Size: 8 in (20.3 cm)
Introduced: 1930
Withdrawn: By 1938
Made to a pair to HN 1397, *Gretchen*
Despite its name, this figure is clearly female

HN 1399 The Young Widow
Designer: L. Harradine
Size: 8 in (20.3 cm)
Introduced: 1930
Withdrawn: 1930
As HN 1418, but light coloured basket
This inappropriately named figure was rapidly withdrawn after its introduction, to be renamed and reissued later with the title *The Little Mother*

HN 1418 The Little Mother (second version, model 648)
Designer: L. Harradine
Introduced: 1930
Withdrawn: By 1938

HN 1641 The Little Mother (second version, model 648)
Introduced: 1934
Withdrawn: By 1949
As HN 1399, but green shawl, pale skirt

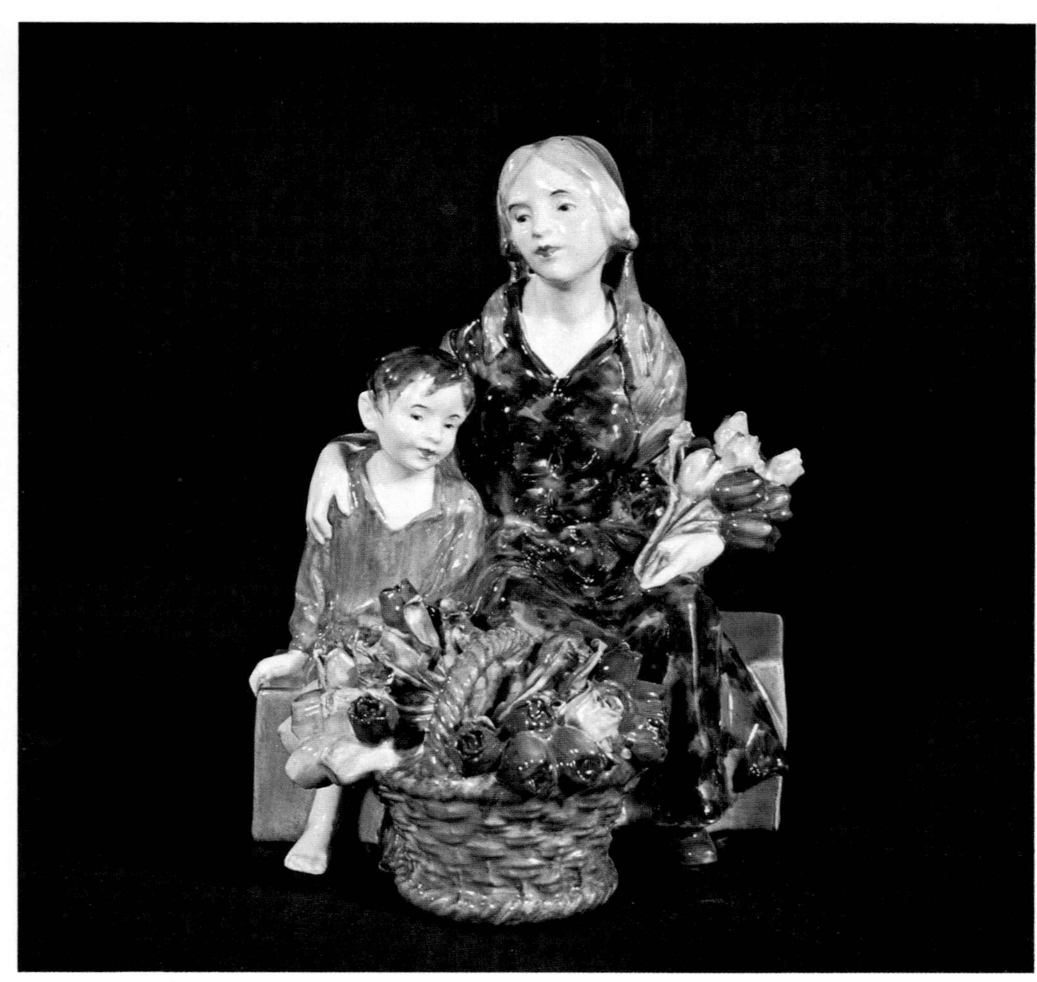

HN 1418 The Little Mother (second version)

HN 1400 The Windmill Lady
Designer: L. Harradine
Size: 8½ in (21.5 cm)
Introduced: 1930
Withdrawn: By 1938

HN 1400 The Windmill Lady

HN 1560, HN 1402 & HN 1440 Miss Demure

HN 1401 ***Chorus Girl***
Introduced: 1930
Withdrawn: By 1938

HN 1402 Miss Demure
Designer: L. Harradine
Size: 7 in (17.7 cm)
Introduced: 1930
Withdrawn: 1975

HN 1440 Miss Demure
Introduced: 1930
Withdrawn: By 1949

HN 1463 Miss Demure
Introduced: 1931
Withdrawn: By 1949
As HN 1402, but green dress

HN 1499 Miss Demure
Introduced: 1932
Withdrawn: By 1938
As HN 1402, but yellow bonnet, pink dress

HN 1560 Miss Demure
Introduced: 1933
Withdrawn: By 1949

HN 1403 The Old Huntsman, Not issued

HN 1401 *Chorus Girl* (illustration from the figure design book)

HN 1404 Betty (second version)

HN 1404 Betty (second version, model 678)
Designer: L. Harradine
Size: $4\frac{1}{2}$ in (11.4 cm)
Introduced: 1930
Withdrawn: By 1938

HN 1405 Betty (second version, model 678)
Introduced: 1930
Withdrawn: By 1938
As HN 1404, but green dress

HN 1407 The Winner

HN 1435 Betty (second version, model 678)
Introduced: 1930
Withdrawn: By 1938
As HN 1404, but mottled multicoloured dress

HN 1436 Betty (second version, model 678)
Introduced: 1930
Withdrawn: By 1938
As HN 1404, but patterned green dress

HN 1406 Flower Seller's Children
See page 134

HN 1408 John Peel & HN 1409 Hunting Squire
(illustrations from the figure design book)

HN 1407 The Winner
Size: 6¾ in (17.1 cm)
Introduced: 1930
Withdrawn: By 1938
Despite its realism, this unusual mounted figure does not appear to represent any actual horse or jockey

HN 1408 John Peel
Introduced: 1930
Withdrawn: 1937
Later reissued with the new title, *The Huntsman*, HN 1815, and made in earthenware.
John Peel, the archetypal huntsman, lived from 1776 to 1854, and was immortalised by the traditional song,
'D'ye ken John Peel with his coat so gay,
D'ye ken John Peel at the break of day.
D'ye ken John Peel when he's far, far away,
With his hounds and his horn in the morning.'
In fact, John Peel hunted on foot, not on horseback, perhaps one of the reasons for the change of name.

HN 1815 The Huntsman (second version, model 673)
Introduced: 1937
Withdrawn: By 1949
As HN 1408, but earthenware

HN 1409 Hunting Squire
Introduced: 1930
Withdrawn: By 1938

HN 2104 Abdullah

HN 1814 The Squire
Introduced: 1937
Withdrawn: By 1949
Renamed *The Squire*, and made in earthenware, this figure is otherwise the same as HN 1409

HN 1410 Abdullah
Designer: L. Harradine
Size: 6 in (15.2 cm)
Introduced: 1930
Withdrawn: By 1938
As HN 2104, but blue cushions, green turban

HN 2104 Abdullah
Introduced: 1953
Withdrawn: 1962

HN 1411 Charley's Aunt (second version, model 681)
Designer: H. Fenton
Introduced: 1930
Withdrawn: By 1938

HN 1554 Charley's Aunt (second version, model 681)
Introduced: 1933
Withdrawn: By 1938
As HN 1411, but purple dress

HN 1412 Pantalettes
See page 199

HN 1413 Margery

HN 1413 Margery
Designer: L. Harradine
Size: $10\frac{3}{4}$ in (27.3 cm)
Introduced: 1930
Withdrawn: By 1949

HN 1411 Charley's Aunt (second version, illustration from the figure design book)

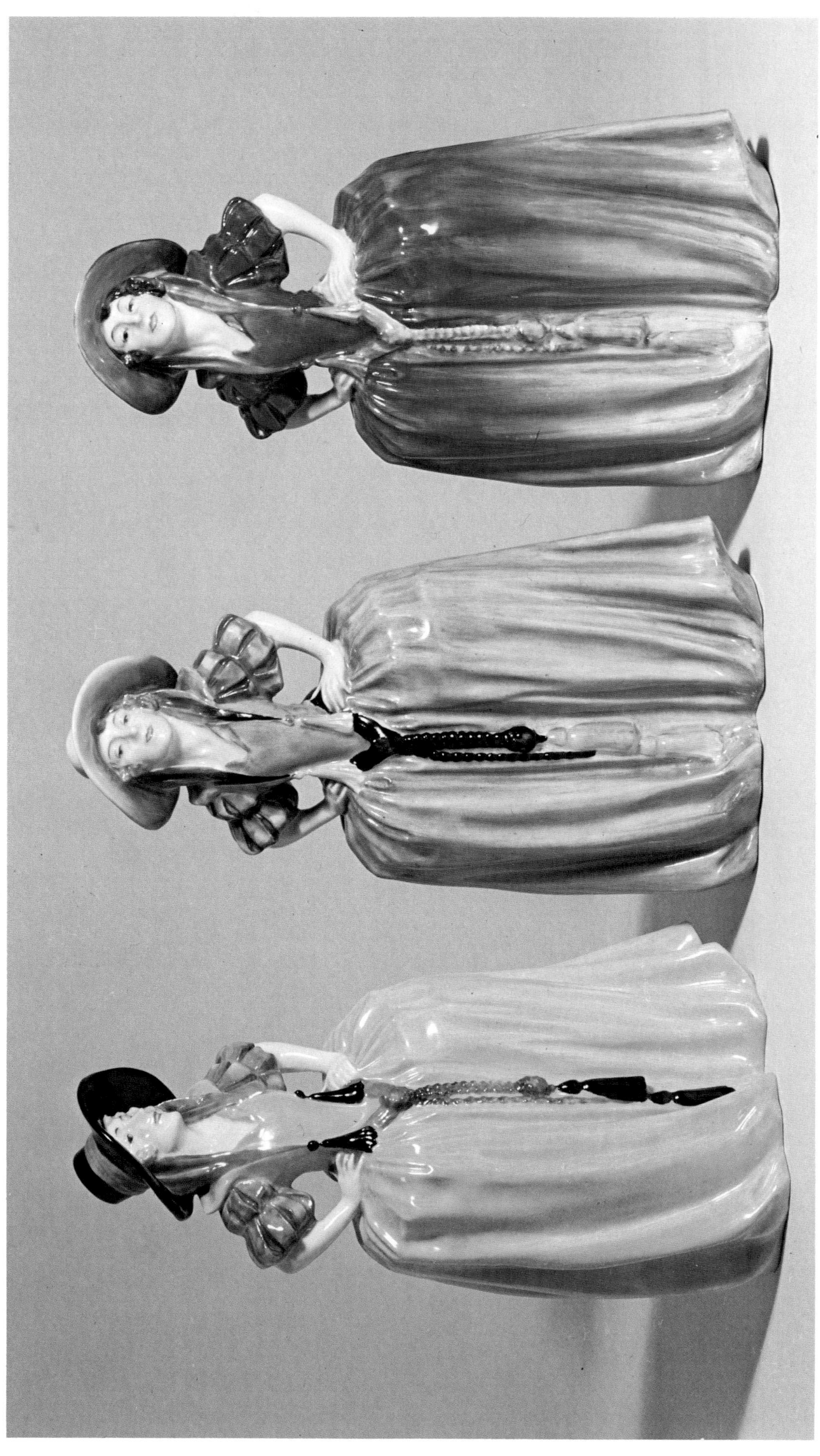

HN 1414, HN 1431 & HN 1567 Patricia

HN 1462 Patricia

HN 1420 & HN 1698 Phyllis

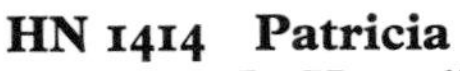

HN 1414 Patricia
Designer: L. Harradine
Size: 8½ in (21.5 cm)
Introduced: 1930
Withdrawn: By 1949
For illustration, see previous page

HN 1431 Patricia
Introduced: 1930
Withdrawn: By 1949
For illustration, see previous page

HN 1462 Patricia
Introduced: 1931
Withdrawn: By 1938

HN 1567 Patricia
Introduced: 1933
Withdrawn: By 1949
For illustration, see previous page

HN 1415 No details available

HN 1416 Rose
See page 200

HN 1417 Marie (second version, model 662)
See page 200

HN 1418 The Little Mother (second version, model 648)
See page 205

HN 1419 Dulcinea
See page 196

HN 1420 Phyllis
Designer: L. Harradine
Size: 9 in (22.8 cm)
Introduced: 1930
Withdrawn: By 1949
Traditionally the name of a country girl or shepherdess, Phyllis may have been taken from the popular poem,
'Phyllis is my only joy,
Faithless as the winds or seas,
Sometimes cunning, sometimes coy,
Yet she never fails to please.'

HN 1430 Phyllis
Introduced: 1930
Withdrawn: By 1938
As HN 1420, but dark blue shawl, striped pink skirt

HN 1421 & HN 1432 Barbara

HN 1486 Phyllis
Introduced: 1931
Withdrawn: By 1949
As HN 1420, but blue shawl, spotted pink overskirt, pink base

HN 1698 Phyllis
Introduced: 1935
Withdrawn: By 1949

HN 1421 Barbara
Designer: L. Harradine
Size: 7¾ in (19.6 cm)
Introduced: 1930
Withdrawn: By 1938

HN 1432 Barbara
Introduced: 1930
Withdrawn: By 1938

HN 1461 Barbara
Introduced: 1931
Withdrawn: By 1938
As HN 1421, but green dress

HN 1427 Darby

HN 1422 Joan

HN 1424 Babette

HN 1422 Joan
Designer: L. Harradine
Size: $5\frac{1}{2}$ in (13.9 cm)
Introduced: 1930
Withdrawn: By 1949
Made as a pair to HN 1427, *Darby*
Darby and Joan, a popular name for an old couple still attached to each other, has been in common use since the 18th century. It occurs frequently in poems and popular songs, for example in R. L. Stevenson's *We have loved of yore:*
'Joan and Darby doze and dream and wake;
Still, in the river of dreams,
Swims the boat of love . . .'

HN 2023 Joan
Introduced: 1949
Withdrawn: 1959
As HN 1422, with minor glaze differences

HN 1423 Babette
Designer: L. Harradine
Size: 5 in (12.7 cm)
Introduced: 1930
Withdrawn: By 1938
As HN 1424, but yellow and red striped costume
Perhaps named after the popular song *Babette*, recorded by Jack Hylton

HN 1424 Babette
Introduced: 1930
Withdrawn: By 1938

HN 1425 The Moor
See page 76

HN 1426 & HN 1429 The Gossips

HN 1428 & HN 1689 Calumet

HN 1426 The Gossips
Designer: L. Harradine
Size: 5¾ in (14.6 cm)
Introduced: 1930
Withdrawn: By 1949
This theme was used by many ceramic modellers, including George Tinworth, who made figure groups with the same title at the Doulton Lambeth factory.

HN 1429 The Gossips
Introduced: 1930
Withdrawn: By 1949

HN 2025 The Gossips
Introduced: 1949
Withdrawn: 1967
As HN 1429, but minor glaze differences

HN 1427 Darby
Designer: L. Harradine
Size: 5½ in (13.9 cm)
Introduced: 1930
Withdrawn: By 1949
Made as a pair to HN 1422, *Joan*
For illustration, see opposite

HN 2024 Darby
Introduced: 1949
Withdrawn: 1959
As HN 1427, but minor glaze differences

HN 1428 Calumet
Designer: C. J. Noke
Size: 6 in (15.2 cm)
Introduced: 1930
Withdrawn: By 1949
The calumet, or tobacco pipe, was of great importance for the North American Indian. The clay or stone bowl, with its long and frequently ornamented reed stem, was used as a symbol of peace and friendship. Smoking the calumet, or pipe of peace, was an expression of brotherhood.

HN 1689 Calumet
Size: 6¾ in (17.1 cm)
Introduced: 1935
Withdrawn: By 1949

HN 2068 Calumet
Introduced: 1950
Withdrawn: 1953
As HN 1689, but minor glaze differences

HN 1429 The Gossips
See page 213

HN 1430 Phyllis
See page 210

HN 1431 Patricia
See page 210

HN 1432 Barbara
See page 211

HN 1433 The Little Bridesmaid (first version, model 700)
Designer: L. Harradine
Size: 5 in (12.7 cm)
Introduced: 1930
Withdrawn: 1951
For illustration, see next page

HN 1434 & HN 1433 The Little Bridesmaid (first version)

HN 1434 The Little Bridesmaid (first version, model 700)
Introduced: 1930
Withdrawn: By 1949

HN 1530 The Little Bridesmaid (first version, model 700)
Introduced: 1932
Withdrawn: By 1938
As HN 1433, but yellow and green dress

HN 1435 Betty (second version, model 678)
See page 207

HN 1436 Betty (second version, model 678)
See page 207

HN 1437 Sweet and Twenty (first version, model 605)
See page 185

HN 1438 Sweet and Twenty (first version, model 605)
See page 185

HN 1439 Columbine (first version, model 563)
See page 185

HN 1440 Miss Demure
See page 206

HN 1441 Child Study
Size: 5 in (12.7 cm)
Introduced: 1931
Withdrawn: By 1938
As HN 1539, but applied flowers on base

HN 1442 Child Study
Size: 6¼ in (15.8 cm)
Introduced: 1931
Withdrawn: By 1938
As HN 1540, applied flowers on base

HN 1443 Child Study
Size: 5 in (12.7 cm)
Introduced: 1931
Withdrawn: By 1938
As HN 1540, applied flowers on base

HN 1444 Pauline

HN 1445 & HN 1513 Biddy

HN 1447 & HN 1555 Marigold

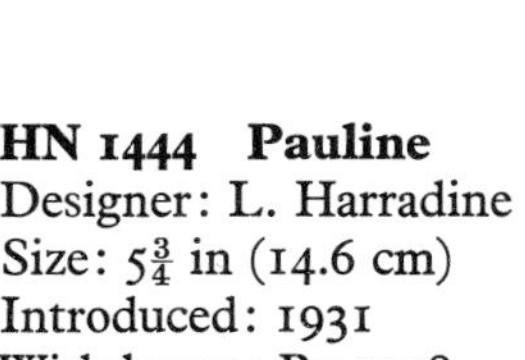

HN 1444 Pauline
Designer: L. Harradine
Size: 5¾ in (14.6 cm)
Introduced: 1931
Withdrawn: By 1938

HN 1445 Biddy
Designer: L. Harradine
Size: 5½ in (13.9 cm)
Introduced: 1931
Withdrawn: By 1938

HN 1500 Biddy
Introduced: 1932
Withdrawn: By 1938
As HN 1445, but yellow dress

HN 1513 Biddy
Introduced: 1932
Withdrawn: 1951

HN 1446 Marietta
See page 195

HN 1447 Marigold
Designer: L. Harradine
Size: 6 in (15.2 cm)
Introduced: 1931
Withdrawn: By 1949

HN 1451 Marigold
Introduced: 1931
Withdrawn: By 1938
As HN 1447, but yellow dress

HN 1555 Marigold
Introduced: 1933
Withdrawn: By 1949

HN 1450 Rita

HN 1448 Rita
Designer: L. Harradine
Size: 7 in (17.7 cm)
Introduced: 1931
Withdrawn: By 1938
As HN 1450, but yellow and pink dress

HN 1450 Rita
Introduced: 1931
Withdrawn: By 1938

HN 1449 The Little Mistress
Designer: L. Harradine
Size: 6 in (15.2 cm)
Introduced: 1931
Withdrawn: By 1949

HN 1450 Rita
See above

HN 1451 Marigold
See above

HN 1452 A Victorian Lady
See page 162

HN 1453 Sweet Anne
See page 191

HN 1454 Negligée
See page 173

HN 1449 The Little Mistress

HN 1455 Molly Malone

HN 1466 All-A-Blooming

HN 1455 Molly Malone
Designer: L. Harradine
Size: 7 in (17.7 cm)
Introduced: 1931
Withdrawn: By 1938
The figure is based on the traditional Irish folk song,
'In Dublin's fair city,
Where girls are so pretty,
I first set my eyes on sweet Molly Malone.
As she wheeled her wheel barrow
Through streets broad and narrow,
Crying cockles and mussels, alive, alive oh!'

HN 1456 Butterfly
See page 158

HN 1457 All-A-Blooming
Designer: L. Harradine
Size: 6½ in (16.5 cm)
Introduced: 1931
As HN 1466, but blue dress.
As the date of withdrawal is not known, it is possible that this version was not actually issued.
This figure was based closely on the Charles Vyse model, *The Flower Girl*, issued in 1928.

HN 1466 All-A-Blooming
Introduced: 1931
Withdrawn: By 1938

HN 1458 Monica
Designer: L. Harradine
Size: 4 in (10.1 cm)
Introduced: 1931
Withdrawn: By 1949

HN 1459 Monica
Introduced: 1931
As HN 1458, but lilac dress.
As the date of withdrawal is not known, it is possible that this version was not actually issued.

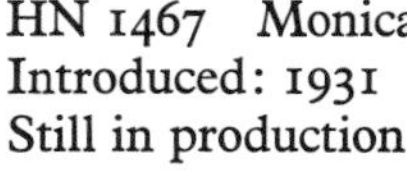

HN 1467 Monica
Introduced: 1931
Still in production

Autumn Leaves, or *The Flower Girl*, modelled by Charles Vyse, introduced in 1928

HN 1458 Monica

HN 1467 Monica

HN 1464 The Carpet Seller

HN 1465 Lady Clare

HN 1460 Paisley Shawl (first version, model 660)
See page 202

HN 1461 Barbara
See page 211

HN 1462 Patricia
See page 210

HN 1463 Miss Demure
See page 206

HN 1464 The Carpet Seller
Designer: L. Harradine
Size: 9¼ in (23.4 cm)
Introduced: 1931
Withdrawn: 1969

HN 1465 Lady Clare
Designer: L. Harradine
Size: 7¾ in (19.6 cm)
Introduced: 1931
Withdrawn: By 1938

HN 1564, HN 1468 & HN 1469 Pamela

HN 1470 Chloe

HN 1479 Chloe

HN 1466 All-A-Blooming
See page 216

HN 1467 Monica
See page 216

HN 1468 Pamela
Designer: L. Harradine
Size: 8 in (20.3 cm)
Introduced: 1931
Withdrawn: By 1938

HN 1469 Pamela
Introduced: 1931
Withdrawn: By 1938

HN 1564 Pamela
Introduced: 1933
Withdrawn: By 1938

HN 1470 Chloe
Designer: L. Harradine
Size 6 in (15.2 cm)
Introduced: 1931
Withdrawn: By 1949
Chloe was a popular song first recorded in 1928, although the style of this figure has more in common with the heroine of Meredith's novel, *A Tale of Chloe*, set in 18th century Bath

HN 1476 Chloe
Introduced: 1931
Withdrawn: By 1938

HN 1479 Chloe
Introduced: 1931
Withdrawn: By 1949

HN 1498 Chloe
Introduced: 1932
Withdrawn: By 1938
As HN 1470, but yellow dress

HN 1765 Chloe
Introduced: 1936
Withdrawn: 1950

HN 1956 Chloe
Introduced: 1940
Withdrawn: By 1949
As HN 1470, but red skirt, green ribbon

HN 1765 Chloe

HN 1476 Chloe

HN 1472, HN 1471 & HN 1550 Annette

HN 1473 Dreamland

HN 1471 Annette
Designer: L. Harradine
Size: 6 in (15.2 cm)
Introduced: 1931
Withdrawn: By 1938
Like HN 1397, *Gretchen,* this figure reflects the Dutch vogue of the 1920s and 1930s

HN 1472 Annette
Introduced: 1931
Withdrawn: By 1949

HN 1550 Annette
Introduced: 1933
Withdrawn: By 1949

HN 1473 Dreamland
Designer: L. Harradine
Size: 4¾ in (12.0 cm)
Introduced: 1931
Withdrawn: By 1938

HN 1481 Dreamland
Introduced: 1931
Withdrawn: By 1938
As HN 1473, but darker sofa, yellow and red costume

HN 1475 In the Stocks (first version)

HN 1474 In the Stocks (first version, model 719)
Designer: L. Harradine
Size: 5¼ in (13.3 cm)
Introduced: 1931
Withdrawn: By 1938
Also known as *Love in the Stocks* and *Love locked in*
As HN 1475, but red dress

HN 1475 In the Stocks (first version, model 719)
Introduced: 1931
Withdrawn: By 1938

HN 1476 Chloe
See page 219

HN 1477 No details available

HN 1478 Sylvia
Designer: L. Harradine
Size: 10½ in (26.6 cm)
Introduced: 1931
Withdrawn: By 1938

HN 1479 Chloe
See page 219

HN 1478 Sylvia

HN 1480 Newhaven Fishwife

HN 1480 Newhaven Fishwife
Designer: H. Fenton
Size: 7¾ in (19.6 cm)
Introduced: 1931
Withdrawn: By 1938
Newhaven is a fishing port on the Firth of Forth, where the fisherwomen traditionally wore striped petticoats, shawls and heavy clogs, and carried the fish in heavy creels, or baskets. Early photographs taken by D. O. Hill between 1843 and 1848 show similarly dressed women at work.

HN 1481 Dreamland
See page 220

HN 1482 Pearly Boy (first version, model 724)
Designer: L. Harradine
Size: 5½ in (13.9 cm)
Introduced: 1931
Withdrawn: By 1949
Pearly Boys and Girls, with their costumes decorated with thousands of buttons, evolved in the 1880s from the traditional cockney coster kings. The first Pearly King was Henry Croft who died in 1930, having collected a large sum for charity during his lifetime, the prime purpose of the Pearly tradition. Hereditary East End families preserve the traditions today, and continue to wear the buttoned costumes, the cartwheel hats and the ostrich plumes.

HN 1482 Pearly Boy & HN 1483 Pearly Girl (first versions)

HN 2036 Pearly Girl & HN 2035 Pearly Boy (second versions)

HN 1547 Pearly Boy (first version, model 724)
Introduced: 1933
Withdrawn: By 1949
As HN 1482, but green jacket, purple trousers

HN 1483 Pearly Girl (first version, model 723)
Designer: L. Harradine
Size: 5½ in (13.9 cm)
Introduced: 1931
Withdrawn: By 1949

HN 1548 Pearly Girl (first version, model 723)
Introduced: 1933
Withdrawn: By 1949
As HN 1483, but purple bodice, green skirt

HN 1484 Jennifer
Designer: L. Harradine
Size: 6½ in (16.5 cm)
Introduced: 1931
Withdrawn: By 1949

HN 1485 Greta
Designer: L. Harradine
Size: 5½ in (13.9 cm)
Introduced: 1931
Withdrawn: 1953

HN 1486 Phyllis
See page 211

HN 1484 Jennifer

HN 1485 Greta

HN 1696, HN 1577 & HN 1487 Suzette

HN 1488 & HN 1700 Gloria

HN 1487 Suzette
Designer: L. Harradine
Size: 7½ in (19 cm)
Introduced: 1931
Withdrawn: 1950

HN 1577 Suzette
Introduced: 1933
Withdrawn: By 1949

HN 1585 Suzette
Introduced: 1933
Withdrawn: By 1938
As HN 1487, but green and yellow dress

HN 1696 Suzette
Introduced: 1935
Withdrawn: By 1949

HN 2026 Suzette
Introduced: 1949
Withdrawn: By 1959
As HN 1487, but minor colour differences

HN 1488 Gloria
Designer: L. Harradine
Size: 7 in (17.7 cm)
Introduced: 1932
Withdrawn: By 1938

HN 1700 Gloria
Introduced: 1935
Withdrawn: By 1938

HN 1489 Marie (second version, model 662)
See page 200

HN 1490 Dorcas
Designer: L. Harradine
Size: 7 in (17.7 cm)
Introduced: 1932
Withdrawn: By 1938
Dorcas is the traditional name for a good and charitable woman, who makes clothes and needlework to help the poor. It originated in the Bible, where Dorcas was referred to as, 'full of good works and alms deeds.' The Dorcas Society, a ladies association connected with the church, was founded for the purpose of making clothes for the poor.

HN 1491 Dorcas
Introduced: 1932
Withdrawn: By 1938

HN 1558 Dorcas
Introduced: 1933
Withdrawn: 1952

HN 1490, HN 1491 & HN 1558 Dorcas

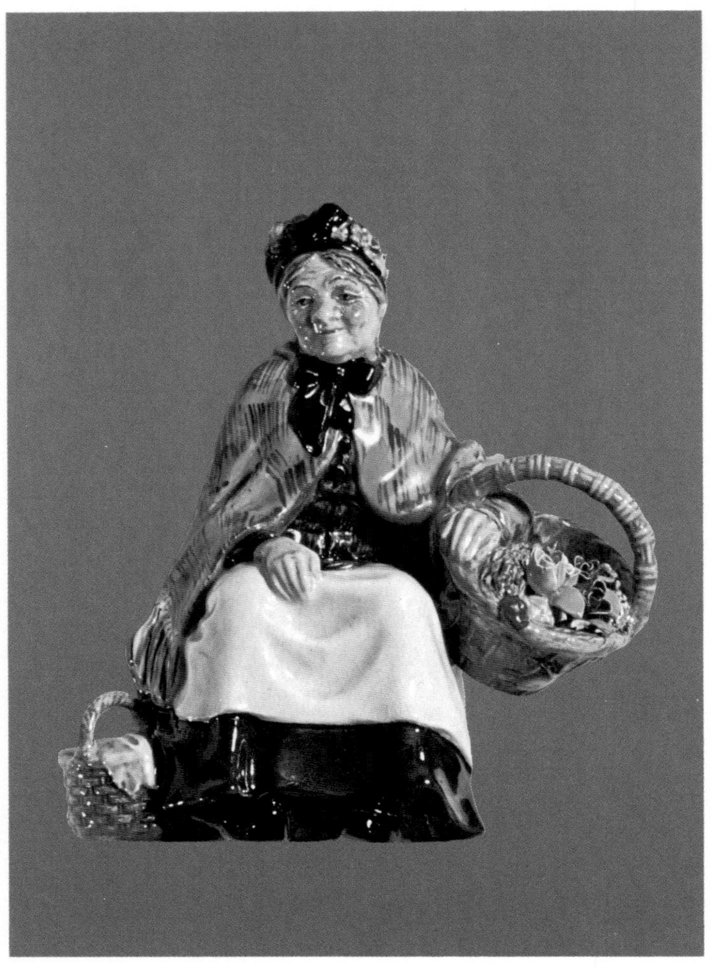

HN 1492 Old Lavender Seller

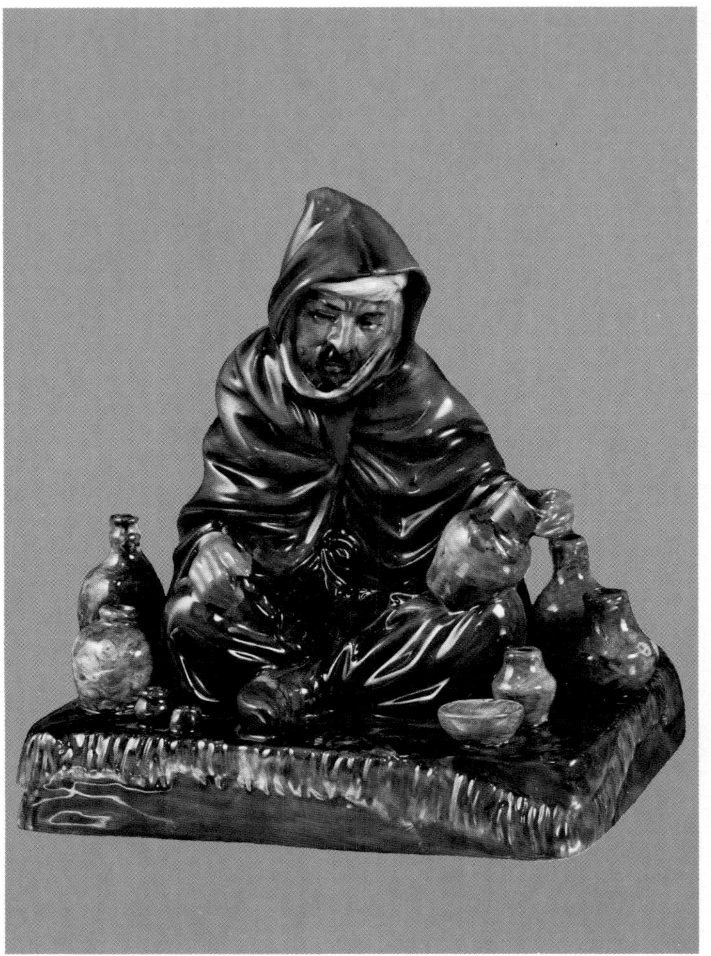

HN 1493 The Potter

HN 1492 Old Lavender Seller
Designer: L. Harradine
Size: $6\frac{1}{2}$ in (16.5 cm)
Introduced: 1932
Withdrawn: By 1949

HN 1571 Old Lavender Seller
Introduced: 1933
Withdrawn: By 1949
As HN 1492, but patterned orange cape

HN 1493 The Potter
Designer: C. J. Noke
Size: $6\frac{3}{4}$ in (17.1 cm)
Introduced: 1932
Still in production
Early versions of this figure have a more complex base, raised on four squat legs.
Unlike the more conventional images of the potter produced by many modellers, including John Broad at Doulton's Lambeth factory, this figure was made to suggest the origins of pottery in the Far and Middle East.

HN 1518 The Potter
Introduced: 1932
Withdrawn: By 1949
As HN 1493, but green cloak

HN 1522 The Potter
Introduced: 1932
Withdrawn: By 1949
As HN 1493, but dark blue and green cloak

HN 1503 Gwendolen

HN 1494 Gwendolen
Designer: L. Harradine
Size: 6 in (15.2 cm)
Introduced: 1932
Withdrawn: By 1938
As HN 1503, but green and pink dress
Perhaps inspired by Gwendolen Fairfax, the heroine of Oscar Wilde's play, *The Importance of Being Ernest.*

HN 1503 Gwendolen
Introduced: 1932
Withdrawn: By 1949

HN 1570 Gwendolen
Introduced: 1933
Withdrawn: By 1949
As HN 1503, but pink dress

HN 1495 Priscilla
See page 194

HN 1496 Sweet Anne
See page 191

HN 1497 Rosamund (second version, model 729)
Designer: L. Harradine
Size: $8\frac{1}{2}$ in (21.5 cm)
Introduced: 1932
Withdrawn: By 1938
This figure is an adapted version of HN 90, *Doris Keene as Cavallini*

HN 1551 Rosamund (second version, model 729)
Introduced: 1933
Withdrawn: By 1938

HN 1498 Chloe
See page 219

HN 1499 Miss Demure
See page 206

HN 1500 Biddy
See page 215

HN 1501 Priscilla
See page 194

HN 1497 & HN 1551 Rosamund (second version)

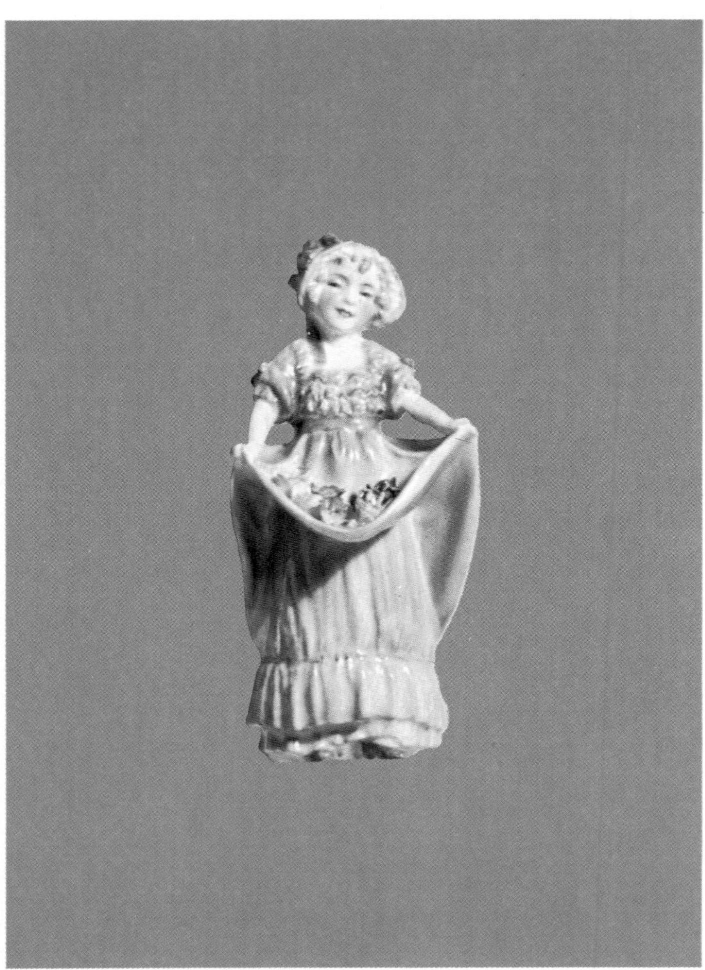

HN 1502 Lucy Ann

HN 1502 Lucy Ann
Designer: L. Harradine
Size: 5¼ in (13.3 cm)
Introduced: 1932
Withdrawn: 1951

HN 1565 Lucy Ann
Introduced: 1933
Withdrawn: By 1938
As HN 1502, but pale green dress

HN 1503 Gwendolen
See page 227

HN 1504 Sweet Maid (first version, model 739)
Designer: L. Harradine
Size: 8 in (20.3 cm)
Introduced: 1932
Withdrawn: By 1938

HN 1505 Sweet Maid (first version, model 739)
Introduced: 1932
Withdrawn: By 1938

HN 1506 Rose
See page 200

HN 1507 Pantalettes
See page 199

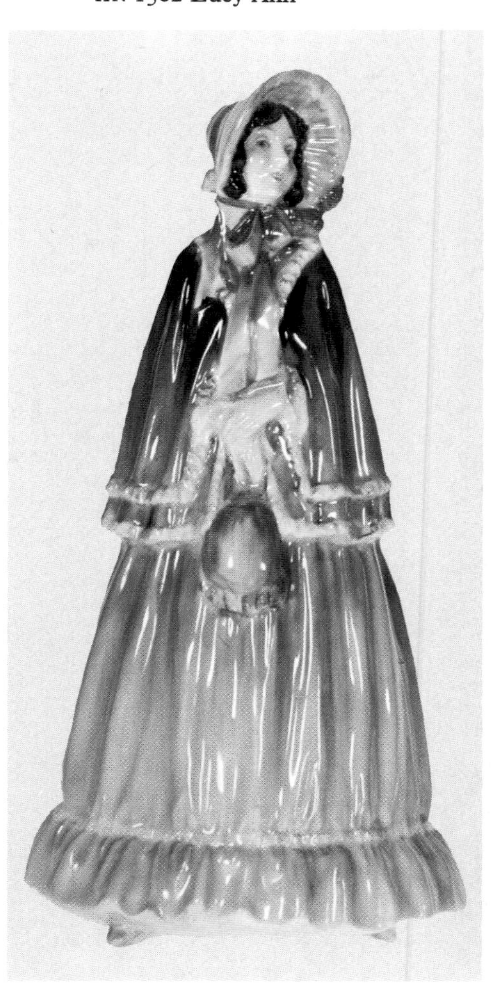

HN 1504 Sweet Maid (first version)

HN 1505 Sweet Maid (first version)

HN 1572 Helen   HN 1509 Helen   HN 1508 Helen

HN 1508 Helen
Designer: L. Harradine
Size: 8 in (20.3 cm)
Introduced: 1932
Withdrawn: By 1938

HN 1509 Helen
Introduced: 1932
Withdrawn: By 1938

HN 1572 Helen
Introduced: 1933
Withdrawn: By 1938

HN 1510 Constance
Designer: L. Harradine
Introduced: 1932
Withdrawn: By 1938
Purple and yellow dress

HN 1511 Constance
Introduced: 1932
Withdrawn: By 1938
Pale pink dress, red handbag

HN 1512 Kathleen
See page 178

HN 1513 Biddy
See page 215

HN 1510 Constance (illustration from the design registration book)

HN 1515 Dolly Vardon

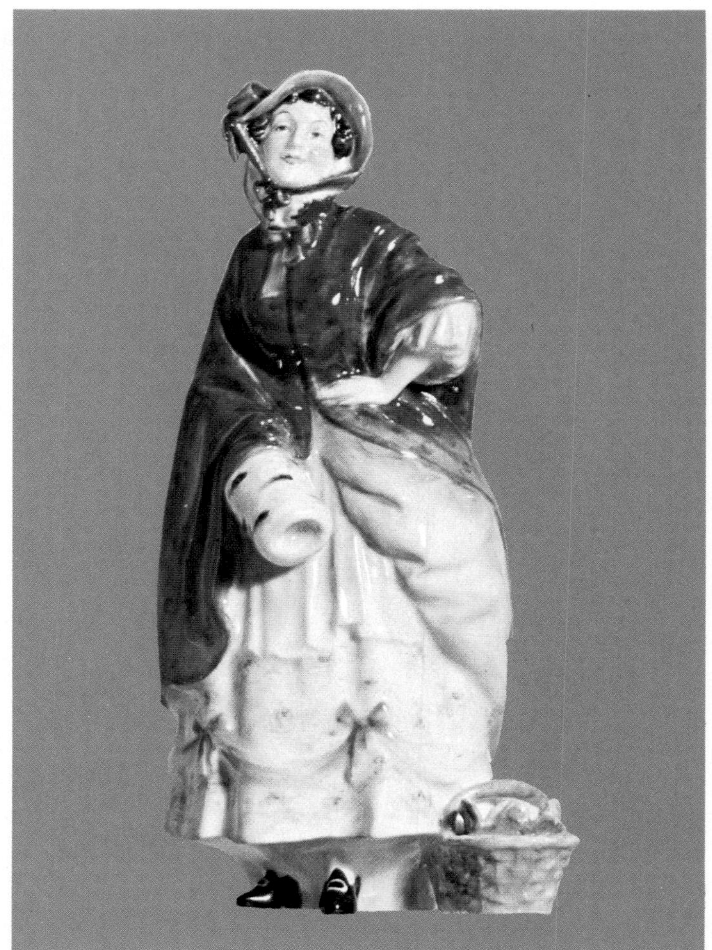

HN 1514 Dolly Vardon

HN 1514 Dolly Vardon
Designer: L. Harradine
Size: 8½ in (21.5 cm)
Introduced: 1932
Withdrawn: By 1938
Dolly Vardon is a character in Dickens' *Barnaby Rudge*: 'A pretty, laughing girl; dimpled, fresh and healthy—the very impersonation of good humour and blooming beauty.' In the book she was loved by Joe Willet and Sid Tappertit. She was seized by the mob during the Gordon riots, was rescued by Joe and subsequently married him.
A Dolly Vardon is also a large-brimmed picture hat, with one side bent downwards and trimmed with flowers.

HN 1515 Dolly Vardon
Introduced: 1932
Withdrawn: By 1949

HN 1516 Cicely
Designer: L. Harradine
Size: 5½ in (13.9 cm)
Introduced: 1932
Withdrawn: By 1949

HN 1516 Cicely

HN 1517 Veronica (first version) HN 1915 Veronica (second version)

HN 1519 Veronica (first version)

HN 1517 Veronica (first version, model 751)
Designer: L. Harradine
Size: 8 in (20.3 cm)
Introduced: 1932
Withdrawn: 1951

HN 1519 Veronica (first version, model 751)
Introduced: 1932
Withdrawn: By 1938

HN 1650 Veronica (first version, model 751)
Introduced: 1934
Withdrawn: By 1949
As HN 1517, but green dress

HN 1943 Veronica (first version, model 751)
Introduced: 1940
Withdrawn: By 1949
As HN 1517, but pink dress, blue hat

HN 1518 The Potter
See page 226

HN 1519 Veronica (first version, model 751)
See above

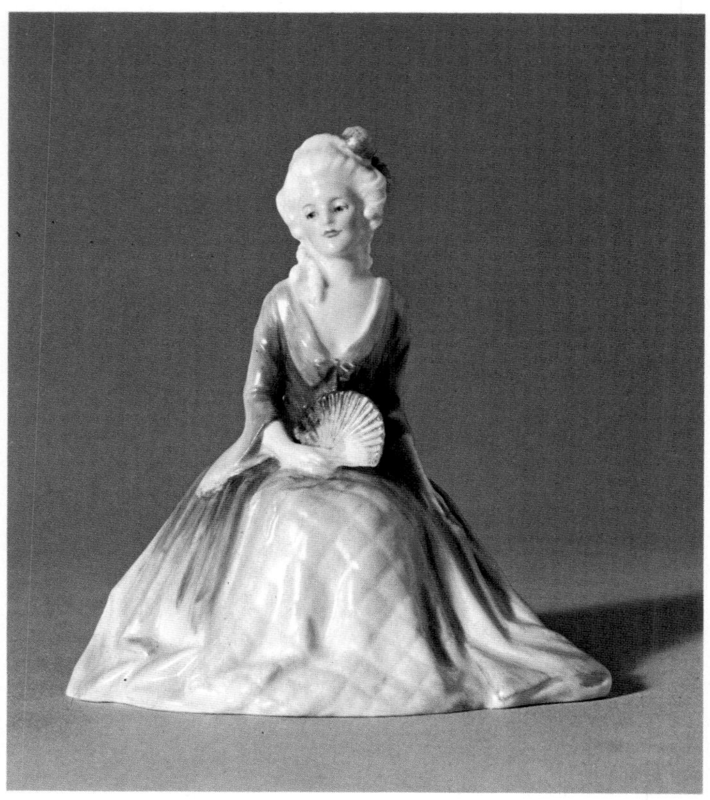

HN 1521 Eugene

HN 1525 Clarissa (first version)

HN 1520 Eugene
Designer: L. Harradine
Size: 5¾ in (14.6 cm)
Introduced: 1932
Withdrawn: By 1938
As HN 1521, but green and pink dress

HN 1521 Eugene
Introduced: 1932
Withdrawn: By 1938

HN 1522 The Potter
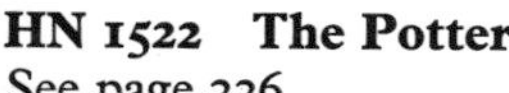
See page 226

HN 1523 & HN 1524 Lisette

HN 1526 Anthea

HN 1527 & HN 1669 Anthea

HN 1523 Lisette
Designer: L. Harradine
Size: $5\frac{1}{4}$ in (13.3 cm)
Introduced: 1932
Withdrawn: By 1938

HN 1524 Lisette
Introduced: 1932
Withdrawn: By 1938

HN 1684 Lisette
Introduced: 1935
Withdrawn: By 1938
As HN 1523, but pink dress, green trim

HN 1525 Clarissa (first version, model 773)
Designer: L. Harradine
Size: 10 in (25.4 cm)
Introduced: 1932
Withdrawn: By 1938
Perhaps inspired by the heroine of the 18th century novel, *Clarissa Marlowe*

HN 1687 Clarissa (first version, model 773)
Introduced: 1935
Withdrawn: By 1949
As HN 1525, but green shawl, pale blue dress

HN 1526 Anthea
Designer: L. Harradine
Size: $6\frac{1}{2}$ in (16.5 cm)
Introduced: 1932
Withdrawn: By 1938
The name Anthea became popular in the 17th century, and was celebrated by a number of poets, including Robert Herrick who wrote *To Anthea:*
'Thou art my life, my love, my heart,
The very eyes of me:
And hast command of every part,
To live and die for thee.'

HN 1527 Anthea
Introduced: 1932
Withdrawn: By 1949

HN 1669 Anthea
Introduced: 1934
Withdrawn: By 1938

HN 1528 Bluebeard (second version)

HN 2105 Bluebeard (second version)

HN 1528 Bluebeard (second version, model 745)
Designer: L. Harradine
Size: 11½ in (29.2 cm)
Introduced: 1932
Withdrawn: By 1949

HN 2105 Bluebeard (second version, model 745)
Introduced: 1953
Still in production

HN 1529 A Victorian Lady
See page 162

HN 1530 The Little Bridesmaid
See page 214

HN 1531 Marie (second version, model 662)
See page 201

HN 1532 *Fairy*
See page 192

HN 1533 *Fairy*
See page 192

HN 1534 *Fairy*
See page 192

HN 1535 *Fairy*
See page 192

HN 1536 *Fairy*
See page 192

HN 1537 & HN 1737 Janet (first version)

HN 1916 Janet (second version) HN 1538 Janet (first version)

HN 1537 Janet (first version, model 785)
Size: 6½ in (16.5 cm)
Introduced: 1932
Still in production

HN 1538 Janet (first version, model 785)
Introduced: 1932
Withdrawn: By 1949

HN 1652 Janet (first version, model 785)
Introduced: 1934
Withdrawn: By 1949
As HN 1537, but red bodice, pink skirt with floral pattern

HN 1737 Janet (first version, model 785)
Introduced: 1935
Withdrawn: By 1949

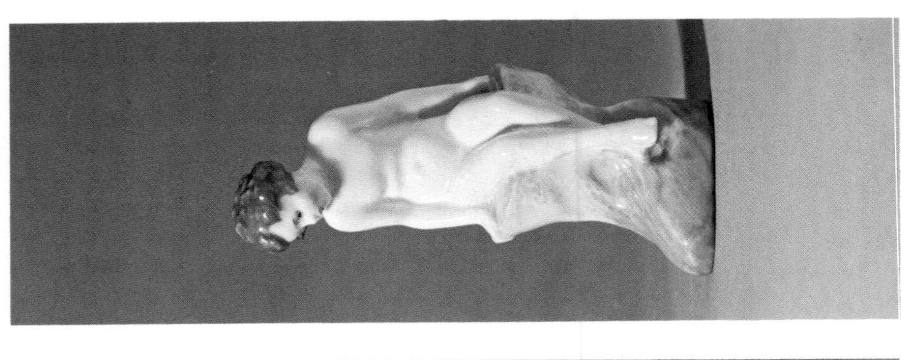

HN 1542

HN 1541 HN 1543 HN 1539 HN 1540 HN 1545 HN 1546 HN 1544

HN 1539 A Saucy Nymph
Size: 4½ in (11.4 cm)
Introduced: 1933
Withdrawn: By 1949
This group of child studies is quite distinctive, although some of the models have been issued before. Each figure has a quotation for a title, and these are printed on the underneath of the base in each case.

HN 1540 'Little Child so Rare and Sweet'
Size: 5 in (12.7 cm)
Introduced: 1933
Withdrawn: By 1949

HN 1541 'Happy Joy. Baby Boy'
Size: 6¼ in (15.8 cm)
Introduced: 1933
Withdrawn: By 1949

HN 1542 'Little Child so Rare and Sweet'
Size: 5 in (12.7 cm)
Introduced: 1933
Withdrawn: By 1949

HN 1543 'Dancing Eyes and Sunny Hair'
Size: 5 in (12.7 cm)
Introduced: 1933
Withdrawn: By 1949

HN 1544 'Do you Wonder where Fairies are that Folk Declare Have Vanished'
Size: 5 in (12.7 cm)
Introduced: 1933
Withdrawn: By 1949

HN 1545 'Called Love, a Little Boy, almost Naked, Wanton, Blind, Cruel now, and then as Kind'
Size: 3½ in (8.8 cm)
Introduced: 1933
Withdrawn: By 1949

HN 1546 'Here a Little Child I Stand'
Size: 6¼ in (15.8 cm)
Introduced: 1933
Withdrawn: 1949
This figure should not be confused with HN 62, *A Child's Grace*, which carries the same Herrick poem.

HN 1547 Pearly Boy (first version, model 724)
See page 222

HN 1548 Pearly Girl (first version, model 723)
See page 223

HN 1549 Sweet and Twenty (first version, model 605)
See page 185

HN 1552 Pinkie

HN 1550 Annette
See page 220

HN 1551 Rosamund (second version, model 729)
See page 227

HN 1552 Pinkie
Designer: L. Harradine
Size: 5 in (12.7 cm)
Introduced: 1933
Withdrawn: By 1938

HN 1553 Pinkie
Introduced: 1933
Withdrawn: By 1938
As HN 1553, but yellow and blue dress

HN 1554 Charley's Aunt (second version, model 681)
See page 208

HN 1555 Marigold
See page 215

HN 1556 Rosina
See page 197

HN 1557 Lady Fayre
See page 180

HN 1558 Dorcas
See page 225

HN 1559 Priscilla
See page 194

HN 1560 Miss Demure
See page 206

HN 1584 Willy-Won't He

HN 1561 Willy-Won't He
Designer: L. Harradine
Size: 6 in (15.2 cm)
Introduced: 1933
Withdrawn: By 1949
As HN 1584, but blue jacket and pink trousers

HN 1584 Willy-Won't He
Introduced: 1933
Withdrawn: By 1949

HN 2150 Willy-Won't He
Introduced: 1955
Withdrawn: 1959
As HN 1584, but minor glaze changes

HN 1562 Gretchen
See page 204

HN 1563 Sweet and Twenty (first version, model 605)
See page 185

HN 1564 Pamela
See page 219

HN 1565 Lucy Ann
See page 228

HN 1566 Estelle

HN 1568 Charmian

HN 1566 Estelle
Designer: L. Harradine
Size: 8 in (20.33 cm)
Introduced: 1933
Withdrawn: By 1938

HN 1802 Estelle
Introduced: 1937
Withdrawn: By 1949
As HN 1566, but pink dress

HN 1567 Patricia
See page 210

HN 1569 Charmian

HN 1568 Charmian
Designer: L. Harradine
Size: 6½ in (16.5 cm)
Introduced: 1933
Withdrawn: By 1938

HN 1569 Charmian
Introduced: 1933
Withdrawn: By 1938

HN 1651 Charmian
Introduced: 1934
Withdrawn: By 1938
As HN 1568, but red bodice, green skirt

HN 1570 Gwendolen
See page 227

HN 1571 Old Lavender Seller
See page 226

HN 1572 Helen
See page 229

HN 1573 Rhoda

HN 1574 Rhoda

HN 1688 Rhoda

HN 1575 Daisy
Designer: L. Harradine
Size: 3½ in (8.8 cm)
Introduced: 1933
Withdrawn: By 1949

HN 1961 Daisy
Introduced: 1941
Withdrawn: By 1949
As HN 1575, but pink dress

HN 1575 Daisy

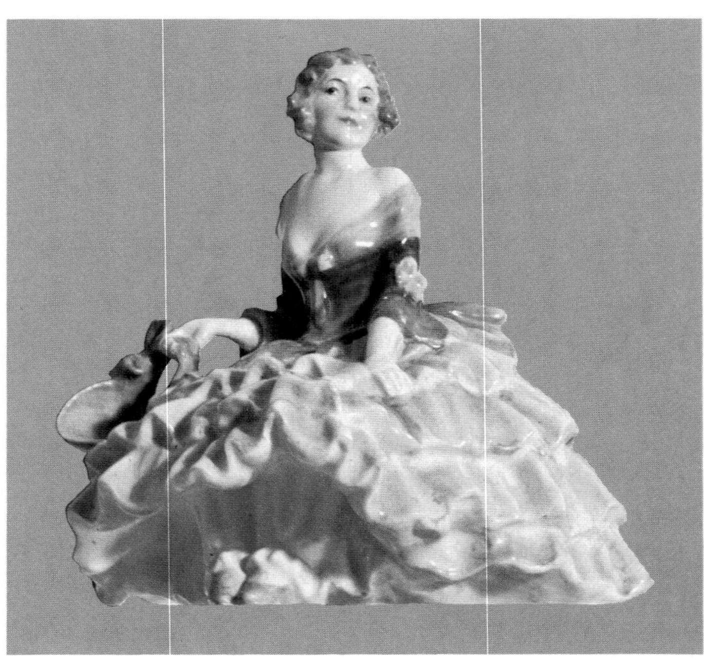

HN 1576 Tildy

HN 1573 Rhoda
Designer: L. Harradine
Size: 10¼ in (26.6 cm)
Introduced: 1933
Withdrawn: By 1949
Perhaps inspired by the heroine of Meredith's novel, *Rhoda Fleming*
For illustration, see previous page

HN 1574 Rhoda
Introduced: 1933
Withdrawn: By 1938
For illustration, see previous page

HN 1688 Rhoda
Introduced: 1935
Withdrawn: By 1949

HN 1576 Tildy
Designer: L. Harradine
Size: 5½ in (13.9 cm)
Introduced: 1933
Withdrawn: By 1938

HN 1859 Tildy
Introduced: 1938
Withdrawn: By 1949
No details of colour available

HN 1578 & HN 1579 The Hinged Parasol

HN 1577 Suzette
See page 225

HN 1578 The Hinged Parasol
Designer: L. Harradine
Size: 6½ in (16.5 cm)
Introduced: 1933
Withdrawn: By 1949

HN 1579 The Hinged Parasol
Introduced: 1933
Withdrawn: By 1949

HN 1580 Rosebud (first version, model 807)
Designer: L. Harradine
Size: 3 in (7.6 cm)
Introduced: 1933
Withdrawn: By 1938
Pink dress

HN 1581 Rosebud (first version, model 807)
Introduced: 1933
Withdrawn: By 1938
Pale dress with flower sprays

HN 1580 Rosebud (first version, illustration from the design registration book)

HN 1582 Marion
Designer: L. Harradine
Size: 6½ in (16.5 cm)
Introduced: 1933
Withdrawn: By 1938
As HN 1583, but green bonnet, pink skirt

HN 1583 Marion
Introduced: 1933
Withdrawn: By 1938

HN 1583 Marion (illustration not in scale)

HN 1648 & HN 1586 Camille

HN 1584 Willy-Won't He
See page 238

HN 1585 Suzette
See page 225

HN 1586 Camille
Designer: L. Harradine
Size: 6½ in (16.5 cm)
Introduced: 1933
Withdrawn: By 1949

HN 1648 Camille
Introduced: 1934
Withdrawn: By 1949

HN 1736 Camille
Introduced: 1935
Withdrawn: By 1949
As HN 1586, but red and white costume

HN 1587 Fleurette
Designer: L. Harradine
Size: 6¾ in (17.1 cm)
Introduced: 1933
Withdrawn: By 1949

HN 1587 Fleurette

HN 1600 & HN 1588 The Bride (first version)

HN 1588 The Bride (first version, model 810)
Designer: L. Harradine
Size: 9½ in (24.1 cm)
Introduced: 1933
Withdrawn: By 1938

HN 1600 The Bride (first version, model 810)
Introduced: 1933
Withdrawn: By 1949

HN 1762 The Bride (first version, model 810)
Introduced: 1936
Withdrawn: By 1949
As HN 1588, but cream dress

HN 1841 The Bride (first version, model 810)
Introduced: 1938
Withdrawn: By 1949
As HN 1588, but blue dress

HN 1589 Sweet and Twenty (second version, model 605a)
Designer: L. Harradine
Size: 3 in (7.6 cm)
Introduced: 1933
Withdrawn: By 1949
For illustration, see HN 1298, page 186

HN 1610 Sweet and Twenty (second version, model 605a)
Introduced: 1933
Withdrawn: By 1938
For illustration, see HN 1298, page 186

HN 1590-1597 Wall Masks

HN 1598 & HN 1599 Clothilde

HN 1598 Clothilde
Designer: L. Harradine
Size: 7¼ in (18.4 cm)
Introduced: 1933
Withdrawn: By 1949

HN 1599 Clothilde
Introduced: 1933
Withdrawn: By 1949

HN 1600 The Bride (first version, model 810)
See page 243

HN 1601-1603 Wall Masks

HN 1605 & HN 1604 The Emir

HN 2095 Ibrahim

HN 1604 The Emir
Designer: C. J. Noke
Size: 7½ in (19 cm)
Introduced: 1933
Withdrawn: By 1949

HN 1605 The Emir
Introduced: 1933
Withdrawn: By 1949

HN 2095 Ibrahim
Size: 7¾ in (19.6 cm)
Introduced: 1952
Withdrawn: 1955
Made in earthenware, this figure is a renamed version of *The Emir*

HN 1606 Falstaff (first version, model 401)
See page 143

HN 1607 Cerise
Designer: L. Harradine
Size: 5¼ in (13.3 cm)
Introduced: 1933
Withdrawn: By 1949

HN 1607 Cerise

HN 1608-1609 Wall Masks

HN 1610 Sweet and Twenty (second version, model 605a)
See page 243

HN 1611-1614 Wall Masks

HN 1615 Bookend, Micawber

HN 1616 Bookend, Tony Weller

HN 1617 Primroses
Designer: L. Harradine
Size: 6½ in (16.5 cm)
Introduced: 1934
Withdrawn: By 1949

HN 1617 Primroses

HN 1618 & HN 1619 Maisie

HN 1620 Rosabell

HN 1618 Maisie
Designer: L. Harradine
Size: 6¼ in (15.8 cm)
Introduced: 1934
Withdrawn: By 1949

HN 1619 Maisie
Introduced: 1934
Withdrawn: By 1949

HN 1621 & HN 1697 Irene

HN 1952 Irene

HN 1620 Rosabell
Designer: L. Harradine
Size: 7 in (17.7 cm)
Introduced: 1934
Withdrawn: By 1938

HN 1621 Irene
Designer: L. Harradine
Size: 6¾ in (17.1 cm)
Introduced: 1934
Withdrawn: 1951
Irene was a popular American musical that was brought to London in 1920, starring Edith Day. It was later turned into a film.

HN 1697 Irene
Introduced: 1935
Withdrawn: By 1949

HN 1952 Irene
Introduced: 1940
Withdrawn: 1950

HN1622 Evelyn
Designer: L. Harradine
Size: 6 in (15.2 cm)
Introduced: 1934
Withdrawn: By 1949

HN 1637 Evelyn
Introduced: 1934
Withdrawn: By 1938

HN 1623 Bookend, Pickwick

HN 1624 No details available

HN 1625 Bookend, Sairey Gamp

HN 1622 & HN 1637 Evelyn

HN 1626 Bonnie Lassie HN 1627 Curly Knob

HN 1626 Bonnie Lassie
Designer: L. Harradine
Size: 5¼ in (13.3 cm)
Introduced: 1934
Withdrawn: 1953
The theme song of Scotland's greatest entertainer, Harry Lauder, included the chorus:
'I love a lassie, a bonnie, bonnie lassie,
She's as pure as the lily in the dell.
She is sweet as the heather,
The bonnie, bloomin' heather,
Mary ma Scotch bluebell.'

HN 1627 Curly Knob
Designer: L. Harradine
Size: 6½ in (16.5 cm)
Introduced: 1934
Withdrawn: By 1949
Although similar in style to HN 1626, *Bonnie Lassie*, this figure may have been inspired by the song *Ma Curly Headed Baby*, recorded in 1932 by Paul Robeson.

HN 1628 Margot
Designer: L. Harradine
Size: 5¾ in (14.6 cm)
Introduced: 1934
Withdrawn: By 1938

HN 1636 Margot
Introduced: 1934
Withdrawn: By 1938
As HN 1628, but red bodice, pink and yellow skirt

HN 1653 Margot
Introduced: 1934
Withdrawn: By 1938

HN 1629 Grizel
Designer: L. Harradine
Size: 7 in (17.7 cm)
Introduced: 1934
Withdrawn: By 1938

HN 1630 Wall Mask

HN 1631 Sweet Anne
See page 191

HN 1632 A Gentlewoman
Designer: L. Harradine
Size: 7¼ in (18.4 cm)
Introduced: 1934
Withdrawn: By 1949

HN 1633 Clemency
Designer: L. Harradine
Size: 7 in (17.7 cm)
Introduced: 1934
Withdrawn: By 1938
For illustration, see page 250

HN 1628 & HN 1653 Margot

HN 1629 Grizel

HN 1632 A Gentlewoman

HN 1643, HN 1634 & HN 1633 Clemency

HN 1634 Clemency
Introduced: 1934
Withdrawn: By 1949

HN 1643 Clemency
Introduced: 1934
Withdrawn: By 1938

HN 1635 Marie (second version, model 662)
See page 201

HN 1636 Margot
See page 248

HN 1637 Evelyn
See page 247

HN 1638 Ladybird
Designer: L. Harradine
Size: $7\frac{3}{4}$ in (19.6 cm)
Introduced: 1934
Withdrawn: By 1949
As HN 1640, but pink costume

HN 1640 Ladybird
Introduced: 1934
Withdrawn: By 1938

HN 1640 Ladybird

HN 1639 & HN 1656 Dainty May

HN 1639 Dainty May
Designer: L. Harradine
Size: 6 in (15.2 cm)
Introduced: 1934
Withdrawn: By 1949

HN 1656 Dainty May
Introduced: 1934
Withdrawn: By 1949

HN 1640 Ladybird
See opposite

HN 1641 The Little Mother (second version, model 648)
See page 205

HN 1642 Granny's Shawl

HN 1647 Granny's Shawl

HN 1642 Granny's Shawl
Designer: L. Harradine
Size: 6 in (15.2 cm)
Introduced: 1934
Withdrawn: By 1949

HN 1647 Granny's Shawl
Introduced: 1934
Withdrawn: By 1949

HN 1643 Clemency
See page 250

HN 1644 & HN 1704 Herminia

HN 1644 Herminia
Designer: L. Harradine
Size: 6½ in (16.5 cm)
Introduced: 1934
Withdrawn: By 1938

HN 1646 Herminia
Introduced: 1934
Withdrawn: By 1938
As HN 1644, but red dress, white stripes

HN 1704 Herminia
Introduced: 1935
Withdrawn: By 1938

HN 1645 Aileen
Designer: L. Harradine
Size: 6 in (15.2 cm)
Introduced: 1934
Withdrawn: By 1938
This is one of a number of figures with Irish names, many of which became popular during the early years of this century.

HN 1664 Aileen
Introduced: 1934
Withdrawn: By 1938
As HN 1645, but pink skirt

HN 1803 Aileen
Introduced: 1937
Withdrawn: By 1949
As HN 1645, but cream dress, blue shawl

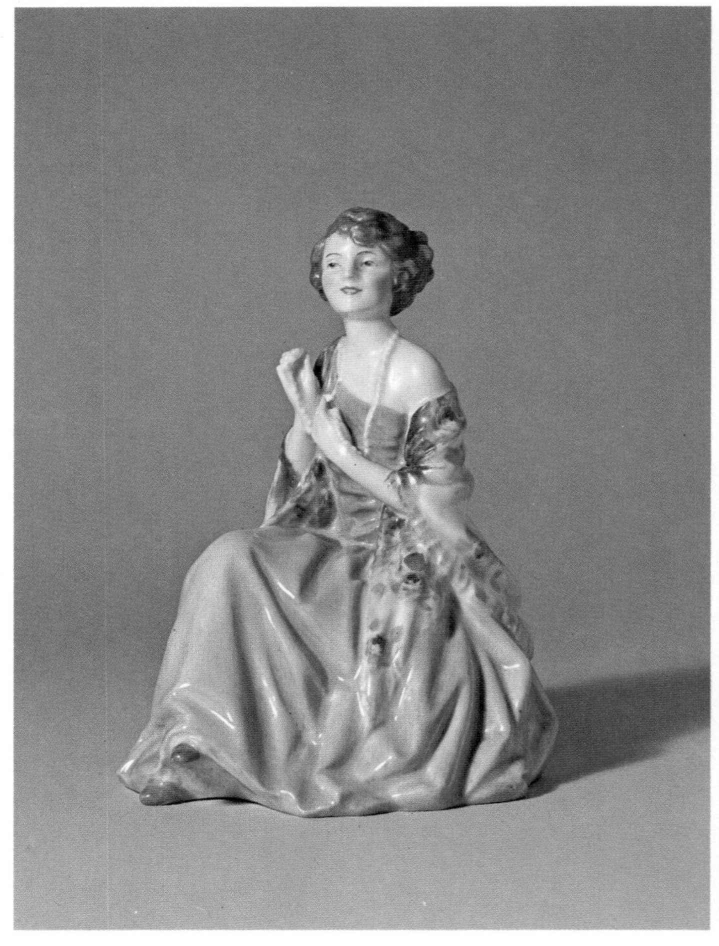

HN 1645 Aileen

HN 1646 Herminia
See opposite

HN 1647 Granny's Shawl
See page 251

HN 1648 Camille
See page 242

HN 1649 Sweet and Twenty (first version, model 605)
See page 185

HN 1650 Veronica (first version, model 751)
See page 231

HN 1651 Charmian
See page 239

HN 1652 Janet (first version, model 785)
See page 235

HN 1653 Margot
See page 248

HN 1654 Rose
See page 200

HN 1655 Marie (second version, model 662)
See page 201

HN 1656 Dainty May
See page 251

HN 1657 The Moor
See page 76

HN 1658–1661 Wall Masks

HN 1662 Delicia
Designer: L. Harradine
Size: 5¾ in (14.6 cm)
Introduced: 1934
Withdrawn: By 1938

HN 1663 Delicia
Introduced: 1934
Withdrawn: By 1938
As HN 1662, but flowered purple, green and yellow skirt

HN 1681 Delicia
Introduced: 1935
Withdrawn: By 1938
As HN 1662, but green and purple dress

HN 1662 Delicia

HN 1665 Miss Winsome

HN 1666 Miss Winsome

HN 1664 Aileen
See page 252

HN 1665 Miss Winsome
Designer: L. Harradine
Size: $6\frac{3}{4}$ in (17.1 cm)
Introduced: 1934
Withdrawn: By 1949

HN 1666 Miss Winsome
Introduced: 1934
Withdrawn: By 1938

HN 1667 Blossom
Designer: L. Harradine
Size: $6\frac{3}{4}$ in (17.1 cm)
Introduced: 1934
Withdrawn: By 1949

HN 1668 Sibell
Designer: L. Harradine
Size: $6\frac{3}{4}$ in (17.1 cm)
Introduced: 1934
Withdrawn: By 1949

HN 1695 Sibell
Introduced: 1935
Withdrawn: By 1949

HN 1667 Blossom

HN 1695 & HN 1668 Sibell

HN 1735 Sibell
Introduced: 1935
Withdrawn: By 1949
As HN 1668, but blue and green dress

HN 1669 Anthea
See page 233

HN 1670 Gillian
Designer: L. Harradine
Size: $7\frac{3}{4}$ in (19.6 cm)
Introduced: 1934
Withdrawn: By 1949

HN 1671–1676 Wall Masks

HN 1670 Gillian

HN 1677 Tinkle Bell HN 1678 Dinky Doo HN 1679 Babie HN 1680 Tootles

HN 1677 Tinkle Bell
Designer: L. Harradine
Size: $4\frac{3}{4}$ in (12.0 cm)
Introduced: 1935
Still in production
Although their style is quite different, both this figure and HN 1680, *Tootles*, would appear to have been named after fairies in J. M. Barrie's *Peter Pan*.

HN 1678 Dinky Doo
Designer: L. Harradine
Size: $4\frac{3}{4}$ in (12.0 cm)
Introduced: 1934
Still in production
A popular song of 1934 was *Inka Dinka Doo*, sung by Jimmy Durante.

HN 1679 Babie
Designer: L. Harradine
Size: $4\frac{3}{4}$ in (12.0 cm)
Introduced: 1935
Still in production

HN 1842 Babie
Introduced: 1938
Withdrawn: By 1949
As HN 1679, but pink dress, green hat and umbrella

HN 1680 Tootles
Designer: L. Harradine
Size: $4\frac{3}{4}$ in (12.0 cm)
Introduced: 1935
Withdrawn: 1975

HN 1681 Delicia
See page 253

HN 1682 Teresa
Designer: L. Harradine
Size: $5\frac{3}{4}$ in (14.6 cm)
Introduced: 1935
Withdrawn: By 1949
This figure is an adaptation of HN 715, *Proposal* (lady)

HN 1683 Teresa
Introduced: 1935
Withdrawn: By 1938
As HN 1682, but pale blue dress

HN 1682 Teresa

HN 1685 Cynthia

HN 1686 Cynthia

HN 1684 Lisette
See page 233

HN 1685 Cynthia
Designer: L. Harradine
Size: $5\frac{3}{4}$ in (14.6 cm)
Introduced: 1935
Withdrawn: By 1949

HN 1686 Cynthia
Introduced: 1935
Withdrawn: By 1949

HN 1687 Clarissa (first version, model 773)
See page 233

HN 1688 Rhoda
See page 240

HN 1689 Calumet
See page 213

HN 1690 June
Designer: L. Harradine
Size: $7\frac{1}{2}$ in (19.0 cm)
Introduced: 1935
Withdrawn: By 1949

HN 1691 June
Introduced: 1935
Withdrawn: By 1949

HN 1690 & HN 1691 June

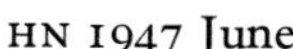

HN 1947 June

HN 1692 Sonia

HN 1947 June
Introduced: 1940
Withdrawn: By 1949

HN 2027 June
Introduced: 1949
Withdrawn: 1952
As HN 1691, but minor glaze changes

HN 1692 Sonia
Designer: L. Harradine
Size: 6½ in (16.5 cm)
Introduced: 1935
Withdrawn: By 1949

HN 1738 Sonia
Introduced: 1935
Withdrawn: By 1949
As HN 1692, but green dress

HN 1693 Virginia
Designer: L. Harradine
Size: 7½ in (19.0 cm)
Introduced: 1935
Withdrawn: By 1949

HN 1694 Virginia
Introduced: 1935
Withdrawn: By 1949

HN 1693 & HN 1694 Virginia

HN 1695 Sibell
See page 254

HN 1696 Suzette
See page 225

HN 1697 Irene
See page 247

HN 1698 Phyllis
See page 211

HN 1699 Marietta
See page 195

HN 1700 Gloria
See page 225

HN 1701 Sweet Anne
See page 191

HN 1702 A Jester (first version, model 170)
See page 85

HN 1703 Charley's Aunt (third version)
Designer: A. Toft
Size: 6 in (15.2 cm)
Introduced: 1935
Withdrawn: By 1938
For illustration, see page 77

HN 1704 Herminia
See page 252

HN 1705 The Cobbler (third version, model 891)
Designer: C. J. Noke
Size: 8 in (20.3 cm)
Introduced: 1935
Withdrawn: By 1949
For illustration, see page 139

HN 1706 The Cobbler (third version, model 891)
Introduced: 1935
Withdrawn: 1969
For illustration, see page 139

HN 1707 Paisley Shawl (first version, model 660)
See page 202

HN 1708 The Bather (first version, model 428)
See page 148

HN 1711 & HN 1710 Camilla

HN 1709 Pantalettes
See page 199

HN 1710 Camilla
Designer: L. Harradine
Size: 7 in (17.7 cm)
Introduced: 1935
Withdrawn: By 1949

HN 1711 Camilla
Introduced: 1935
Withdrawn: By 1949

HN 1713 & HN 1712 Daffy Down Dilly

HN 1712 Daffy Down Dilly
Designer: 1935
Size: $8\frac{1}{4}$ in (20.9 cm)
Introduced: 1935
Withdrawn: 1975
Later versions of this figure were also made with the head at a different angle. The title is taken from a traditional nursery rhyme,
'Daffy-down-Dilly is new come to town,
With a yellow petticoat and a green gown.'
Daffy Down Dilly is a popular name for a yellow daffodil.

HN 1713 Daffy Down Dilly
Introduced: 1935
Withdrawn: By 1949

HN 1714 Millicent
Designer: L. Harradine
Introduced: 1935
Withdrawn: By 1949

HN 1715 Millicent
Introduced: 1935
Withdrawn: By 1949
As HN 1714, but flowered shawl and purple dress

HN 1860 Millicent
Introduced: 1938
Withdrawn: 1949
No details of colour available

HN 1716 Diana
Designer: L. Harradine
Size: $5\frac{3}{4}$ in (14.6 cm)
Introduced: 1935
Withdrawn: By 1949
As HN 1717, but pink blouse, blue skirt

HN 1717 Diana
Introduced: 1935
Withdrawn: By 1949

HN 1714 Millicent (illustration from the figure design book)

HN 1717 Diana

HN 1986 Diana

HN 1986 Diana
Introduced: 1946
Withdrawn: 1975

HN 1718 Kate Hardcastle
Designer: L. Harradine
Size: 8¼ in (20.9 cm)
Introduced: 1935
Withdrawn: By 1949
Kate Hardcastle is the heroine of Goldsmith's comedy, *She Stoops to Conquer*, written in 1773, a spirited girl who masquerades as a barmaid to overcome the shyness of her lover, the young son of Sir Charles Marlow.

HN 1719 Kate Hardcastle
Introduced: 1935
Withdrawn: By 1949
For illustration, see next page

HN 1734 Kate Hardcastle
Introduced: 1935
Withdrawn: By 1949
For illustration, see next page

HN 1861 Kate Hardcastle
Introduced: 1938
Withdrawn: By 1949
For illustration, see next page

HN 1919 Kate Hardcastle
Introduced: 1939
Withdrawn: By 1949
As HN 1718, but red overskirt, green dress, black base

HN 2028 Kate Hardcastle
Introduced: 1949
Withdrawn: 1952
As HN 1719, but minor glaze differences

HN 1718 Kate Hardcastle

HN 1719 & HN 1734 Kate Hardcastle

HN 1721 & HN 1720 Frangcon

HN 1861 Kate Hardcastle

HN 1723 The Coming of Spring

HN 1720 Frangcon
Designer: L. Harradine
Size: $7\frac{1}{2}$ in (19.0 cm)
Introduced: 1935
Withdrawn: By 1949
This figure may be named after the famous actress and singer Gwen Frangcon Davies, who made her name with her performance in the light opera, *The Immortal Hour*, between 1920 and 1926. She later starred in plays by Shakespeare and Bernard Shaw, and in 1934 played Mary Stuart in *Queen of Scots*.

HN 1721 Frangcon
Introduced: 1935
Withdrawn: 1949

HN 1722 The Coming of Spring
Designer: L. Harradine
Size: $12\frac{1}{2}$ in (31.7 cm)
Introduced: 1935
Withdrawn: By 1949
As HN 1723, but pink costume
This figure, and several that follow, such as *Celia*, *Dawn* and *The Awakening*, are in a dramatically different style that relates closely to sculpture of the period and anticipates the models designed by Richard Garbe.

HN 1723 The Coming of Spring
Introduced: 1935
Withdrawn: By 1949

HN 1725 & HN 1724 Ruby

HN 1726 Celia

HN 1728 The New Bonnet

HN 1724 Ruby
Designer: L. Harradine
Size: $5\frac{1}{4}$ in (13.3 cm)
Introduced: 1935
Withdrawn: By 1949

HN 1725 Ruby
Introduced: 1935
Withdrawn: By 1949

HN 1726 Celia
Designer: L. Harradine
Size: $11\frac{1}{2}$ in (29.2 cm)
Introduced: 1935
Withdrawn: By 1949

HN 1727 Celia
Introduced: 1935
Withdrawn: By 1949

HN 1728 The New Bonnet
Designer: L. Harradine
Size: 7 in (17.7 cm)
Introduced: 1935
Withdrawn: By 1949

HN 1957 The New Bonnet
Introduced: 1940
Withdrawn: 1949

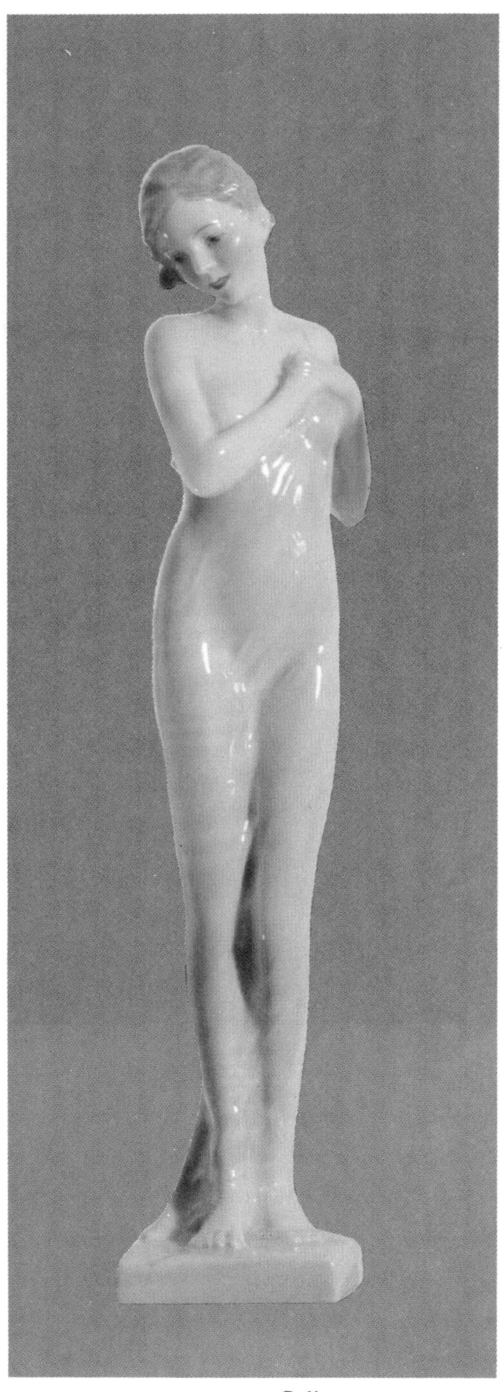

HN 1727 Celia

HN 1957 The New Bonnet

HN 1729 Vera
Designer: L. Harradine
Size: $4\frac{1}{4}$ in (10.7 cm)
Introduced: 1935
Withdrawn: By 1938
This unusual figure and its pair, HN 1741, *Gladys*, are the only head and shoulder models in the HN range.

HN 1730 Vera
Introduced: 1935
Withdrawn: By 1938
As HN 1729, but green costume

HN 1729 Vera HN 1740 Gladys

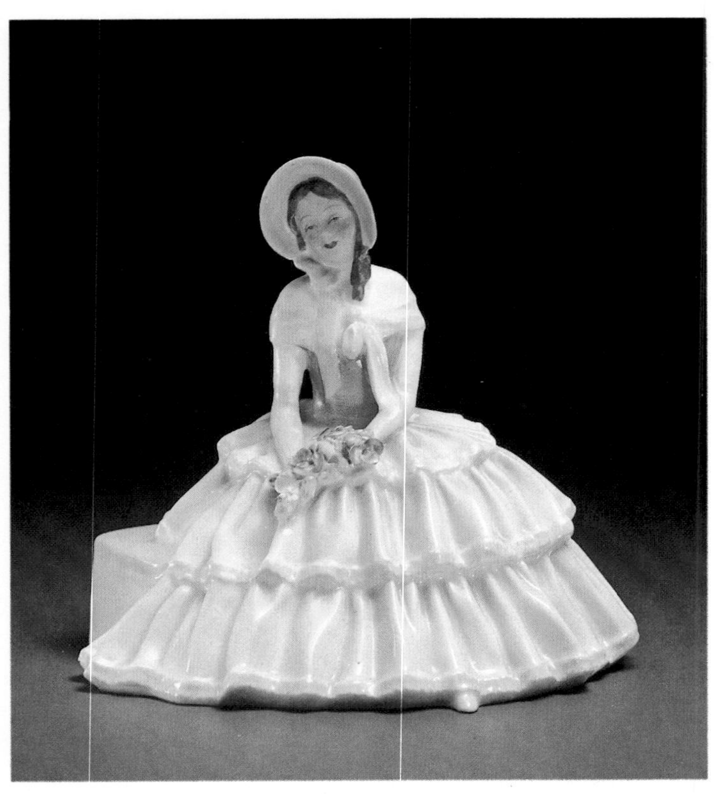

HN 1731 Daydreams

HN 1944 Daydreams

HN 1731 Daydreams
Designer: L. Harradine
Size: $5\frac{1}{2}$ in (13.9 cm)
Introduced: 1935
Still in production

HN 1732 Daydreams
Introduced: 1935
Withdrawn: By 1949
As HN 1731, but pale blue dress, pink trim

HN 1944 Daydreams
Introduced: 1940
Withdrawn: By 1949

HN 1733 Wall Mask

HN 1734 Kate Hardcastle
See page 261

HN 1735 Sibell
See page 255

HN 1736 Camille
See page 242

HN 1737 Janet (first version, model 785)
See page 235

HN 1738 Sonia
See page 258

HN 1739 Paisley Shawl (first version, model 660)
See page 202

HN 1740 Gladys
Designer: L. Harradine
Size: 5 in (12.7 cm)
Introduced: 1935
Withdrawn: By 1949
For illustration, see previous page

HN 1741 Gladys
Introduced: 1935
Withdrawn: By 1938
As HN 1740, but pink costume

HN 1742 Sir Walter Raleigh　　　HN 2015 Sir Walter Raleigh

HN 1742 Sir Walter Raleigh
Designer: L. Harradine
Size: $10\frac{1}{2}$ in (26.6 cm)
Introduced: 1935
Withdrawn: By 1949
Born in Devon in 1552, Raleigh was a brilliant soldier, sailor, scholar and diplomat. For long a favourite of Queen Elizabeth, he sailed to America in 1584, bringing back cotton, potatoes and tobacco, none of which had been seen before in Europe. Later, after losing the Queen's favour, he was committed to the Tower of London, where he wrote some of his finest poetry. In 1618 he was finally executed by James I, who had been persuaded that Raleigh was plotting against him, an accusation that had no justification.

HN 1751 Sir Walter Raleigh
Size: $11\frac{1}{2}$ in (29.2 cm)
Introduced: 1936
Withdrawn: By 1949
Earthenware model. As HN 2015, but with minor glaze differences

HN 2015 Sir Walter Raleigh
Introduced: 1948
Withdrawn: 1955

HN 1743 & HN 1744 Mirabel

HN 1743 Mirabel
Designer: L. Harradine
Size: $7\frac{3}{4}$ in (19.6 cm)
Introduced: 1935
Withdrawn: By 1949

HN 1744 Mirabel
Introduced: 1935
Withdrawn: By 1949

HN 1745 The Rustic Swain
Designer: L. Harradine
Size: $5\frac{1}{4}$ in (13.3 cm)
Introduced: 1935
Withdrawn: By 1949
This figure was later adapted and reissued as HN 1899, *Midsummer Noon*

HN 1746 The Rustic Swain
Introduced: 1935
Withdrawn: By 1949
As HN 1745, but man in green costume

HN 1747 Afternoon Tea
Designer: Mrs Pleydell Railston
Size: $5\frac{1}{4}$ in (13.3 cm)
Introduced: 1935
Still in production

HN 1748 Afternoon Tea
Introduced: 1935
Withdrawn: By 1949
As HN 1747, but green dress

HN 1745 The Rustic Swain (illustration from the figure design book)

HN 1747 Afternoon Tea

HN 1749 Pierrette (third version, model 659)
See page 202

HN 1750 Folly
See page 193

HN 1751 Sir Walter Raleigh
See page 267

HN 1752 Regency
Designer: L. Harradine
Size: 8 in (20.3 cm)
Introduced: 1936
Withdrawn: By 1949
With her smart riding clothes, this figure takes her title from the Regency of the Prince of Wales, 1811–20, a period of high fashion.

HN 1753 Eleanore
Designer: L. Harradine
Size: 7 in (17.7 cm)
Introduced: 1936
Withdrawn: By 1949
As HN 1754, but blue bodice, green and pink skirt

HN 1754 Eleanore
Introduced: 1936
Withdrawn: By 1949

HN 1752 Regency

HN 1754 Eleanore

HN 1755 The Court Shoemaker

HN 1756 Lizana

HN 1759 The Orange Lady

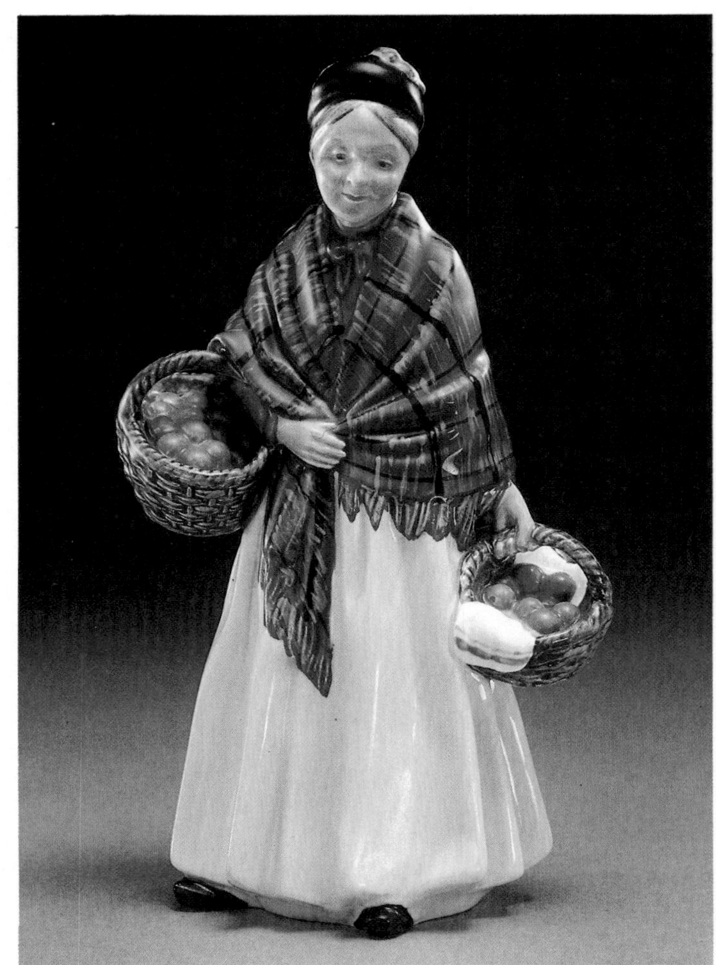

HN 1953 The Orange Lady

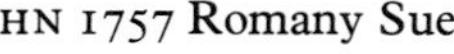
HN 1757 Romany Sue

HN 1758 Romany Sue

HN 1755 The Court Shoemaker
Designer: L. Harradine (?)
Size: $6\frac{3}{4}$ in (17.1 cm)
Introduced: 1936
Withdrawn: By 1949
In the pattern book this figure is shown with quite different colours; the lady has a red dress, the man a green coat. The version illustrated is not recorded.

HN 1756 Lizana
Designer: L. Harradine
Size: $8\frac{1}{2}$ in (21.5 cm)
Introduced: 1936
Withdrawn: By 1949

HN 1761 Lizana
Introduced: 1936
Withdrawn: By 1938
As HN 1756, but green dress, leopard-skin cloak

HN 1757 Romany Sue
Designer: L. Harradine
Size: $9\frac{1}{2}$ in (24.1 cm)
Introduced: 1936
Withdrawn: By 1949
Like many of the street sellers, this figure reflects the popular romantic interest in romanies, or gypsies, an interest expressed both by the paintings of Augustus John and by songs, such as Cole Porter's *Gypsy in Me*, included in the 1935 show *Anything Goes*.

HN 1758 Romany Sue
Introduced: 1936
Withdrawn: By 1949

HN 1759 The Orange Lady
Designer: L. Harradine
Size: $8\frac{3}{4}$ in (22.2 cm)
Introduced: 1936
Withdrawn: 1975
Perhaps inspired by the traditional street cry:
'Here's oranges nice,
At a very small price,
I sell them all two for a penny.
Ripe, juicy and sweet,
Just fit for to eat,
So customers buy a good many.'

HN 1953 The Orange Lady
Introduced: 1940
Withdrawn: 1975

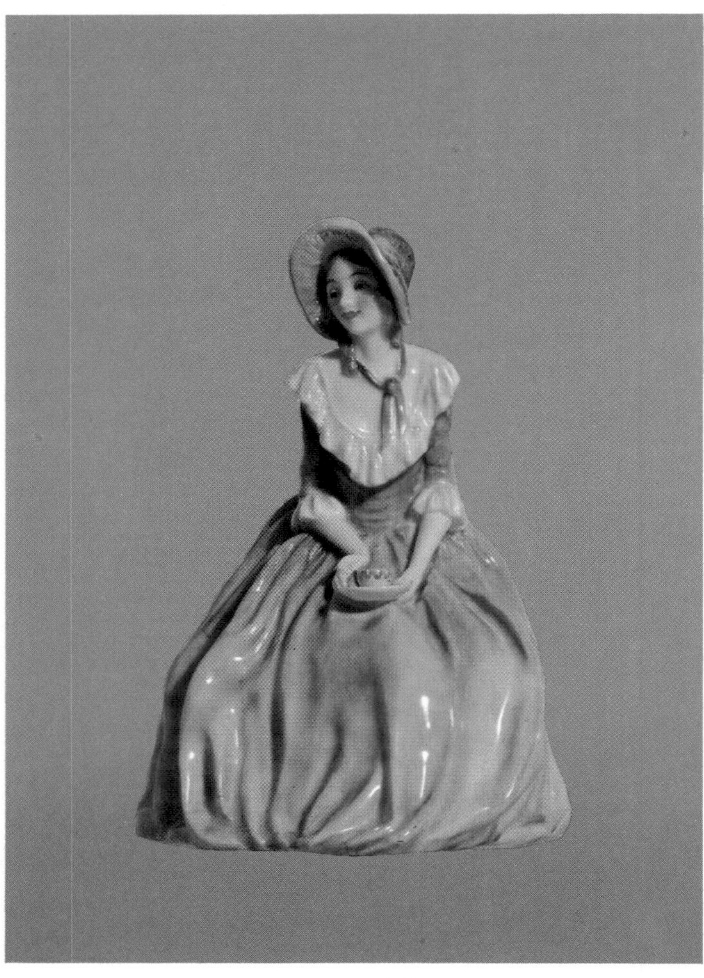

HN 1760 4 o'Clock

HN 1760 4 o'Clock
Designer: L. Harradine
Size: 6 in (15.2 cm)
Introduced: 1936
Withdrawn: By 1949

HN 1761 Lizana
See page 271

HN 1762 The Bride (first version, model 810)
See page 243

HN 1763 Windflower (first version, model 926)
Designer: L. Harradine
Size: 7¼ in (18.4 cm)
Introduced: 1936
Withdrawn: By 1949
The windflower is the common name for the wood anemone, which grows in sandy woodlands.

HN 1764 Windflower (first version, model 926)
Introduced: 1936
Withdrawn: By 1949

HN 2029 Windflower (first version, model 926)
Introduced: 1949
Withdrawn: 1952
Although slightly larger, this later version has the same model number.

HN 2029 Windflower (first version)

HN 1764 & HN 1763 Windflower (first version)

HN 1766 Nana

HN 1767 Nana

HN 1768 Ivy

HN 1765 Chloe
See page 219

HN 1766 Nana
Designer: L. Harradine
Size: $4\frac{3}{4}$ in (12.0 cm)
Introduced: 1936
Withdrawn: By 1949

HN 1767 Nana
Introduced: 1936
Withdrawn: By 1949

HN 1768 Ivy
Designer: L. Harradine
Size: $4\frac{3}{4}$ in (12.0 cm)
Introduced: 1936
Still in production

HN 1769 Ivy
Introduced: 1936
Withdrawn: By 1938
Details of colour not recorded

HN 1771 & HN 1770 Maureen

HN 1770 Maureen
Designer: L. Harradine
Size: $7\frac{1}{2}$ in (19.0 cm)
Introduced: 1936
Withdrawn: 1959

HN 1771 Maureen
Introduced: 1936
Withdrawn: By 1949

HN 1773 Delight HN 1772 Delight

HN 1772 Delight
Designer: L. Harradine
Size: 6¾ in (17.1 cm)
Introduced: 1936
Withdrawn: 1967

HN 1773 Delight
Introduced: 1936
Withdrawn: By 1949

Primavera, ivory carving by Richard Garbe, 1926 (Victoria & Albert Museum, London)

HN 1774 Spring (second version, model 796)
Designer: R. Garbe
Size: 21 in (53.3 cm)
Introduced: 1933
Limited edition of 100, sold out by 1939
As HN 1827, but matt ivory finish
This figure is taken directly from an ivory carving executed by Garbe in 1926, now in the Victoria and Albert Museum, London
Richard Garbe R.A. (1876–1957) was a leading British sculptor of the 1920s and 1930s. He exhibited widely throughout his lifetime, including 108 times at the Royal Academy and many of his works are included in national art collections. He was Professor of Sculpture at the Royal College of Art from 1929 to 1946, and most of his work for Doulton was produced during the early years of this professorship. Some of his models were produced specifically for Doulton, while others were adapted from stone and ivory carvings exhibited previously at the Royal Academy and elsewhere. He designed models for production at both Lambeth and Burslem factories.
So close a relationship between a contemporary artist and a large industrial company is rare in the history of English ceramics.

HN 1827 Spring (second version, model 796)
Introduced: 1937
Withdrawn: By 1949
The later, tinted versions of the Garbe figures were made in unlimited editions, and some were produced as lamp bases.

HN 1831 The Cloud
(illustrations not in scale)

HN 1774 Spring (second version)

HN 1869 Dryad of the Pines

HN 1776 West Wind (illustration not in scale)

HN 1775 Salome
Designer: R. Garbe
Introduced: 1933
Limited edition of 100, sold out by 1939
Matt ivory finish
Although no example of this model has been traced, it is likely that Garbe was inspired by the first public performance in 1931 of Oscar Wilde's play, *Salome*, previously banned since its original publication in 1893. In the play Salome performs the famous erotic veil dance in order to win the reward of John the Baptist's head.

HN 1828 Salome
Introduced: 1937
Withdrawn: By 1949
Tinted finish

HN 1776 West Wind
Designer: R. Garbe
Size: 14½ in (36.8 cm)
Introduced: 1933
Limited edition of 25, sold out by 1939
Matt ivory finish

HN 1826 West Wind
Introduced: 1937
Withdrawn: By 1949
Tinted finish

HN 1777 Spirit of the Wind
Designer: R. Garbe
Introduced: 1933
Limited edition of 50, sold out by 1939
As HN 1825, but matt ivory finish

HN 1825 Spirit of the Wind
Introduced: 1937
Withdrawn: By 1949

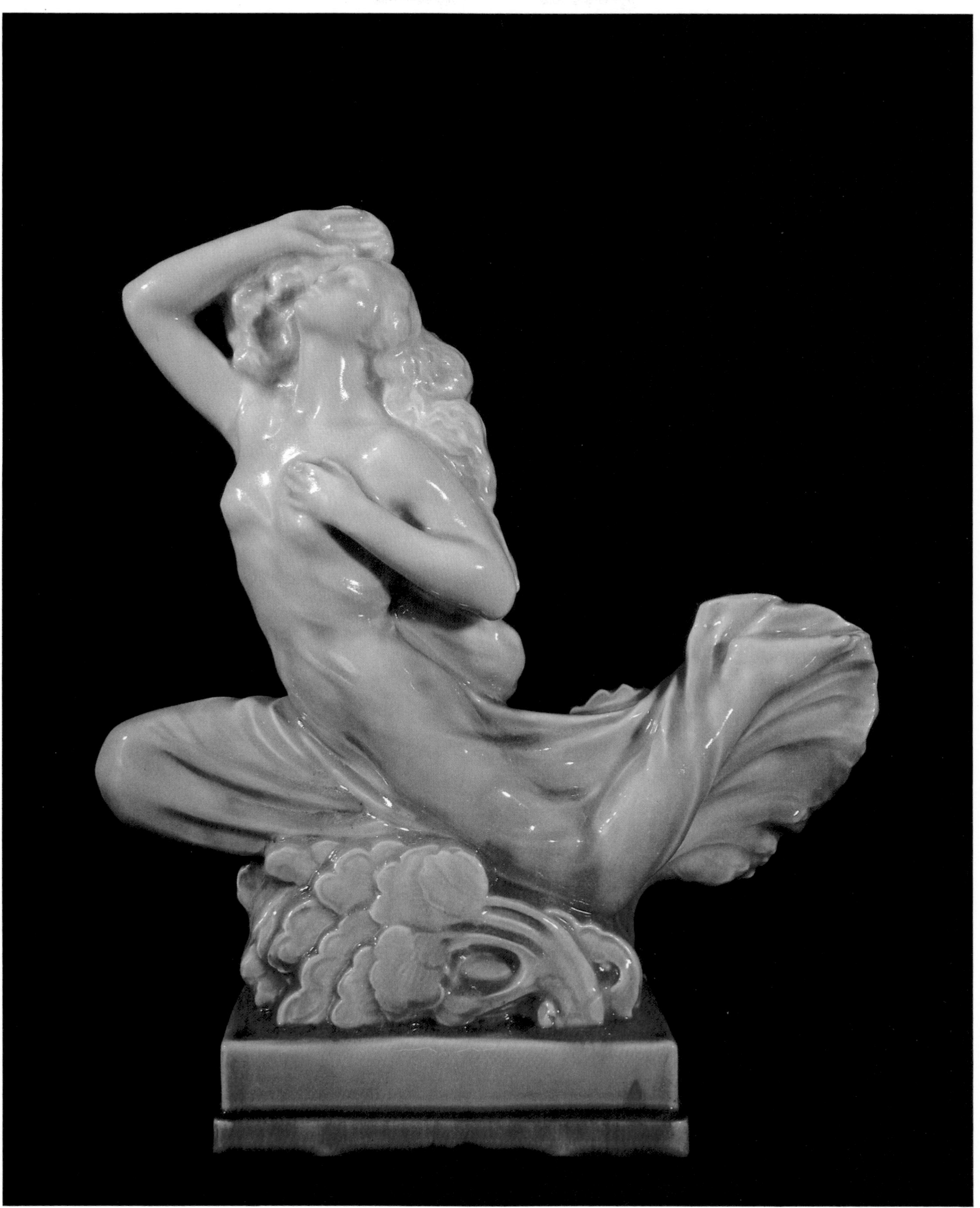

HN 1825 Spirit of the Wind (illustration not in scale)

HN 1778 Beethoven (illustration not in scale)

HN 1778 Beethoven
Designer: R. Garbe
Size: 22 in (55.8 cm)
Introduced: 1933
Limited edition of 25, sold out by 1939
Matt ivory glaze
Also known as *Sonata Pathétique*, this model was based on a sculpture exhibited by Garbe in the Royal Academy in 1931.

HN 1779 Bird Model (Macaw by R. Garbe)

HN 1829 Bird Model (Macaw by R. Garbe)

HN 1780 Lady of the Snows
Designer: R. Garbe
Introduced: 1933
No further information available

HN 1830 Lady of the Snows
Introduced: 1937
Withdrawn: By 1949
Tinted model

HN 1781–1786 Wall Masks (R. Garbe)

HN 1787–1790 No details available

HN 1792 Henry VIII (second version)

HN 1791 Old Balloon Seller and Bulldog (illustration from an old catalogue)

HN 1791 Old Balloon Seller and Bulldog (K1)
Designer: L. Harradine
Size: 7 in (17.7 cm) (without base)
Introduced: 1932
Withdrawn: By 1938
This combination figure, mounted on a mahogany stand, was actually introduced in 1932, although it was not given an HN number until 1936.

HN 1912 Old Balloon Seller and Bulldog
Introduced: 1939
Withdrawn: By 1949
No details available

HN 1792 Henry VIII (second version, model 841)
Designer: C. J. Noke
Size: 11½ in (29.2 cm)
Introduced: 1933
Limited edition of 200, sold out by 1939

HN 1794 & HN 1793 This Little Pig

HN 1795 M' Lady's Maid
(illustration from an old catalogue)

HN 1793 This Little Pig
Designer: L. Harradine
Size: 4 in (10.1 cm)
Introduced: 1936
Still in production
Based on the popular nursery rhyme, *This Little Pig Went to Market*, used by young children to count their toes.

HN 1794 This Little Pig
Introduced: 1936
Withdrawn: By 1949

HN 1795 M'Lady's Maid
Designer: L. Harradine
Size: 9 in (22.8 cm)
Introduced: 1936
Withdrawn: By 1949

HN 1822 M'Lady's Maid
Introduced: 1937
Withdrawn: By 1949
As HN 1795, but multicoloured dress

HN 1796 Hazel
Designer: L. Harradine
Size: 5¼ in (13.3 cm)
Introduced: 1936
Withdrawn: By 1949
As HN 1797, but green dress

HN 1797 Hazel
Introduced: 1936
Withdrawn: By 1949

HN 1798 Lily
Designer: L. Harradine
Size: 5 in (12.7 cm)
Introduced: 1936
Withdrawn: By 1949

HN 1799 Lily
Introduced: 1936
Withdrawn: By 1949
As HN 1798, but blue shawl, green dress

HN 1800 St George (first version, model 191)
See page 115

HN 1801 An Old King
See page 111

HN 1802 Estelle
See page 238

HN 1803 Aileen
See page 252

HN 1797 Hazel HN 1798 Lily

HN 1832 Granny

HN 1805 & HN 1806 To Bed

HN 1807 Spring Flowers

HN 1804 Granny
Designer: L. Harradine
Size: 7 in (17.7 cm)
Introduced: 1937
Withdrawn: By 1949
As HN 1832, but grey dress, purple and brown chequered shawl

HN 1832 Granny
Introduced: 1937
Withdrawn: By 1949

HN 1805 To Bed
Designer: L. Harradine
Size: 6 in (15.2 cm)
Introduced: 1937
Withdrawn: 1959

HN 1806 To Bed
Introduced: 1937
Withdrawn: By 1949

HN 1807 Spring Flowers
Designer: L. Harradine
Size: 7¼ in (18.4 cm)
Introduced: 1937
Withdrawn: 1959

HN 1945 Spring Flowers
Introduced: 1940
Withdrawn: By 1949
As HN 1807, but green skirt, pink overskirt

HN 1809 Cissie HN 1813 Forget-me-not

HN 1810 Bo-Peep (second version)

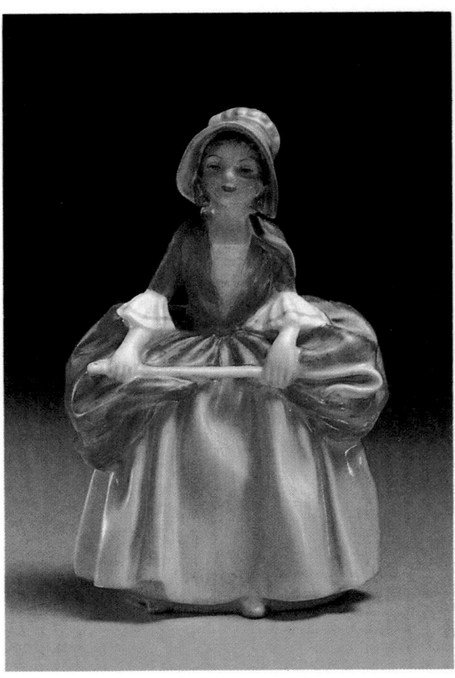

HN 1811 Bo-Peep (second version)

HN 1808 Cissie
Designer: L. Harradine
Size: 5 in (12.7 cm)
Introduced: 1937
Withdrawn: 1951
As HN 1809, but green dress

HN 1809 Cissie
Introduced: 1937
Still in production

HN 1810 Bo-Peep (second version, model 944)
Designer: L. Harradine
Size: 5 in (12.7 cm)
Introduced: 1937
Withdrawn: By 1949

HN 1811 Bo-Peep (second version, model 944)
Introduced: 1937
Still in production

HN 1812 Forget-me-not
Designer: L. Harradine
Size: 6 in (15.2 cm)
Introduced: 1937
Withdrawn: By 1949
As HN 1813, but pink dress, green ribbon

HN 1813 Forget-me-not
Introduced: 1937
Withdrawn: By 1949

HN 1814 The Squire
See page 208

HN 1815 The Huntsman (second version, model 673)
See page 207

HN 1816–1817 Wall Masks

HN 1818 Miranda

HN 1818 Miranda
Designer: L. Harradine
Size: 8½ in (21.5 cm)
Introduced: 1937
Withdrawn: By 1949

HN 1819 Miranda
Introduced: 1937
Withdrawn: By 1949
As HN 1818, but green skirt

HN 1820 Reflections
Designer: L. Harradine
Size: 5 in (12.7 cm)
Introduced: 1937
Withdrawn: By 1938
As HN 1821, but red dress, lilac sofa

HN 1821 Reflections
Introduced: 1937
Withdrawn: By 1938

HN 1847 Reflections
Designer: L. Harradine
Introduced: 1938
Withdrawn: By 1949
Although there was actually only one version of this figure, in later models the girl wears a poke bonnet instead of the mob-cap.

HN 1847 Reflections

HN 1821 Reflections (illustration from the figure design book)

HN 1848 Reflections
Introduced: 1938
Withdrawn: By 1949
As HN 1847, but green skirt

HN 1822 M'Lady's Maid
See page 280

HN 1823–1824 Wall Masks

HN 1825 Spirit of the Wind
See page 276

HN 1826 West Wind
See page 276

HN 1834 Top o' the Hill

Letter from the publishers Raphael Tuck Ltd., granting Royal Doulton permission to reproduce their design by Molly Benatar

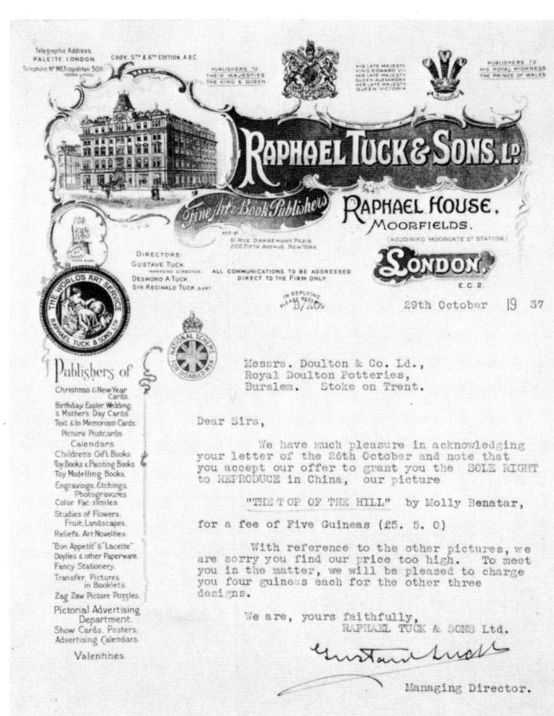

Telegraphic Address PALETTE. LONDON
Code 5th & 6th Edition A.B.C.
Telephone Nº METropolitan 5011

PUBLISHERS TO THEIR MAJESTIES THE KING & QUEEN

HIS LATE MAJESTY KING EDWARD VII, HER LATE MAJESTY QUEEN ALEXANDRA, HER LATE MAJESTY QUEEN VICTORIA

PUBLISHERS TO HIS ROYAL HIGHNESS THE PRINCE OF WALES

RAPHAEL TUCK & SONS. LD.

Fine Art & Book Publishers

RAPHAEL HOUSE,
MOORFIELDS.
(ADJOINING MOORGATE ST STATION)
LONDON,
E.C. 2.

61 Rue Dareemont Paris
200 Fifth Avenue New York

DIRECTORS
GUSTAVE TUCK
MANAGING DIRECTOR
DESMOND A TUCK
SIR REGINALD TUCK BART

ALL COMMUNICATIONS TO BE ADDRESSED DIRECT TO THE FIRM ONLY

THE WORLDS ART SERVICE — RAPHAEL TUCK & SONS LTD

NATIONAL SCHEME FOR DISABLED MEN

In replying please refer B/AO

29th October 1937

Publishers of
Christmas & New Year Cards
Birthday, Easter, Wedding & Mother's Day Cards
Text & In Memoriam Cards
Picture Postcards
Calendars
Childrens Gift Books
Toy Books & Painting Books
Toy Modelling Books
Engravings, Etchings, Photogravures
Color Fac-similes
Studies of Flowers, Fruit, Landscapes
Reliefs, Art Novelties
"Bon Appetit" & "Lacette" Doylies & other Paperware
Fancy Stationery
Transfer Pictures in Booklets
Zag Zaw Picture Puzzles
Pictorial Advertising Department
Show Cards, Posters, Advertising Calendars
Valentines

Messrs. Doulton & Co. Ld.,
Royal Doulton Potteries,
Burslem. Stoke on Trent.

Dear Sirs,

We have much pleasure in acknowledging your letter of the 26th October and note that you accept our offer to grant you the SOLE RIGHT to REPRODUCE in China, our picture

"THE TOP OF THE HILL" by Molly Benatar,

for a fee of Five Guineas (£5. 5. 0)

With reference to the other pictures, we are sorry you find our price too high. To meet you in the matter, we will be pleased to charge you four guineas each for the other three designs.

We are, yours faithfully,
RAPHAEL TUCK & SONS Ltd.

Gustave Tuck

Managing Director.

HN 1833 Top o' the Hill

HN 1849 Top o' the Hill

HN 1827 Spring
See page 274

HN 1828 Salome
See page 274

HN 1829 Bird Model (Macaw)

HN 1830 Lady of the Snows
See page 274

HN 1831 The Cloud
Designer: R. Garbe
Size: 23 in (58.4 cm)
Introduced: 1937
Withdrawn: By 1949
See illustration page 275

HN 1832 Granny
See page 281

HN 1833 Top o' the Hill
Designer: L. Harradine
Size: 7 in (17.7 cm)
Introduced: 1937
Withdrawn: 1971
The original design for this model, by Molly Benatar, was purchased from the Christmas card, calendar and book publishers, Raphael Tuck & Sons Ltd, the source for many figures of this period.

HN 1834 Top o' the Hill
Introduced: 1937
Still in production

HN 1849 Top o' the Hill
Introduced: 1938
Withdrawn: 1975

HN 1835 Verena
Designer: L. Harradine
Size: 8¼ in (20.9 cm)
Introduced: 1938
Withdrawn: By 1949

HN 1854 Verena
Introduced: 1938
Withdrawn: By 1949
As HN 1835, but green dress

HN 1836 Vanessa
Designer: L. Harradine
Size: 7½ in (19.0 cm)
Introduced: 1938
Withdrawn: By 1949

HN 1838 Vanessa
Introduced: 1938
Withdrawn: By 1949
For illustration, see next page

HN 1835 Verena

HN 1836 Vanessa

HN 1838 Vanessa HN 1840 Christine (first version)

HN 1837
Mariquita
(illustration
from an old
catalogue)

"Mariquita" (8 in.)
HN 1837 .. 45/-

HN 1837 Mariquita
Designer: L. Harradine
Size: 8 in (20.3 cm)
Introduced: 1938
Withdrawn: By 1949

HN 1838 Vanessa
See above

HN 1839 Christine (first version, model 939)
Designer: L. Harradine
Size: 7¾ in (19.6 cm)
Introduced: 1938
Withdrawn: By 1949
As HN 1840, but lilac dress, blue shawl

HN 1840 Christine (first version, model 939)
Introduced: 1938
Withdrawn: By 1949

HN 1841 The Bride (first version, model 810)
See page 243

HN 1842 Babie
See page 256

HN 1843 Biddy Penny Farthing
Designer: L. Harradine
Size: 9 in (22.8 cm)
Introduced: 1938
Still in production

HN 1844 Odds and Ends
Designer: L. Harradine
Size: 8 in (20.3 cm)
Introduced: 1938
Withdrawn: By 1949
Made as a pair to HN 1843, *Biddy Penny Farthing*. These two pedlar figures were designed to complement the existing series of street sellers.

HN 1845 Modena
Designer: L. Harradine
Size: 7¼ in (18.4 cm)
Introduced: 1938
Withdrawn: By 1949
As HN 1846, but blue dress

HN 1846 Modena
Introduced: 1938
Withdrawn: By 1949

HN 1847 Reflections
See page 283

HN 1843 Biddy Penny Farthing

HN 1844 Odds and Ends

HN 1846 Modena

HN 1850 Antoinette (first version)

HN 1851 Antoinette (first version)

HN 1848 Reflections
See page 283

HN 1849 Top o' the Hill
See page 285

HN 1850 Antoinette (first version, model 980)
Designer: L. Harradine
Size: 8¼ in (20.9 cm)
Introduced: 1938
Withdrawn: By 1949
Inspired by the film *Marie Antoinette*, starring Norma Shearer and Tyrone Power, first shown in 1938, which was based on the story of the Queen of Louis XVI who died at the guillotine in 1793.

HN 1851 Antoinette (first version, model 980)
Introduced: 1938
Withdrawn: By 1949

HN 1852 The Mirror
Designer: L. Harradine
Size: 7½ in (18.4 cm)
Introduced: 1938
Withdrawn: By 1949

HN 1853 The Mirror
Introduced: 1938
Withdrawn: By 1949
As HN 1852, but blue costume

HN 1852 The Mirror

HN 2030 Memories

HN 1856 Memories

HN 1854 Verena
See page 285

HN 1855 Memories
Designer: L. Harradine
Size: 6 in (15.2 cm)
Introduced: 1938
Withdrawn: By 1949
As HN 1856, but green bodice and hat, red skirt
Based on a Raphael Tuck design by Stanislaus Longley, used for the Royal Christmas card in 1937.

HN 1856 Memories
Introduced: 1938
Withdrawn: By 1949

HN 1857 Memories
Introduced: 1938
Withdrawn: By 1949
As HN 1856, but red bodice with red and lilac skirt

HN 2030 Memories
Introduced: 1949
Withdrawn: 1959
For illustration, see previous page

HN 1858 Dawn
Designer: L. Harradine
Size: 10¼ in (26.0 cm)
Introduced: 1938
Withdrawn: By 1949
Early versions of this figure were also made with a head-dress, see illustration.

"Dawn" (10¼ in.)
HN 1858 .. 25/-

HN 1859 Tildy
See page 240

HN 1860 Millicent
See page 260

HN 1861 Kate Hardcastle
See page 261

HN 1862 Jasmine
Designer: L. Harradine
Size: 7½ in (19.0 cm)
Introduced: 1938
Withdrawn: By 1949

HN 1862 Jasmine

HN 1858 Dawn

HN 1863 Jasmine
Introduced: 1938
Withdrawn: By 1949

HN 1876 Jasmine
Introduced: 1938
Withdrawn: By 1949
As HN 1862, but flowered blue coat with pink trim

HN 1864 Sweet and Fair
Designer: L. Harradine
Size: 7½ in (19.0 cm)
Introduced: 1938
Withdrawn: By 1949
As HN 1865, but blue shawl with pink dress

HN 1865 Sweet and Fair
Introduced: 1938
Withdrawn: By 1949

HN 1863 Jasmine

HN 1867 Wedding Morn

HN 1865 Sweet and Fair

HN 1866 Wedding Morn
Designer: L. Harradine
Size: 10½ in (26.6 cm)
Introduced: 1938
Withdrawn: By 1949
As HN 1867, but cream dress

HN 1867 Wedding Morn
Introduced: 1938
Withdrawn: By 1949

HN 1868 Serena

HN 1870 Little Lady Make Believe

HN 1868 Serena
Designer: L. Harradine
Size: 11 in (27.9 cm)
Introduced: 1938
Withdrawn: By 1949

HN 1869 Dryad of the Pines
Designer: R. Garbe
Size: 23 in (58.4 cm)
Introduced: 1938
Withdrawn: By 1949
For illustration, see page 275

HN 1871 & HN 1872 Annabella

HN 1870 Little Lady Make Believe
Designer: L. Harradine
Size: 6 in (15.2 cm)
Introduced: 1938
Withdrawn: By 1949
Probably inspired by the popular song of the same title first published in 1938, and recorded by both Gracie Fields and Bing Crosby.

HN 2031 Granny's Heritage

HN 1871 Annabella
Designer: L. Harradine
Size: $4\frac{3}{4}$ in (12.0 cm)
Introduced: 1938
Withdrawn: By 1949

HN 1872 Annabella
Introduced: 1938
Withdrawn: By 1949

HN 1875 Annabella
Introduced: 1938
Withdrawn: 1949
As HN 1871, but red dress

HN 1873 Granny's Heritage
Designer: L. Harradine
Size: $6\frac{1}{4}$ in (15.8 cm)
Introduced: 1938
Withdrawn: By 1949
As HN 2031, but red flowered shawl on granny, child in green dress

HN 1874 Granny's Heritage
Introduced: 1938
Withdrawn: By 1949
As HN 2031, but granny in blue shawl, green skirt

HN 2031 Granny's Heritage
Introduced: 1949
Withdrawn: 1969

HN 1875 Annabella
See above

HN 1876 Jasmine
See page 290

HN 1877 Jean
Designer: L. Harradine
Size: $7\frac{1}{4}$ in (18.4 cm)
Introduced: 1938
Withdrawn: By 1949
Perhaps named in memory of the actress Jean Harlow, who died in 1937.

HN 1878 Jean
Introduced: 1938
Withdrawn: By 1949
As HN 1877, but green dress, red shawl

HN 2032 Jean
Introduced: 1949
Withdrawn: 1959

HN 1877 Jean

HN 2032 Jean

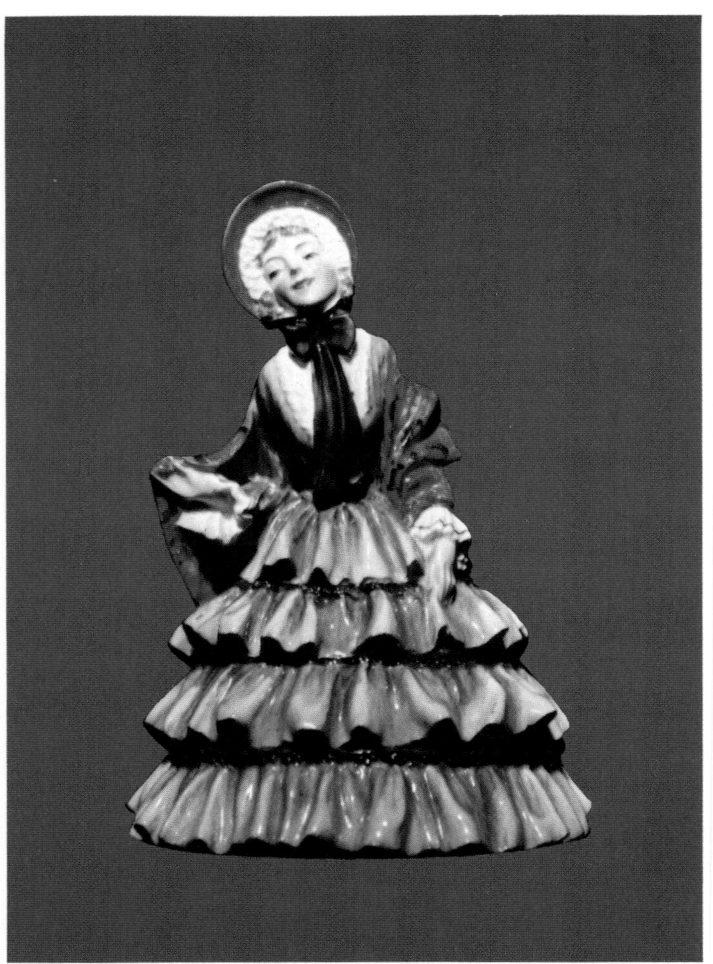

HN 1879 Bon Jour

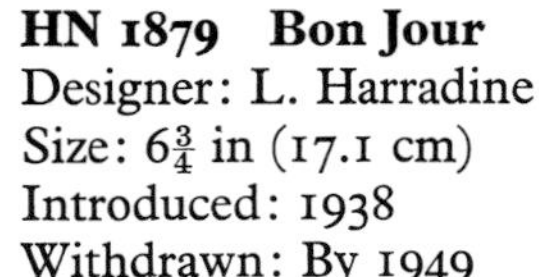

HN 1879 Bon Jour
Designer: L. Harradine
Size: $6\frac{3}{4}$ in (17.1 cm)
Introduced: 1938
Withdrawn: By 1949

HN 1888 Bon Jour
Introduced: 1938
Withdrawn: By 1949

HN 1888 Bon Jour (illustration from an old catalogue)

HN 1881 Lambeth Walk (illustration from an old catalogue)

"The Lambeth Walk" (10 in.)
HN 1881 .. .. 45/-

HN 1887 & HN 1882 Nell Gwynn

Player's cigarette card of Nell Gwynn, the design on which the figure was based

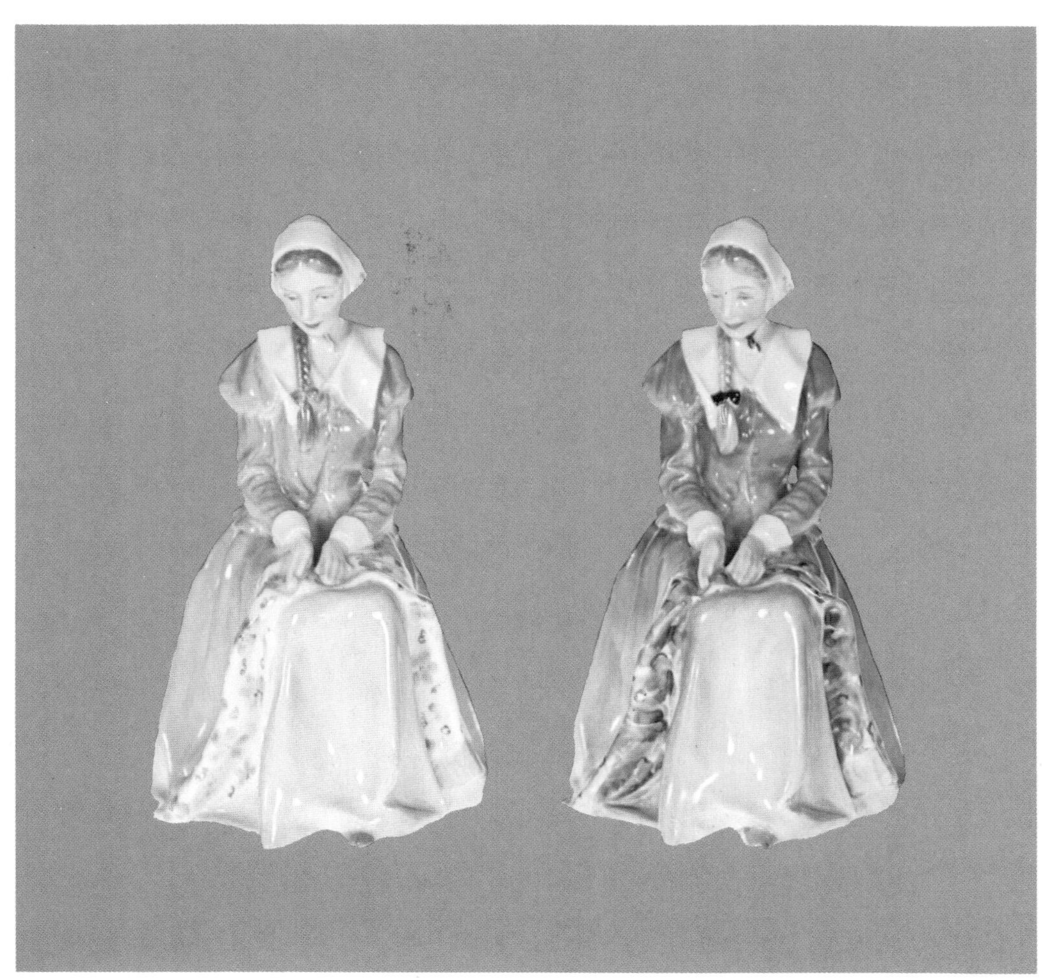

HN 1884 & HN 1883 Prudence

HN 1880 The Lambeth Walk
Designer: L. Harradine
Size: 10 in (25.4 cm)
Introduced: 1938
Withdrawn: By 1949
As HN 1881, but blue dress
The Lambeth Walk was a hit song of 1937, sung by Lupino Lane in the show *Me and My Girl*. A bright, spirited and infectious dance tune, the song started a dance craze that swept across the country.

HN 1881 The Lambeth Walk
Introduced: 1938
Withdrawn: By 1949

HN 1882 Nell Gwynn
Designer: L. Harradine
Size: 6½ in (16.5 cm)
Introduced: 1938
Withdrawn: By 1949
Based on a cigarette card in a series of twenty-five *Famous Beauties* issued by Player's, and perhaps inspired by the film *Nell Gwynn*, first shown in 1937, which starred Anna Neagle and Sir Cedric Hardwick.
Nell Gwynn, the chestnut-haired Cockney orange seller, trollop, actress and mistress of Charles II, has probably inspired more books, plays, paintings, films and legends than any other female performer in the English theatre. She became the king's mistress in 1669 and remained a firm favourite; on his death-bed he is reported to have said: 'Let not poor Nelly starve'.

HN 1887 Nell Gwynn
Introduced: 1938
Withdrawn: By 1949

HN 1883 Prudence
Designer: L. Harradine
Size: 6¾ in (17.1 cm)
Introduced: 1938
Withdrawn: By 1949

HN 1884 Prudence
Introduced: 1938
Withdrawn: By 1949

HN 1885 & HN 1886 Nadine

HN 2037 Goody Two Shoes

HN 1885 Nadine
Designer: L. Harradine
Size: 7¼ in (18.4 cm)
Introduced: 1938
Withdrawn: By 1949

HN 1886 Nadine
Introduced: 1938
Withdrawn: By 1949

HN 1887 Nell Gwynn
See previous page

HN 1888 Bon Jour
See previous page

HN 1889 Goody Two Shoes
Designer: L. Harradine
Size: 4¾ in (12.0 cm)
Introduced: 1938
Withdrawn: By 1949
As HN 2037, but green dress
The title is taken from a traditional English nursery tale apparently written by Oliver Goldsmith in about 1760, although the figure was actually based on a Raphael Tuck illustration, *The Merry Month of May*, drawn by Molly Benatar.

HN 1905 Goody Two Shoes
Introduced: 1939
Withdrawn: By 1949
As HN 2037, pink skirt, red overdress

HN 2037 Goody Two Shoes
Introduced: 1949
Still in production

HN 1890 Lambing Time
Designer: L. Harradine
Size: 9¼ in (23.4 cm)
Introduced: 1938
Still in production

HN 1891 Pecksniff (second version, model 385)
See page 141

HN 1892 Uriah Heep (second version, model 384)
See page 141

HN 1893 Fat Boy (second version, model 381)
See page 141

HN 1894 Mr Pickwick (second version, model 379)
See page 141

HN 1895 Mr Micawber (second version, model 380)
See page 141

HN 1896 Sairey Gamp (second version, model 382)
See page 141

HN 1890 Lambing Time

HN 1897 Miss Fortune

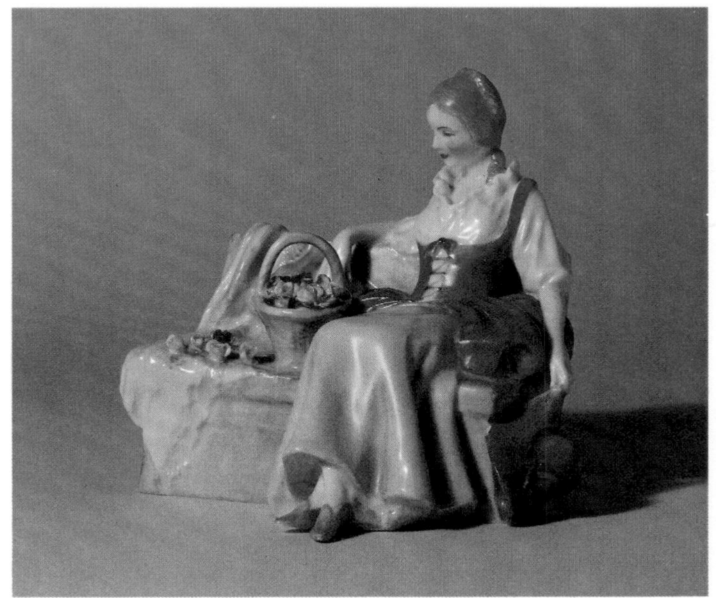

HN 1899 Midsummer Noon

HN 1897 Miss Fortune
Designer: L. Harradine
Size: $5\frac{3}{4}$ in (14.6 cm)
Introduced: 1938
Withdrawn: By 1949
Based on the Raphael Tuck calendar design, *A Rosy Ruse*

HN 1898 Miss Fortune
Introduced: 1938
Withdrawn: By 1949
As HN 1897, but green and yellow shawl, mauve dress

HN 1899 Midsummer Noon
Designer: L. Harradine
Size: $4\frac{1}{2}$ in (11.4 cm)
Introduced: 1939
Withdrawn: By 1949
This figure is an adapted version of HN 1745, *The Rustic Swain.*

HN 1900 Midsummer Noon
Introduced: 1939
Withdrawn: By 1949
As HN 1899, but blue dress

HN 2033 Midsummer Noon
Introduced: 1949
Withdrawn: By 1955
As HN 1899, but minor colour differences

HN 1901 Penelope

HN 1904 Rhythm

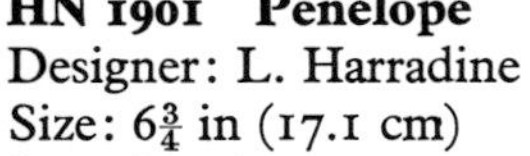

HN 1901 Penelope
Designer: L. Harradine
Size: $6\frac{3}{4}$ in (17.1 cm)
Introduced: 1939
Withdrawn: 1975
Based on a calendar illustration, *The Seamstress*, drawn by Anne Rochester for the publishers Valentine and Sons. Penelope, the wife of Ulysses, kept her suitors at bay by undoing at night all the embroidery she had completed during the day until her husband returned from his adventures.

HN 1902 Penelope
Introduced: 1939
Withdrawn: By 1949
As HN 1901, but green petticoat, blue bodice, mauve and blue striped skirt

HN 1903 Rhythm
Designer: L. Harradine
Size: $6\frac{3}{4}$ in (17.1 cm)
Introduced: 1939
Withdrawn: By 1949
As HN 1904, but pink dress

HN 1904 Rhythm
Introduced: 1939
Withdrawn: By 1949

HN 1905 Goody Two Shoes
See page 296

HN 1906 Lydia
Designer: L. Harradine
Size: $4\frac{1}{4}$ in (10.7 cm)
Introduced: 1939
Withdrawn: By 1949
As HN 1907, but orange/pink overdress, pale pink flowered underskirt.
Based on a design by Molly Benatar, *The Bluebird's Message*, published by Raphael Tuck.

HN 1907 Lydia
Introduced: 1939
Withdrawn: By 1949

HN 1908 Lydia
Introduced: 1939
Still in production

HN 1907 & HN 1908 Lydia

HN 1910 & HN 1909 Honey

HN 1909 Honey
Designer: L. Harradine
Size: 6¾ in (17.1 cm)
Introduced: 1939
Withdrawn: By 1949
Based on a design by Stanislaus Longley used for publicity purposes by Liberty of Regent Street.

HN 1910 Honey
Introduced: 1939
Withdrawn: 1949

HN 1963 Honey
Introduced: 1941
Withdrawn: By 1949
As HN 1909, but red dress, blue hat strings and shawl

HN 1911 Autumn Breezes

HN 1913 Autumn Breezes

HN 1934 Autumn Breezes

HN 2147 Autumn Breezes

HN 1911 Autumn Breezes
Designer: L. Harradine
Size: 7½ in (19.0 cm)
Introduced: 1939
Withdrawn: 1976
Based on a calendar design, *Autumn Glory*, painted by Stanislaus Longley.

HN 1913 Autumn Breezes
Introduced: 1939
Withdrawn: 1971

HN 1934 Autumn Breezes
Introduced: 1940
Still in production

HN 2147 Autumn Breezes
Introduced: 1955
Withdrawn: 1971

HN 1912 Old Balloon Seller and Bulldog
See page 279

HN 1913 Autumn Breezes
See above

HN 1914 Paisley Shawl (second version, model 1030)
Designer: L. Harradine
Size: 6½ in (16.5 cm)
Introduced: 1939
Withdrawn: By 1949
For illustration, see page 203

HN 1988 Paisley Shawl (second version, model 1030)
Introduced: 1946
Withdrawn: 1975
As HN 1914, but cream and yellow skirt, red bonnet

HN 1915 Veronica (second version, model 1031)
Designer: L. Harradine
Size: 5¾ in (14.6 cm)
Introduced: 1939
Withdrawn: By 1949
For illustration, see page 231

HN 1916 Janet (second version, model 1032)
Designer: L. Harradine
Size: 5 in (12.7 cm)
Introduced: 1939
Withdrawn: By 1949
For illustration, see page 235

HN 1964 Janet (second version, model 1032)
Introduced: 1941
Withdrawn: 1949
As HN 1916, but pink dress

HN 1917 Meryll
Designer: L. Harradine
Size: 6¾ in (17.1 cm)
Introduced: 1939
Withdrawn: 1940
As HN 1940, but red jacket and green skirt.
For reasons that are not absolutely clear this figure was renamed *Toinette* shortly after its introduction, and was reissued as HN 1940, in a different colour scheme.
The model was based on the Molly Benatar painting, *The Robin's Message.*

HN 1940 Toinette
Introduced: 1940
Withdrawn: By 1949

HN 1940 Toinette (illustration from an old catalogue)

The Robin's Message, a Raphael Tuck calendar design by Molly Benatar

HN 1918 Sweet Suzy
Designer: L. Harradine
Size: 6½ in (16.5 cm)
Introduced: 1939
Withdrawn: By 1949
Based on a Molly Benatar design, *Tulip Time*, published by Raphael Tuck.

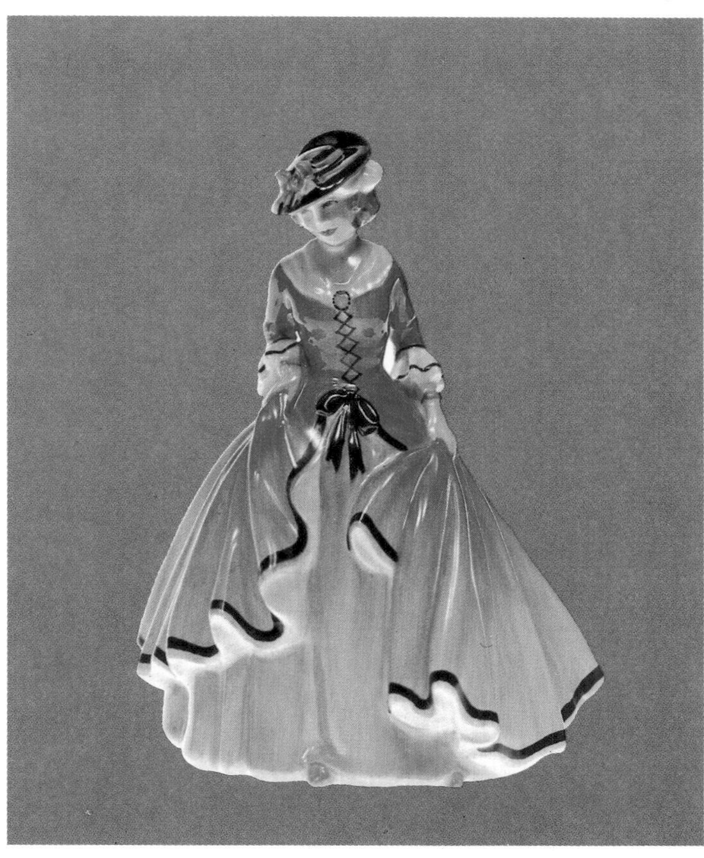

HN 1918 Sweet Suzy

HN 1919 Kate Hardcastle
See page 261

HN 1920 Windflower (second version, model 977)
Designer: L. Harradine
Size: 11 in (27.9 cm)
Introduced: 1939
Withdrawn: By 1949
Multicoloured skirt, red bodice, black base

HN 1939 Windflower (second version, model 977)
Introduced: 1940
Withdrawn: 1949
Flowered pink skirt, blue hat and gloves

HN 1921 Roseanna
Designer: L. Harradine
Size: 8 in (20.3 cm)
Introduced: 1940
Withdrawn: By 1949
As HN 1926, but green dress
Based on a Stanislaus Longley design, *Lady and Roses*, originally used as a calendar and Christmas card.

HN 1926 Roseanna
Introduced: 1940
Withdrawn: 1959

HN 1922 Spring Morning
Designer: L. Harradine
Size: $7\frac{1}{4}$ in (18.4 cm)
Introduced: 1940
Withdrawn: 1973
Based on a calendar design by Molly Benatar, *The Call of the Winds*, published by Raphael Tuck.

HN 1923 Spring Morning
Introduced: 1940
Withdrawn: By 1949

HN 1924 Fiona (first version, model 1040)
Designer: L. Harradine
Size: $5\frac{3}{4}$ in (14.6 cm)
Introduced: 1940
Withdrawn: By 1949

HN 1925 Fiona (first version, model 1040)
Introduced: 1940
Withdrawn: By 1949
As HN 1933, but green skirt

HN 1933 Fiona (first version, model 1040)
Introduced: 1940
Withdrawn: By 1949

HN 1926 Roseanna
See above

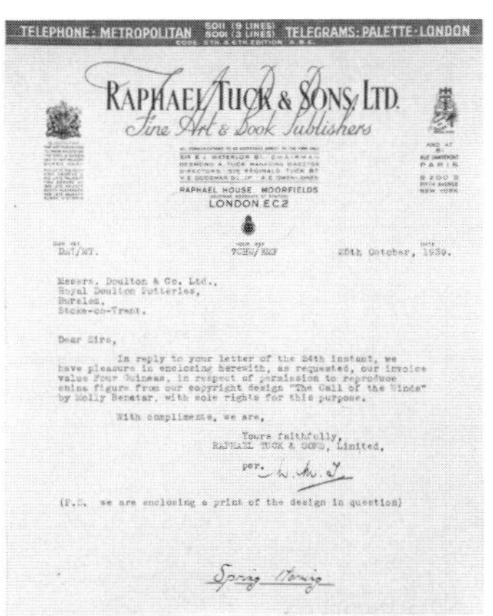
TELEPHONE: METROPOLITAN 5011 (9 LINES) 5001 (3 LINES) TELEGRAMS: PALETTE·LONDON

RAPHAEL TUCK & SONS, LTD.
Fine Art & Book Publishers

RAPHAEL HOUSE MOORFIELDS
LONDON E.C.2

October, 1939.

Messrs. Doulton & Co. Ltd.,
Royal Doulton Potteries,
Burslem,
Stoke-on-Trent.

Dear Sirs,

In reply to your letter of the 24th instant, we have pleasure in enclosing herewith, as requested, our invoice value Four Guineas, in respect of permission to reproduce china figure from our copyright design "The Call of the Winds" by Molly Benatar, with sole rights for this purpose.

With compliments, we are,

Yours faithfully,
RAPHAEL TUCK & SONS, Limited,
per.

(P.S. we are enclosing a print of the design in question)

Spring Morning

Letter from Raphael Tuck and Co., giving Doulton permission to model a figure on *The Call of the Winds* design

The Call of the Winds, a Raphael Tuck calendar design by Molly Benatar

HN 1926 Roseanna

HN 1922 Spring Morning

HN 1923 Spring Morning

HN 1924 Fiona (first version)

HN 1933 Fiona (first version)

HN 1946 Marguerite

Meriel

HN 1927 The Awakening (illustration from the figure design book)

HN 1927 The Awakening
Designer: L. Harradine
Introduced: 1940
Withdrawn: By 1949

HN 1928 Marguerite
Designer: L. Harradine
Size: 8 in (20.3 cm)
Introduced: 1940
Withdrawn: 1959
As HN 1946, but pink dress
Based on a design by Stanislaus Longley, *Summer Breezes*.

HN 1929 Marguerite
Introduced: 1940
Withdrawn: 1949
As HN 1946, but pink fading to yellow at the bottom of dress

HN 1930 Marguerite
Introduced: 1940
Withdrawn: By 1949
As HN 1946, but blue dress with purple stripes

HN 1946 Marguerite
Introduced: 1940
Withdrawn: By 1949

HN 1931 Meriel
Designer: L. Harradine
Size: $7\frac{1}{4}$ in (18.4 cm)
Introduced: 1940
Withdrawn: By 1949
Pink dress

HN 1932 Meriel
Introduced: 1940
Withdrawn: By 1949
Green dress

HN 1933 Fiona (first version, model 1040)
See page 302

HN 1934 Autumn Breezes
See page 301

HN 1935 Sweeting

HN 1938 Sweeting

HN 1937 Miss Muffet HN 1936 Miss Muffet

HN 1935 Sweeting
Designer: L. Harradine
Size: 6 in (15.2 cm)
Introduced: 1940
Withdrawn: 1973

HN 1938 Sweeting
Introduced: 1940
Withdrawn: By 1949

HN 1936 Miss Muffet
Designer: L. Harradine
Size: $5\frac{1}{2}$ in (13.3 cm)
Introduced: 1940
Withdrawn: 1967
Based on a calendar design by Molly Benatar, *When Hearts are Young*. The figure is named after the traditional nursery rhyme about Little Miss Muffet and the spider, but the style does not really fit the rhyme.

HN 1937 Miss Muffet
Introduced: 1940
Withdrawn: 1952

HN 2038 Peggy

HN 1938 Sweeting
See previous page

HN 1939 Windflower (second version, model 977)
See page 302

HN 1940 Toinette
See page 301

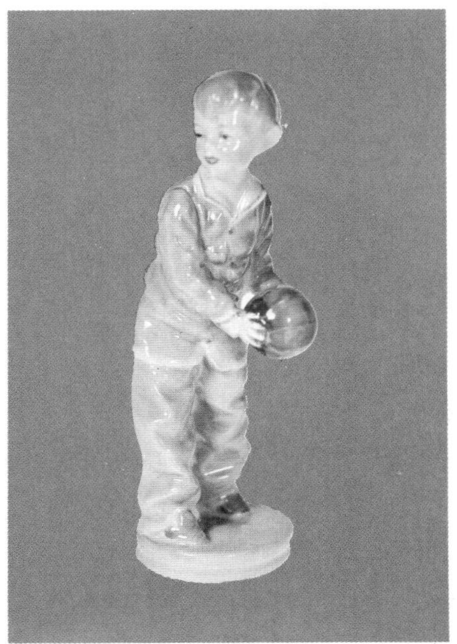

HN 1942 Pyjams

HN 1941 Peggy
Designer: L. Harradine
Size: 5 in (12.7 cm)
Introduced: 1940
Withdrawn: By 1949
As HN 2038, but minor glaze differences

HN 2038 Peggy
Introduced: 1949
Still in production

HN 1948 Lady Charmian

HN 1949 Lady Charmian

HN 1950 & HN 1951 Claribel

HN 1942 Pyjams
Designer: L. Harradine
Size: 5¼ in (13.3 cm)
Introduced: 1940
Withdrawn: By 1949

HN 1943 Veronica (first version, model 751)
See page 231

HN 1944 Daydreams
See page 266

HN 1945 Spring Flowers
See page 281

HN 1946 Marguerite
See page 304

HN 1947 June
See page 258

HN 1948 Lady Charmian
Designer: L. Harradine
Size: 7¾ in (19.6 cm)
Introduced: 1940
Withdrawn: 1973
Based on a calendar design by Stanislaus Longley

HN 1949 Lady Charmian
Introduced: 1940
Withdrawn: 1975

HN 1950 Claribel
Designer: L. Harradine
Size: 4¾ in (12.0 cm)
Introduced: 1940
Withdrawn: By 1949

HN 1951 Claribel
Introduced: 1940
Withdrawn: 1949

HN 1952 Irene
See page 247

HN 1953 Orange Lady
See page 271

HN 1954 The Balloon Man
Designer: L. Harradine
Size: 7½ in (19.0 cm)
Introduced: 1940
Still in production
Perhaps inspired by the poem,
The Balloon Man, by Rose Fyleman:
'He always comes on market days
And holds balloons—a lovely bunch—
And in the market square he stays,
And never seems to think of lunch.
They're red and purple, blue and green,
And when it's a sunny day
Tho' carts and people get between
You see 'em shining far away.'

HN 1954 The Balloon Man

HN 1955 Lavinia
Designer: L. Harradine
Size: 5 in (12.7 cm)
Introduced: 1940
Still in production

HN 1956 Chloe
See page 219

HN 1957 The New Bonnet
See page 264

HN 1958 Lady April
Designer: L. Harradine
Size: 7 in (17.7 cm)
Introduced: 1940
Withdrawn: 1959

HN 1965 Lady April
Introduced: 1941
Withdrawn: 1949
As HN 1958, but green dress

HN 1959 The Choice
Designer: L. Harradine
Introduced: 1941
Withdrawn: 1949
As HN 1960, but red dress

HN 1955 Lavinia

HN 1960 The Choice
Introduced: 1941
Withdrawn: 1949

HN 1961 Daisy
See page 240

HN 1962 Genevieve
Designer: L. Harradine
Size: 7 in (17.7 cm)
Introduced: 1941
Withdrawn: 1975

HN 1958 Lady April

HN 1967 Lady Betty

HN 1960 The Choice (illustration from the figure design book)

HN 1963 Honey
See page 299

HN 1964 Janet (second version, model 1032)
See page 301

HN 1965 Lady April
See opposite

HN 1966 Orange Vendor
See page 94

HN 1967 Lady Betty
Designer: L. Harradine
Size: $6\frac{1}{2}$ in (16.5 cm)
Introduced: 1941
Withdrawn: 1951

HN 1968 Madonna of the Square
See page 68

HN 1969 Madonna of the Square
See page 68

HN 1971 Springtime (illustration from the figure design book)

Springtime, a Raphael Tuck calendar design by Lancelot Roberts

HN 1970 Milady
Designer: L. Harradine
Size: $6\frac{1}{2}$ in (16.5 cm)
Introduced: 1941
Withdrawn: 1949

HN 1971 Springtime
Designer: L. Harradine
Introduced: 1941
Withdrawn: 1949
Based on a design for a calendar by Lancelot Roberts, published by Raphael Tuck.

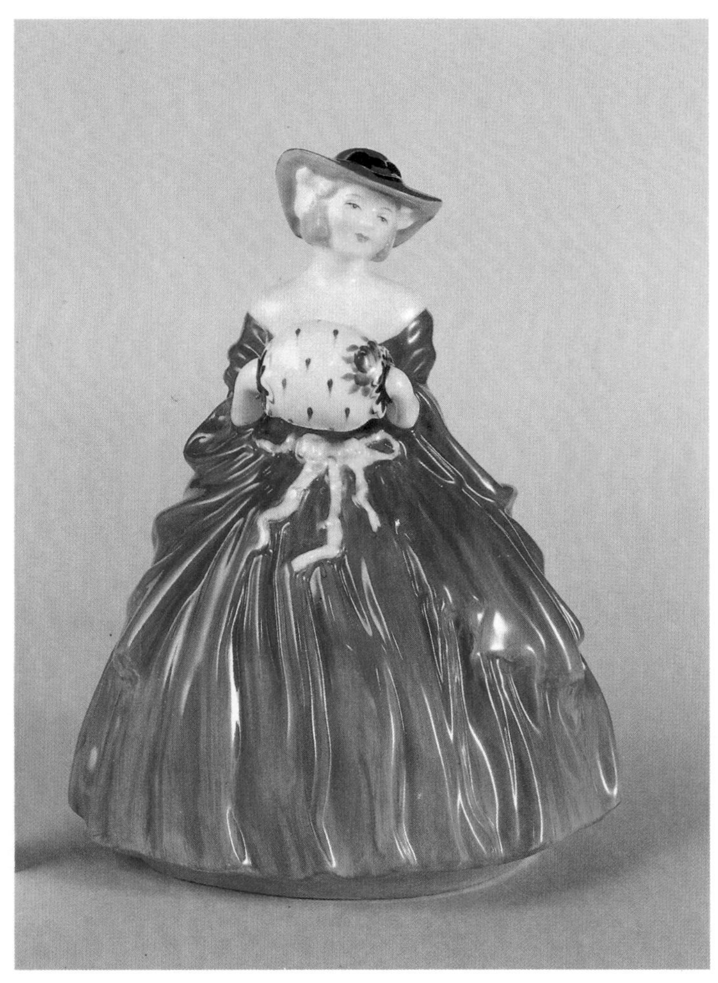

HN 1962 Genevieve

HN 1970 Milady

HN 1972 Regency Beau

HN 1973 The Corinthian

HN 1975 The Shepherd (fourth version)

HN 2094 Uncle Ned

HN 1974 Forty Winks

HN 1976 Easter Day

HN 2039 Easter Day

HN 1972 Regency Beau
Designer: H. Fenton
Size: 8 in (20.3 cm)
Introduced: 1941
Withdrawn: 1949
This figure, and those that follow, HN 1973, 1974 and 1975, may have been based on designs by Harradine, for he was unable to send any actual models to Burslem during the German occupation of the Channel Islands. Few new models were introduced during the war, but earlier models continued to be made in limited quantities.

HN 1973 The Corinthian
Designer: H. Fenton
Size: 7¾ in (19.6 cm)
Introduced: 1941
Withdrawn: 1949
It is possible that these two figures were inspired by Georgette Heyer's novels *Regency Buck* and *The Corinthian*, published in 1935 and 1940. Both represent young men of fashion of the Regency period, a time early in the 19th century when style was based on excessive attention to costume, manner and social etiquette. The high priest of the style was Beau Brummell.

HN 1974 Forty Winks
Designer: H. Fenton
Size: 6¾ in (17.1 cm)
Introduced: 1945
Withdrawn: 1973
Made as a pair to HN 2094, *Uncle Ned*

HN 1975 The Shepherd (fourth version, model 1190)
Designer: H. Fenton
Size: 8½ in (21.5 cm)
Introduced: 1945
Withdrawn: 1975

HN 1976 Easter Day
Designer: Margaret Davies
Size: 7½ in (19.0 cm)
Introduced: 1945
Withdrawn: 1951
The traditional Easter Day parade in London's Hyde Park was established by Queen Victoria, who also started the fashion of wearing new bonnets for the occasion. More recently the event has inspired shows such as Irving Berlin's *Easter Parade*.

HN 2039 Easter Day
Introduced: 1949
Withdrawn: 1969

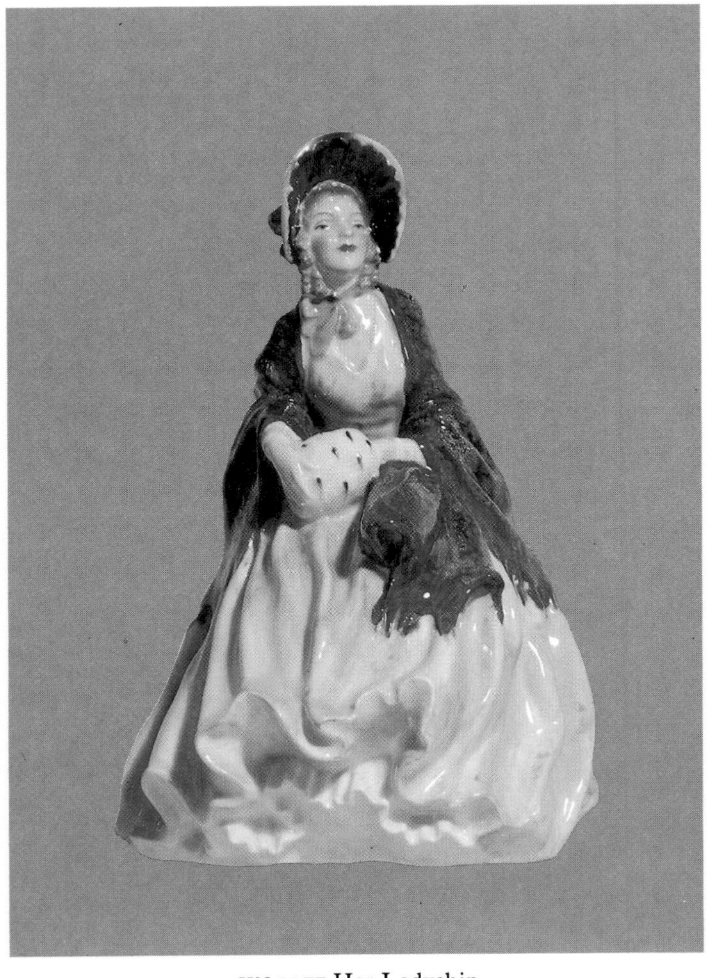

HN 1977 Her Ladyship

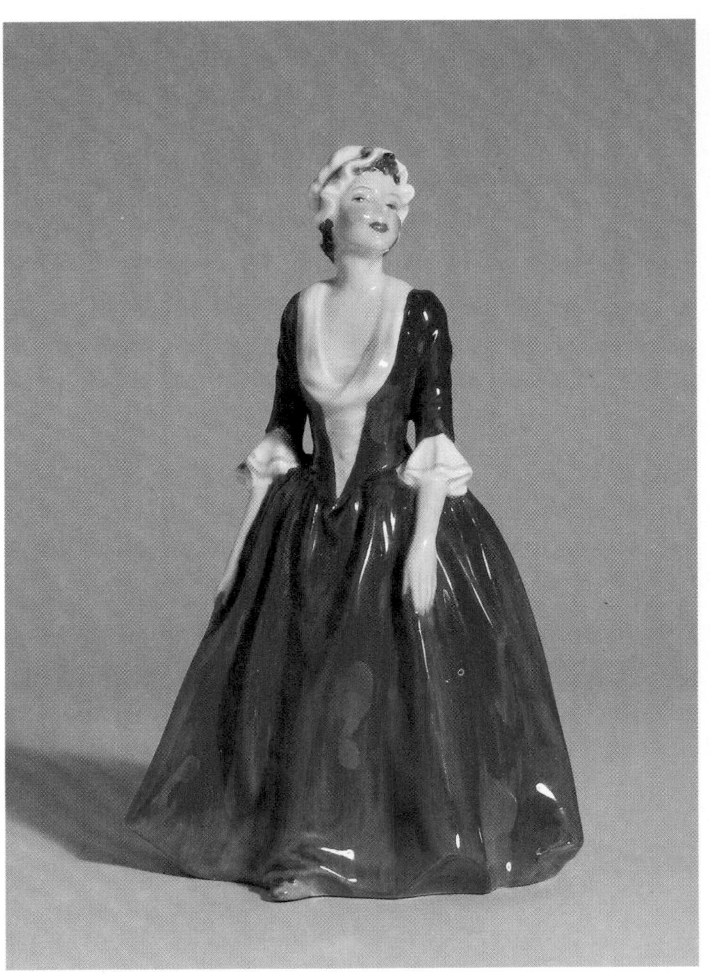

HN 1980 Gwynneth

HN 1977 Her Ladyship
Designer: L. Harradine
Size: 7 in (17.7 cm)
Introduced: 1945
Withdrawn: 1959

HN 1978 Bedtime
Designer: L. Harradine
Size: $5\frac{1}{2}$ in (13.9 cm)
Introduced: 1945
Still in production

HN 1979 Gollywog
Designer: L. Harradine
Size: $5\frac{1}{4}$ in (13.3 cm)
Introduced: 1945
Withdrawn: 1959
Traditionally one of the most popular soft toys, the gollywog first appeared in 1895, inspired by the Florence Upton children's book *The Adventures of Two Dutch Dolls and a Gollywog.*

HN 1978 Bedtime

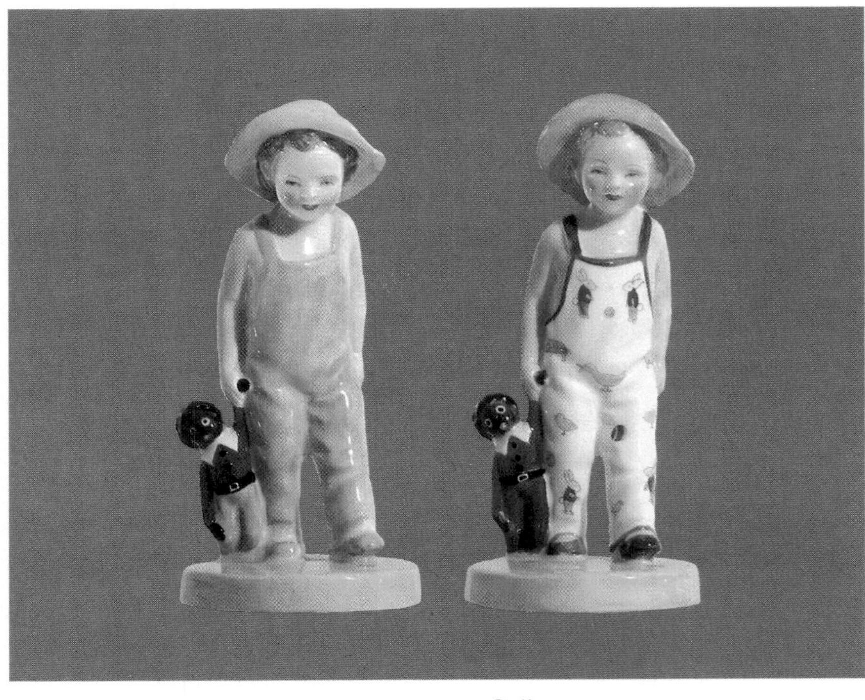

HN 2040 & HN 1979 Gollywog

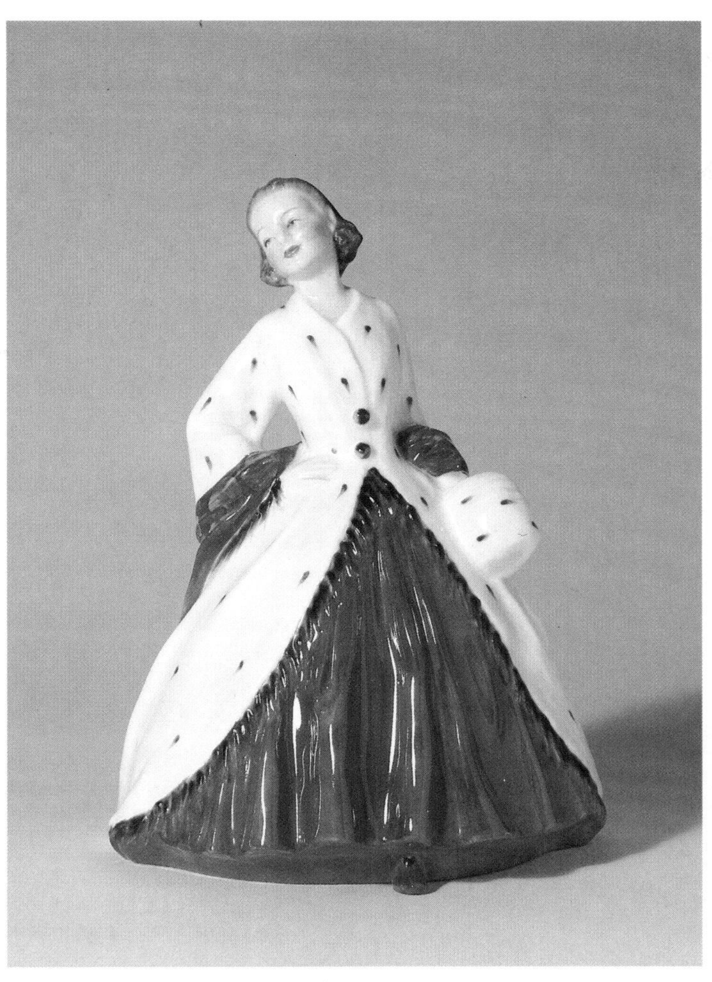

HN 1981 The Ermine Coat

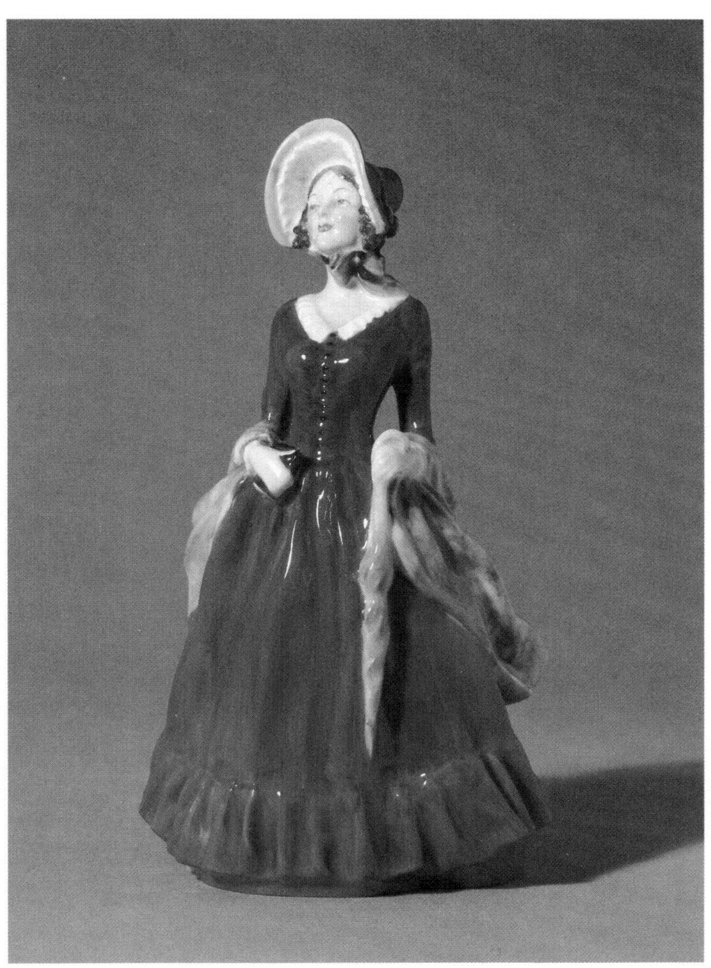

HN 1982 Sabbath Morn

HN 2040 Gollywog
Introduced: 1949
Withdrawn: 1959

HN 1980 Gwynneth
Designer: L. Harradine
Size: 7 in (17.7 cm)
Introduced: 1945
Withdrawn: 1952

HN 1981 The Ermine Coat
Designer: L. Harradine
Size: $6\frac{3}{4}$ in (17.1 cm)
Introduced: 1945
Withdrawn: 1967

HN 1982 Sabbath Morn
Designer: L. Harradine
Size: $7\frac{1}{4}$ in (18.4 cm)
Introduced: 1945
Withdrawn: 1959

HN 1983 Rosebud (second version, model 1174)
Designer: L. Harradine
Size: $7\frac{1}{2}$ in (19.0 cm)
Introduced: 1945
Withdrawn: 1952
The title is taken from a poem by Robert Herrick:
'Gather ye rosebuds while ye may,
Old time is still a flying:
And this same flower that smiles today
Tomorrow will be dying.'

HN 1983 Rosebud (second version)

HN 1984 The Patchwork Quilt

HN 1989 Margaret

HN 1984 The Patchwork Quilt
Designer: L. Harradine
Size: 6 in (15.2 cm)
Introduced: 1945
Withdrawn: 1959

HN 1985 Darling (second version, model 1264)
Designer: Charles Vyse
Size: 5¼ in (13.3 cm)
Introduced: 1946
Still in production
For illustration, see page 65

HN 1986 Diana
See page 261

HN 1987 Paisley Shawl (first version, model 660)
See page 202

HN 1988 Paisley Shawl (second version, model 1030)
See page 301

HN 1989 Margaret
Designer: L. Harradine
Size: 7¼ in (18.4 cm)
Introduced: 1947
Withdrawn: 1959

HN 1990 Mary Jane
Designer: L. Harradine
Size: 7½ in (19.0 cm)
Introduced: 1947
Withdrawn: 1959

HN 1991 Market Day
Designer: L. Harradine
Size: 7¼ in (18.4 cm)
Introduced: 1947
Withdrawn: 1955

HN 1991 Country Lass
Introduced: 1975
Still in production
This renamed version of *Market Day*, reintroduced in 1975, was at first incorrectly numbered as HN 2099, and a number of figures were issued before the mistake was rectified.

HN 1992 Christmas Morn
Designer: Margaret Davies
Size: 7 in (17.7 cm)
Introduced: 1947
Still in production

HN 1990 Mary Jane

HN 1992 Christmas Morn

HN 1991 Country Lass

HN 1991 Market Day

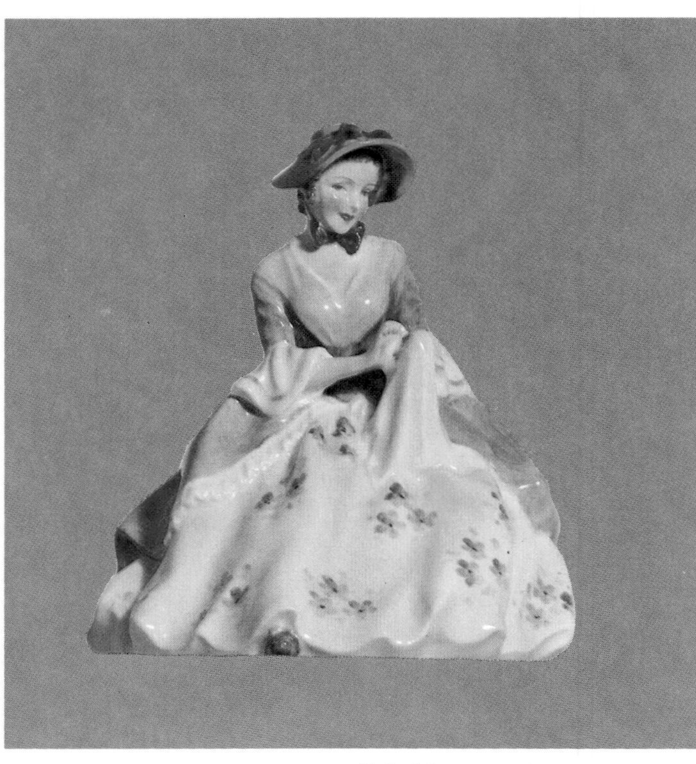

HN 1993 Griselda

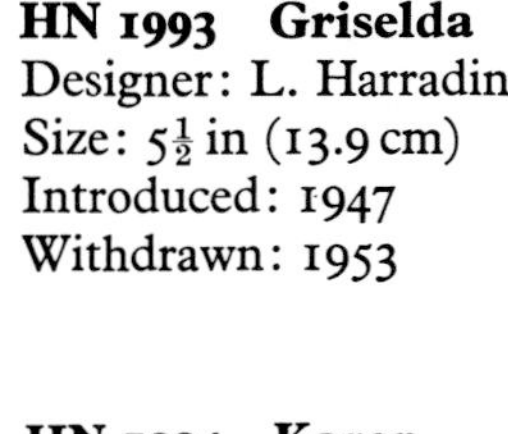

HN 1993 Griselda
Designer: L. Harradine
Size: $5\frac{1}{2}$ in (13.9 cm)
Introduced: 1947
Withdrawn: 1953

HN 1994 Karen
Designer: L. Harradine
Size: 8 in (20.3 cm)
Introduced: 1947
Withdrawn: 1955
With her stylish Edwardian riding costume, this model seems to belong to an earlier period of figure production.

HN 1995 Olivia
Designer: L. Harradine
Size: $7\frac{1}{2}$ in (19.0 cm)
Introduced: 1947
Withdrawn: 1951
Although this figure was probably inspired by the heroine of Shakespeare's comedy *Twelfth Night*, she may also have been named after the film actress, Olivia de Havilland.

HN 1994 Karen

HN 1995 Olivia

HN 1996 Prue

HN 1997 Belle o' the Ball

HN 1999 & HN 1998 Collinette

HN 1996 Prue
Designer: L. Harradine
Size: $6\frac{3}{4}$ in (17.1 cm)
Introduced: 1947
Withdrawn: 1955

HN 1997 Belle o' the Ball
Designer: L. Harradine
Size: 6 in (15.2 cm)
Introduced: 1947
Still in production

HN 1998 Collinette
Designer: L. Harradine
Size: $7\frac{1}{4}$ in (18.4 cm)
Introduced: 1947
Withdrawn: 1949

HN 1999 Collinette
Introduced: 1947
Withdrawn: 1949

HN 2000 & HN 2001 Jacqueline

HN 2000 Jacqueline
Designer: L. Harradine
Size: 7¼ in (18.4 cm)
Introduced: 1947
Withdrawn: 1951

HN 2001 Jacqueline
Introduced: 1947
Withdrawn: 1951

HN 2002 Bess
Designer: L. Harradine
Size: 7¼ in (18.4 cm)
Introduced: 1947
Withdrawn: 1969

HN 2003 Bess
Introduced: 1947
Withdrawn: 1950

HN 2002 & HN 2003 Bess

HN 2004 A' Courting

HN 2004 A 'Courting
Designer: L. Harradine
Size: $7\frac{1}{4}$ in (18.4 cm)
Introduced: 1947
Withdrawn: 1953

HN 2005 Henrietta Maria
Designer: Margaret Davies
Size: $9\frac{1}{4}$ in (23.4 cm)
Introduced: 1948
Withdrawn: 1953
This set of eight figures was designed to illustrate important lady characters in English history, between 1080 and 1860. They were designed, modelled and decorated in styles that depicted faithfully the costumes and colours of the period represented.
Henrietta Maria, daughter of Henry IV of France, was the Queen of Charles I. She lived from 1609 to 1666, and helped Charles to develop one of the most cultured, attractive, and dignified courts in Europe. Her influence was cut short by Charles' execution after the Civil War.
For illustration, see next page

HN 2006 The Lady Anne Nevill
Designer: Margaret Davies
Size: $9\frac{1}{2}$ in (24.1 cm)
Introduced: 1948
Withdrawn: 1953
The Lady Anne Nevill, 1456–1485, was the unwilling Queen of Richard III, having been forced to marry him following the death of her first husband, Edward, Prince of Wales, at the Battle of Tewkesbury. Her short life was one of the tragedies of the Wars of the Roses.
For illustration, see next page

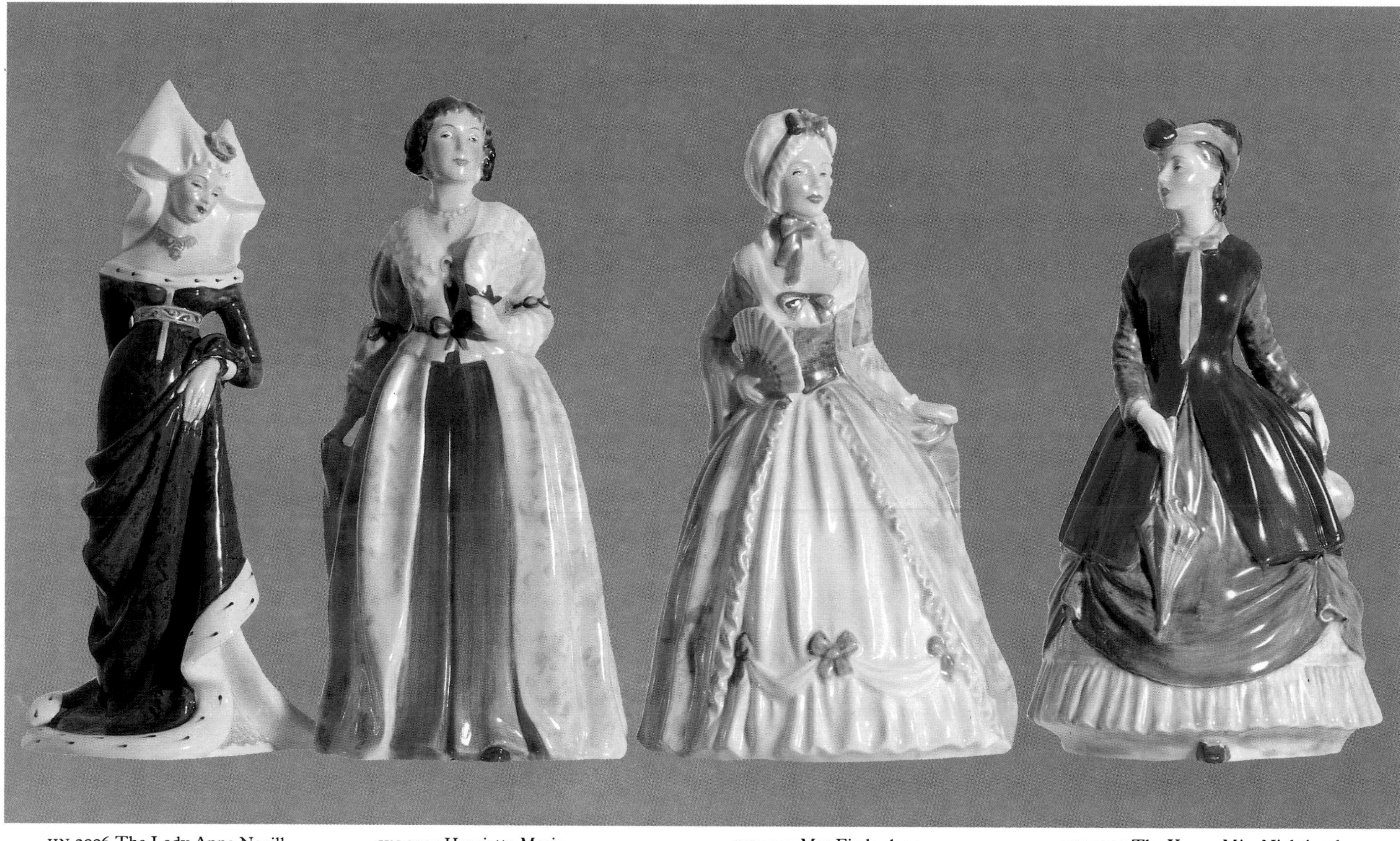

HN 2006 The Lady Anne Nevill

HN 2005 Henrietta Maria

HN 2007 Mrs Fitzherbert

HN 2010 The Young Miss Nightingale

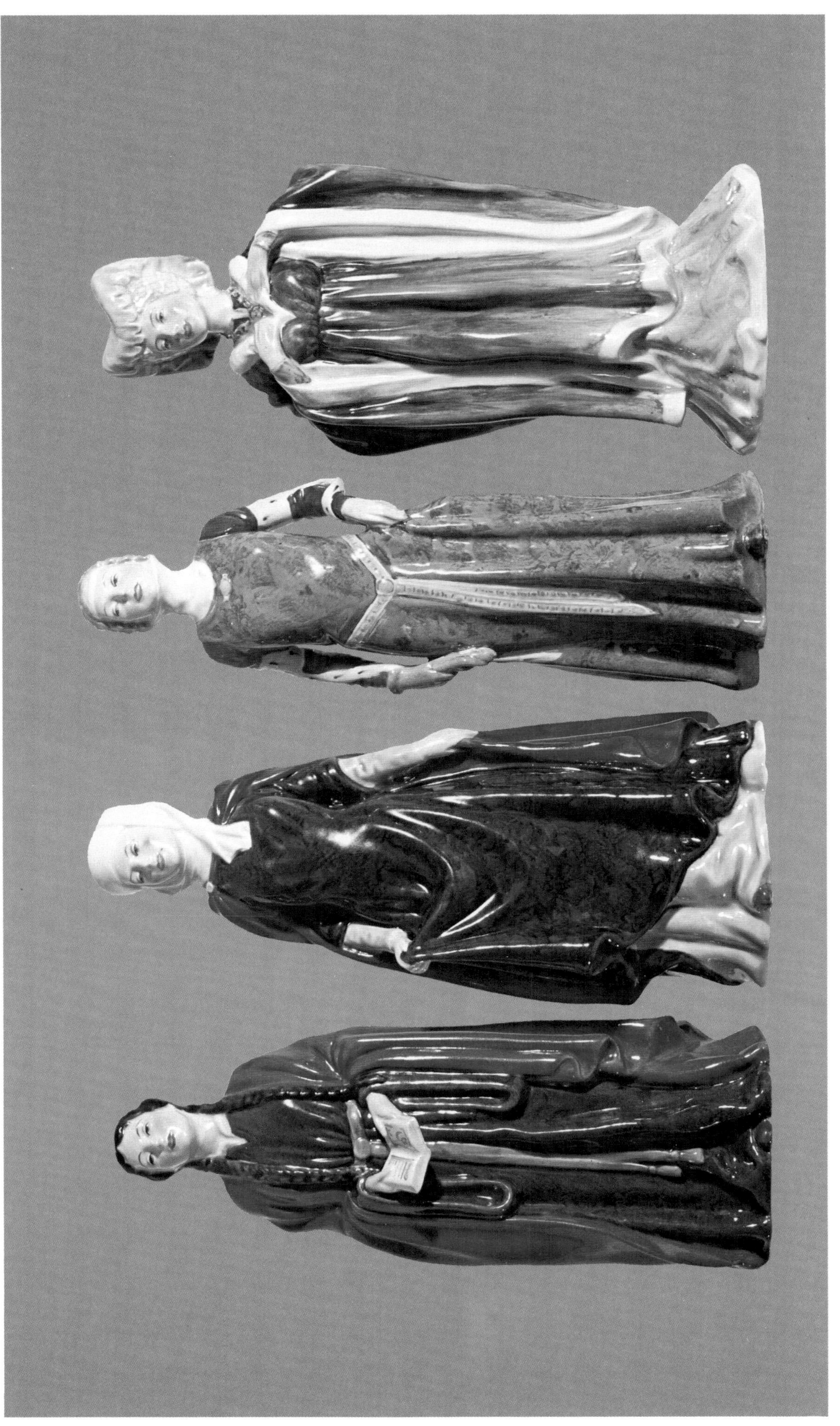

HN 2011 Matilda

HN 2009 Eleanor of Provence

HN 2008 Philippa of Hainault

HN 2012 Margaret of Anjou

HN 2007 Mrs Fitzherbert
Designer: Margaret Davies
Size: 9 in (22.8 cm)
Introduced: 1948
Withdrawn: 1953
Maria Fitzherbert, 1756–1837, was deeply loved by the Prince of Wales, the future George IV. Despite religious and social objections, they were eventually canonically married, but the marriage was not recognised by the State. Her devotion, dignity and self-effacement endeared her to the Royal Family, especially after George's death.
For illustration, see page 320

HN 2008 Philippa of Hainault
Designer: Margaret Davies
Size: $9\frac{1}{2}$ in (24.1 cm)
Introduced: 1948
Withdrawn: 1953
Philippa of Hainault, 1314–1369, was Queen of Edward III, who ruled at a time when the mature tradition of chivalry filled the English Court with pageantry and colour. Her husband and her son, the Black Prince, were above all men of war, but she is remembered for her courtesy, gentleness and clemency.
For illustration, see previous page

HN 2009 Eleanor of Provence
Designer: Margaret Davies
Size: $9\frac{1}{2}$ in (24.1 cm)
Introduced: 1948
Withdrawn: 1953
Eleanor of Provence, 1222–1291, was the Queen of Henry III. Although unpopular in England, she was renowned in her own country for her beauty and artistic abilities. After the death of her husband, she withdrew to a convent and devoted herself to charitable work. She lived to see her son, Edward I, become one of the greatest English monarchs.
For illustration, see previous page

HN 2010 The Young Miss Nightingale
Designer: Margaret Davies
Size: 9 in (22.8 cm)
Introduced: 1948
Withdrawn: 1953
Despite the wealth and brilliance of her background, Florence Nightingale devoted her life, not to a husband and comfort, but to humanity. She established her reputation during the Crimean War when she made an efficient field hospital out of the chaos to which official indifference had condemned the wounded British soldiers. She then dedicated her life to making nursing an honourable profession.
For illustration, see page 320

HN 2011 Matilda
Designer: Margaret Davies
Size: 9 in (22.8 cm)
Introduced: 1948
Withdrawn: 1953
Matilda, 1080–1118, was the Queen of Henry I. She has gone down in history as 'Good Queen Maud' because of unwearying care for the poor and the sick. The daughter of Margaret, Queen of Scotland, she linked together the Saxon and Norman Royal families.
For illustration, see previous page

HN 2012 Margaret of Anjou
Designer: Margaret Davies
Size: $9\frac{1}{4}$ in (23.4 cm)
Introduced: 1948
Withdrawn: 1953
This figure appears to be a remodelled version of HN 43, *A Lady of the Time of Henry VI*
Margaret of Anjou, 1430–1482, was the Queen of Henry VI. She came to England from France at a time when there was no love lost between the two countries, as a pledge of peace. She was then deeply involved in the Wars of the Roses, rallying the supporters of the Red Rose to defend her husband. When the White Rose triumphed, she was flung into the Tower of London, Henry having been brutally murdered.
For illustration, see previous page

HN 2013 Angelina
Designer: L. Harradine
Size: 7 in (17.7 cm)
Introduced: 1948
Withdrawn: 1951
For illustration, see page 325

HN 2014 Jane
Designer: L. Harradine
Size: $6\frac{1}{4}$ in (15.8 cm)
Introduced: 1948
Withdrawn: 1951
For illustration, see page 325

HN 2015 Sir Walter Raleigh
See page 267

HN 2016 A Jester (first version, model 170)
See page 85

HN 2017 Silks and Ribbons
Designer: L. Harradine
Size: $6\frac{1}{4}$ in (15.8 cm)
Introduced: 1949
Still in production
A late addition to the street seller series, this figure is modelled on the traditional pedlar lady, a familiar character from the fairground.

HN 2018 Parson's Daughter
See page 106

HN 2019 Minuet
Designer: Margaret Davies
Size: $7\frac{1}{4}$ in (18.4 cm)
Introduced: 1949
Withdrawn: 1971
One of the most popular dance forms, the minuet first came to England in the late 17th century. It reigned supreme at both court and assembly rooms as a test of elegance, deportment and skill until about 1800, after which date its popularity gradually declined. The minuet was included in symphonies and suites by many composers, including Handel, Bach and Mozart.

HN 2017 Silks and Ribbons

HN 2020 Deidre

HN 2066 Minuet
Introduced: 1950
Withdrawn: 1955

HN 2020 Deidre
Designer: L. Harradine
Size: 7 in (17.7 cm)
Introduced: 1949
Withdrawn: 1955

Original designer's model for the figure, Minuet

HN 2019 Minuet

HN 2066 Minuet

HN 2021 Blithe Morning

HN 2065 Blithe Morning

HN 2022 & HN 2165 Janice

Painting of Lady Jane Grey (National Portrait Gallery, London)

HN 2021 Blithe Morning
Designer: L. Harradine
Size: 7 in (17.7 cm)
Introduced: 1949
Withdrawn: 1971

HN 2065 Blithe Morning
Introduced: 1950
Withdrawn: 1973

HN 2022 Janice
Designer: Margaret Davies
Size: $7\frac{1}{4}$ in (18.4 cm)
Introduced: 1949
Withdrawn: 1955
Despite the name, this figure is clearly meant to represent Lady Jane Grey, who was made heir to the throne by the Duke of Northumberland. On the death of Edward VI in 1553, she reluctantly accepted the crown. She only reigned for a matter of days before being executed, to make way for Queen Mary. She was only 17 at her death. The figure is based on a painting of Lady Jane, now in the National Portrait Gallery, London.

HN 2165 Janice
Introduced: 1955
Withdrawn: 1965

HN 2023 Joan
See page 212

HN 2024 Darby
See page 213

HN 2025 Gossips
See page 213

HN 2026 Suzette
See page 225

HN 2027 June
See page 258

HN 2028 Kate Hardcastle
See page 261

HN 2029 Windflower (first version)
See page 302

HN 2030 Memories
See page 290

HN 2031 Granny's Heritage
See page 293

HN 2032 Jean
See page 293

HN 2033 Midsummer Morn
See page 297

HN 2034 Madonna of the Square
See page 68

HN 2035 Pearly Boy (second version)
Designer: L. Harradine
Size: $5\frac{1}{2}$ in (13.9 cm)
Introduced: 1949
Withdrawn: 1959
For illustration, see page 222

HN 2036 Pearly Girl (second version)
Designer: L. Harradine
Size: $5\frac{1}{2}$ in (13.9 cm)
Introduced: 1949
Withdrawn: 1959
For illustration, see page 222

HN 2037 Goody Two Shoes
See page 296

HN 2038 Peggy
See page 306

HN 2039 Easter Day
See page 311

HN 2040 Gollywog
See page 312

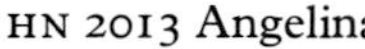
HN 2013 Angelina

HN 2014 Jane

HN 2041 The Broken Lance
Designer: Margaret Davies
Size: $8\frac{3}{4}$ in (22.2 cm)
Introduced: 1949
Withdrawn: 1975

HN 2042 Owd Willum
Designer: L. Harradine
Size: $6\frac{3}{4}$ in (17.1 cm)
Introduced: 1949
Withdrawn: 1973

HN 2043 The Poacher
Designer: L. Harradine
Size: $6\frac{1}{4}$ in (15.8 cm)
Introduced: 1949
Withdrawn: 1959

HN 2044 Mary Mary
Designer: L. Harradine
Size: 5 in (12.7 cm)
Introduced: 1949
Withdrawn: 1973
This is the first of a series of child figures, based on popular nursery rhymes.

HN 2041 The Broken Lance

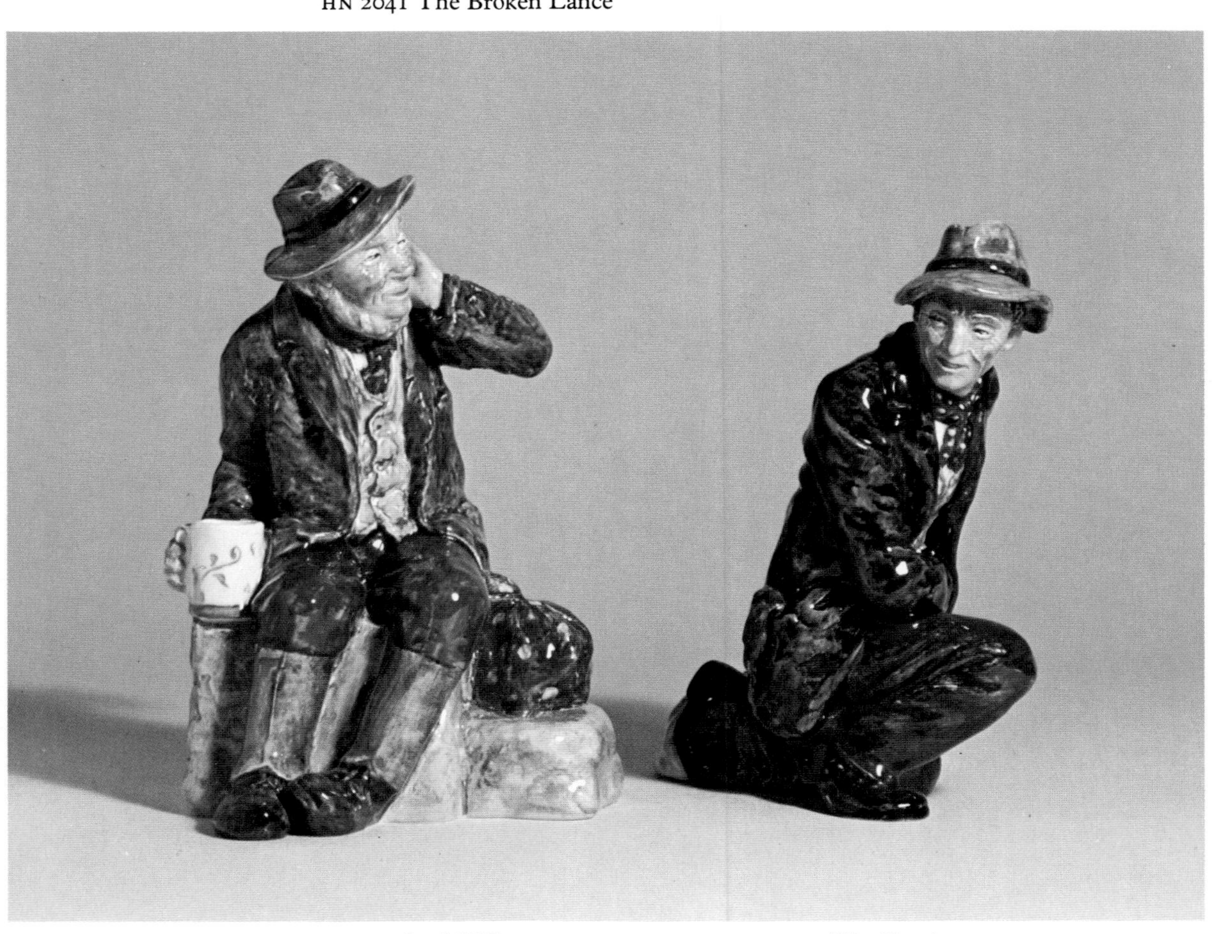

HN 2042 Owd Willum HN 2043 The Poacher

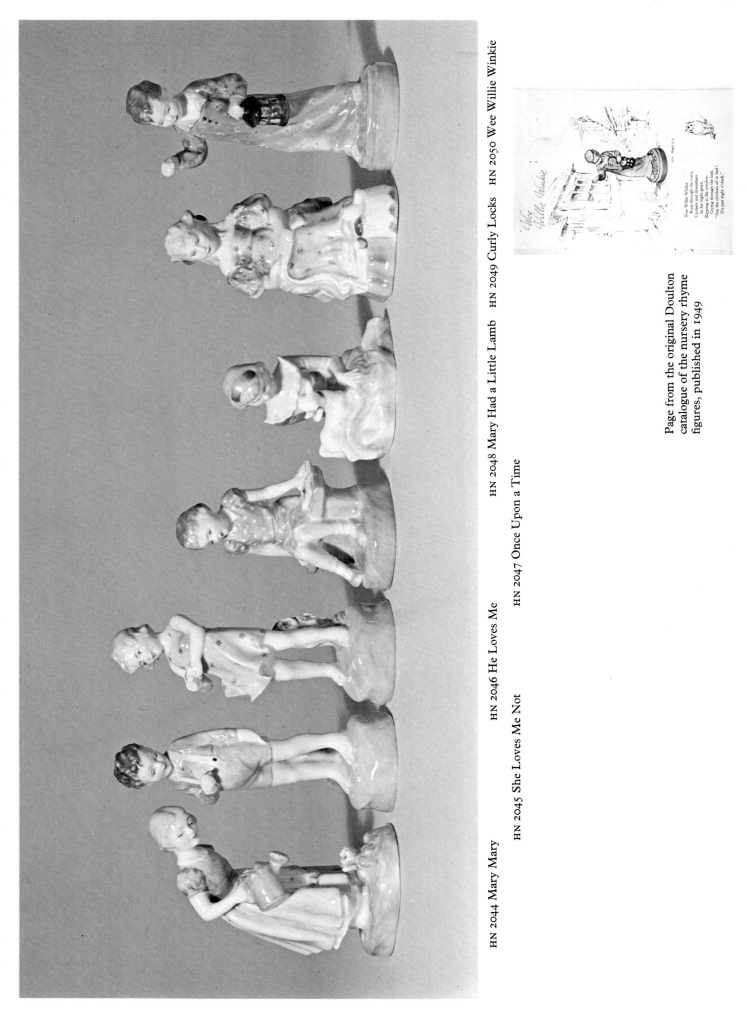

HN 2044 Mary Mary

HN 2045 She Loves Me Not

HN 2046 He Loves Me

HN 2047 Once Upon a Time

HN 2048 Mary Had a Little Lamb

HN 2049 Curly Locks

HN 2050 Wee Willie Winkie

Wee Willie Winkie

Wee Willie Winkie
Runs through the town,
Upstairs and downstairs
In his night-gown,
Rapping at the window,
Crying through the lock,
"Are the children all in bed?
It's past eight o'clock."

Page from the original Doulton catalogue of the nursery rhyme figures, published in 1949

HN 2045 She Loves Me Not
Designer: L. Harradine
Size: 5 in (12.7 cm)
Introduced: 1949
Withdrawn: 1962
For illustration, see previous page

HN 2046 He Loves Me
Designer: L. Harradine
Size: $5\frac{1}{2}$ in (13.9 cm)
Introduced: 1949
Withdrawn: 1962
For illustration, see previous page

HN 2047 Once Upon a Time
Designer: L. Harradine
Size: $4\frac{1}{4}$ in (10.7 cm)
Introduced: 1949
Withdrawn: 1955
For illustration, see previous page

HN 2048 Mary Had a Little Lamb
Designer: Margaret Davies
Size: $3\frac{1}{2}$ in (8.9 cm)
Introduced: 1949
Still in production
For illustration, see previous page

HN 2049 Curly Locks
Designer: Margaret Davies
Size: $4\frac{1}{2}$ in (11.4 cm)
Introduced: 1949
Withdrawn: 1953
For illustration, see previous page

HN 2053 The Gaffer HN 2052 Grandma

HN 2051 St George (second version)

HN 2050 Wee Willie Winkie
Designer: Margaret Davies
Size: $5\frac{1}{4}$ in (13.3 cm)
Introduced: 1949
Withdrawn: 1953
For illustration, see previous page

HN 2051 St George (second version, model 1356)
Designer: Margaret Davies
Size: $7\frac{1}{4}$ in (18.4 cm)
Introduced: 1950
Still in production

HN 2052 Grandma
Designer: L. Harradine
Size: $6\frac{3}{4}$ in (17.1 cm)
Introduced: 1950
Withdrawn: 1959

HN 2053 The Gaffer
Designer: L. Harradine
Size: $7\frac{1}{2}$ in (19.0 cm)
Introduced: 1950
Withdrawn: 1959
A popular term for an elderly rustic respected for his age and experience, gaffer has been in common use since the 18th century. In Fielding's novel *Joseph Andrews*, published in 1742, there occurs the line: 'Mr Andrews was esteemed to be the only son of Gaffer and Gammer Andrews.' Gammer is likely to be a contraction of Grandma.

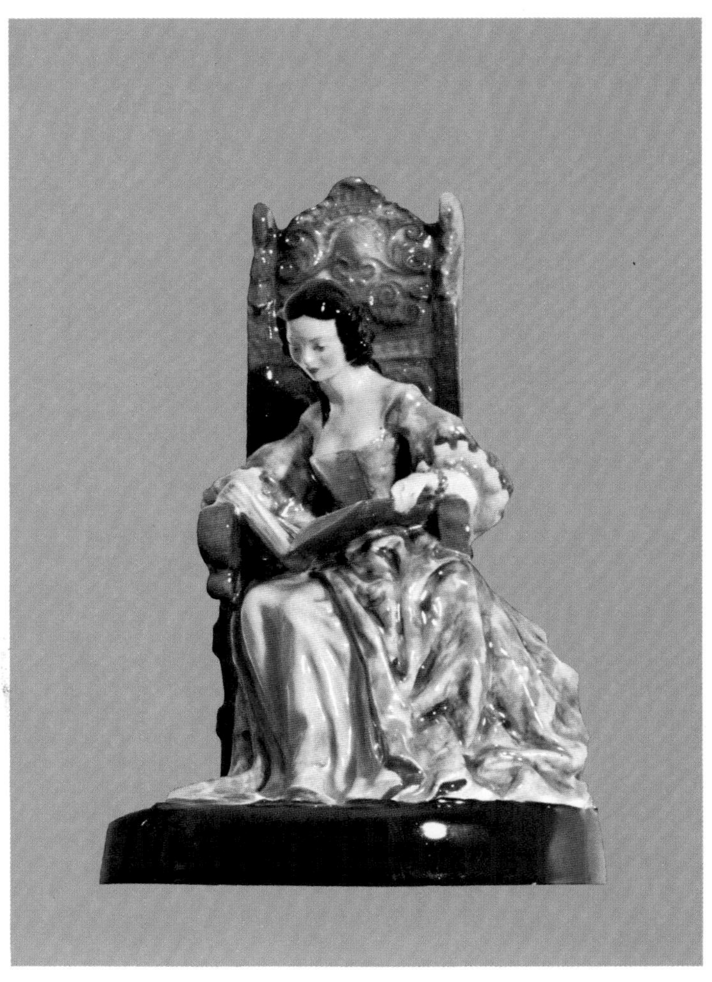

HN 2055 The Leisure Hour

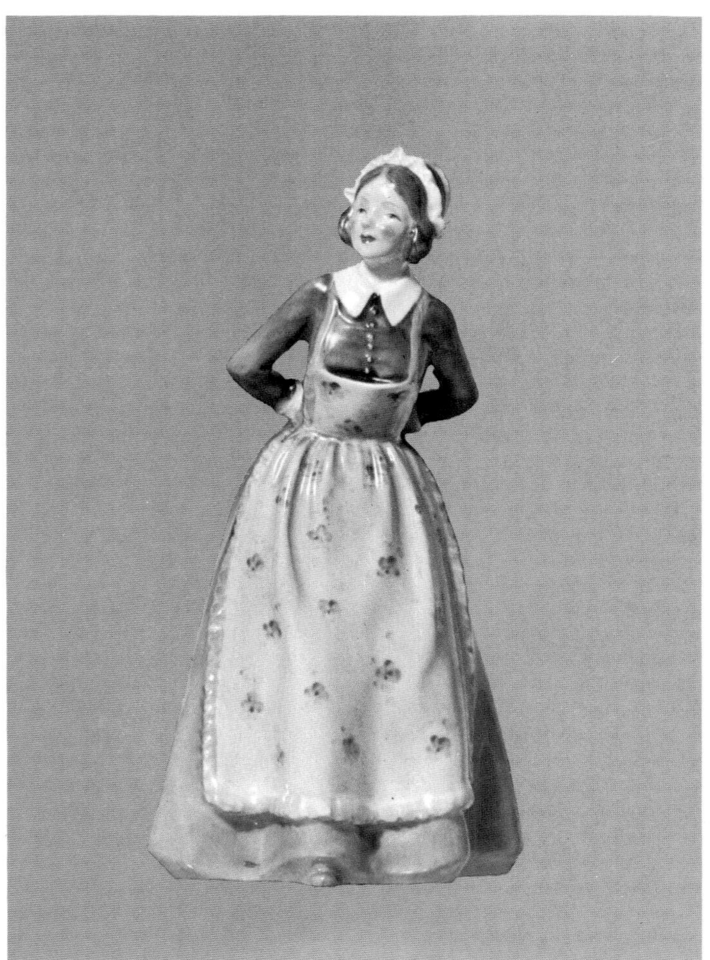

HN 2056 Susan

HN 2054 Falstaff (second version, model 353)
See page 150

HN 2055 The Leisure Hour
Designer: Margaret Davies
Size: 6¾ in (17.1 cm)
Introduced: 1950
Withdrawn: 1965
The Leisure Hour was the title of a popular ladies' magazine, concerned largely with romance, stories and pastimes.

HN 2056 Susan
Designer: L. Harradine
Size: 7 in (17.7 cm)
Introduced: 1950
Withdrawn: 1959
Susan was a traditional name for a servant girl, emphasised by the costume of this figure.

HN 2057 The Jersey Milkmaid
Designer: L. Harradine
Size: 6¾ in (17.1 cm)
Introduced: 1950
Withdrawn: 1959
Jersey cows are renowned for their rich milk, with a high cream content.

HN 2057 The Jersey Milkmaid

HN 2057 The Milkmaid

HN 2058 Hermione

HN 2057 The Milkmaid
Size: 6¾ in (17.1 cm)
Introduced: 1975
Still in production
This renamed version of *The Jersey Milkmaid*, reintroduced in 1975, was at first incorrectly numbered as HN 2100, and a number of figures were issued before the mistake was rectified.

HN 2059 The Bedtime Story

HN 2058 Hermione
Designer: Margaret Davies
Size: 7¼ in (18.4 cm)
Introduced: 1950
Withdrawn: 1952

HN 2059 The Bedtime Story
Designer: L. Harradine
Size: 4½ in (11.4 cm)
Introduced: 1950
Still in production

HN 2060 Jack
Designer: L. Harradine
Size: 5½ in (13.9 cm)
Introduced: 1950
Withdrawn: 1971

HN 2061 Jill
Designer: L. Harradine
Size: 5½ in (13.9 cm)
Introduced: 1950
Withdrawn: 1971

HN 2062 Little Boy Blue
Designer: L. Harradine
Size: 5½ in (13.9 cm)
Introduced: 1950
Withdrawn: 1973

HN 2060 Jack HN 2062 Little Boy Blue HN 2061 Jill HN 2063 Little Jack Horner HN 2064 My Pretty Maid

HN 2063 Little Jack Horner
Designer: L. Harradine
Size: $4\frac{1}{2}$ in (11.4 cm)
Introduced: 1950
Withdrawn: 1953

HN 2064 My Pretty Maid
Designer: L. Harradine
Size: $5\frac{1}{2}$ in (13.9 cm)
Introduced: 1950
Withdrawn: 1954

HN 2065 Blithe Morning
See page 325

HN 2066 Minuet
See page 323

HN 2067 St George (first version, model 191)
See page 115

HN 2068 Calumet
See page 213

HN 2069 Farmer's Wife
Designer: L. Harradine
Size: $9\frac{1}{4}$ in (23.4 cm)
Introduced: 1951
Withdrawn: 1955

HN 2069 Farmer's Wife

HN 2070 Bridget

HN 2071 Bernice

HN 2072 The Rocking Horse

HN 2073 Vivienne

HN 2074 Marianne

HN 2070 Bridget
Designer: L. Harradine
Size: 7¾ in (19.6 cm)
Introduced: 1951
Withdrawn: 1973

HN 2071 Bernice
Designer: Margaret Davies
Size: 8 in (20.3 cm)
Introduced: 1951
Withdrawn: 1953

HN 2072 The Rocking Horse
Designer: L. Harradine
Size: 7 in (17.7 cm)
Introduced: 1951
Withdrawn: 1953
Perhaps inspired by the film *The Rocking Horse Winner*, first shown in 1949 and starring John Mills and Valerie Hobson. The story concerned a boy with second sight whose affinity with his rocking horse enabled him to select the winners of actual horse races.

HN 2073 Vivienne
Designer: L. Harradine
Size: 7¾ in (19.6 cm)
Introduced: 1951
Withdrawn: 1967
This figure is the first of a small group having a distinctly French flavour.

HN 2074 Marianne
Designer: L. Harradine
Size: 7¼ in (18.4 cm)
Introduced: 1951
Withdrawn: 1953

HN 2075 French Peasant
Designer: L. Harradine
Size: 9½ in (24.1 cm)
Introduced: 1951
Withdrawn: 1955

HN 2075 French Peasant

HN 2076 Promenade

HN 2077 Rowena

HN 2076 Promenade
Designer: Margaret Davies
Size: 8 in (20.3 cm)
Introduced: 1951
Withdrawn: 1953

HN 2077 Rowena
Designer: L. Harradine
Size: 7½ in (19.0 cm)
Introduced: 1951
Withdrawn: 1955

HN 2078 Elfreda
Designer: L. Harradine
Size: 7¼ in (18.4 cm)
Introduced: 1951
Withdrawn: 1955

HN 2079 Damaris
Designer: Margaret Davies
Size: 7½ in (19.0 cm)
Introduced: 1951
Withdrawn: 1952

HN 2080 Jack Point
See page 99

HN 2081 Princess Badoura
Designers: H. Tittensor, Harry E. Stanton, F. Van Allen Phillips
Size: 20 in (50.8 cm)
Introduced: 1952
Still in production
Although this grand figure was only added to the HN series in 1952, it had in fact been produced considerably earlier. It was based on a model exhibited at the Wembley Exhibition of 1924 by Harry E. Stanton, at that time Master-in-Charge of Burslem School of Art. The story of Princess Badoura is taken from *The Arabian Nights*, and concerns the beautiful Badoura and her love for Prince Kaimar.
For illustration, see frontispiece

HN 2082 The Moor
See page 76

HN 2083 No details available

HN 2084 King Charles I
See page 118

HN 2078 Elfreda

HN 2079 Damaris

The original model for Princess Badoura by Harry E. Stanton (illustration taken from the 1924 Wembley Exhibition catalogue)

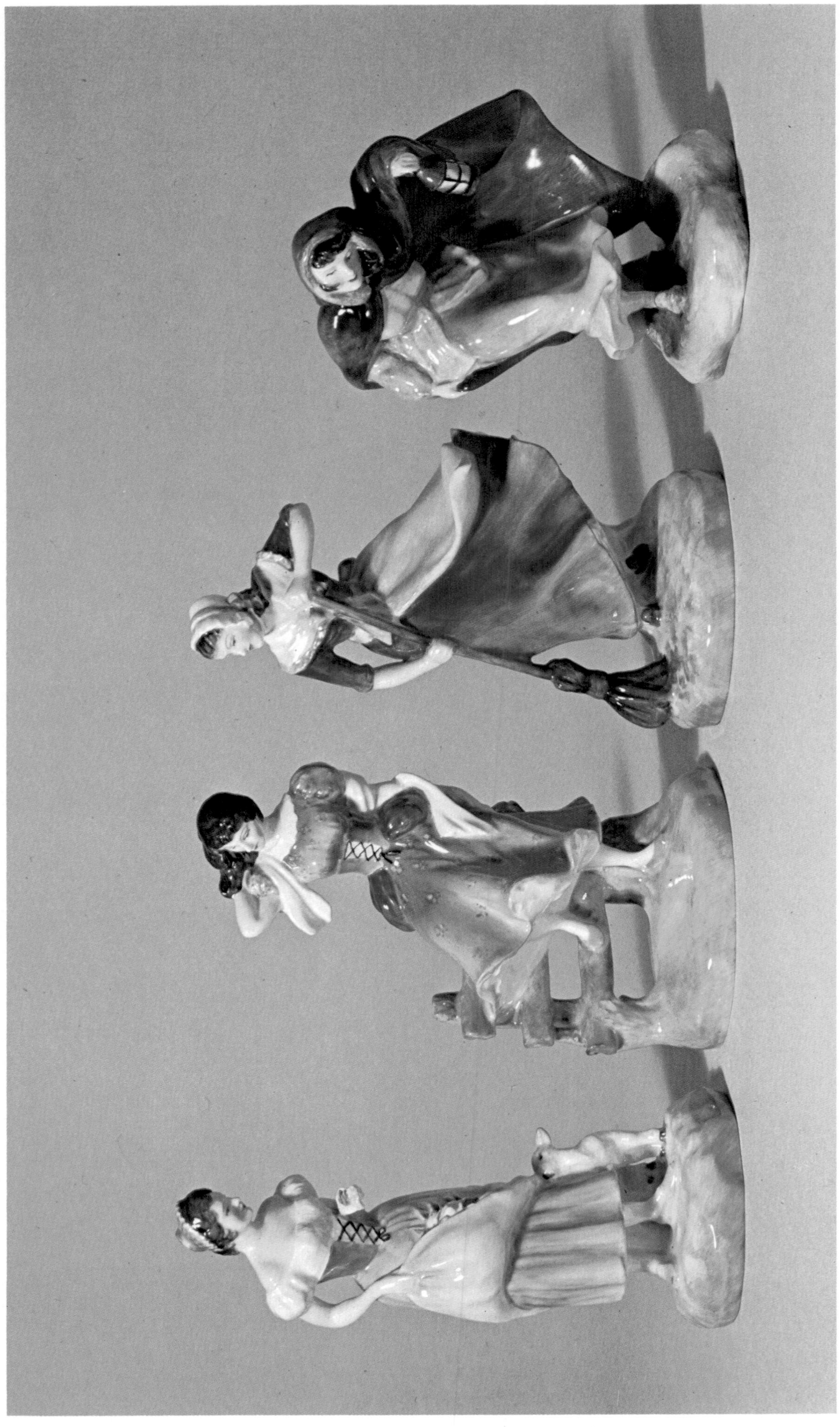

The Seasons (second version): HN 2085 Spring, HN 2086 Summer, HN 2087 Autumn, HN 2088 Winter

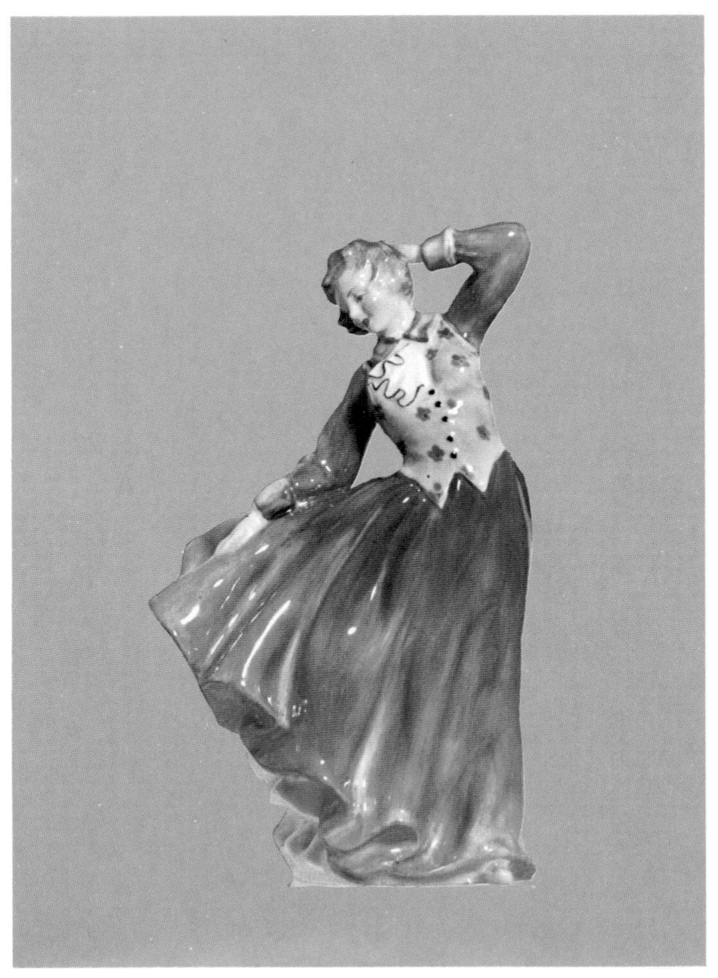

HN 2089 Judith

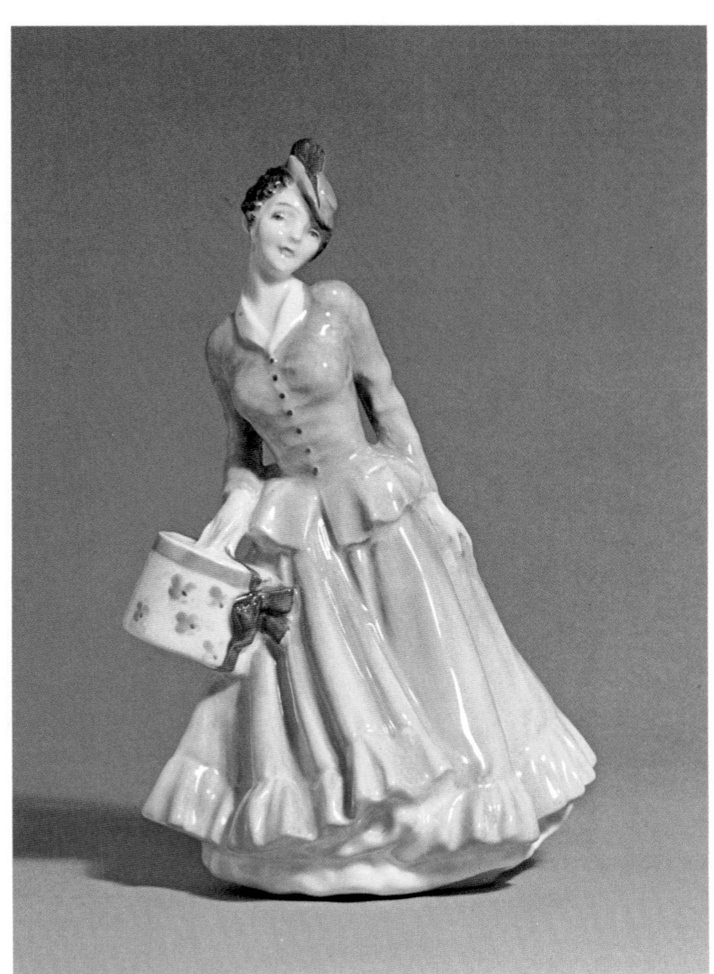

HN 2090 Midinette (second version)

HN 2085–2088 The Seasons (second version)
Designer: Margaret Davies
Introduced: 1952
Withdrawn: 1959

HN 2085 Spring (model 1394)
Size: $7\frac{3}{4}$ in (19.6 cm)

HN 2086 Summer (model 1395)
Size: $7\frac{1}{4}$ in (18.4 cm)

HN 2087 Autumn (model 1400)
Size: $7\frac{1}{4}$ in (18.4 cm)

HN 2088 Winter (model 1402)
Size: $6\frac{1}{4}$ in (15.8 cm)

HN 2089 Judith
Designer: L. Harradine
Size: $6\frac{3}{4}$ in (17.1 cm)
Introduced: 1952
Withdrawn: 1959

HN 2090 Midinette (second version, model 1831)
Designer: L. Harradine
Size: $7\frac{1}{4}$ in (18.4 cm)
Introduced: 1952
Withdrawn: 1965

HN 2091 Rosemary
Designer: L. Harradine
Size: 7 in (17.7 cm)
Introduced: 1952
Withdrawn: 1959

HN 2091 Rosemary

HN 2092 Sweet Maid (second version)

HN 2093 Georgiana

HN 2092 Sweet Maid (second version, model 1325)
Designer: L. Harradine
Size: 7¼ in (18.4 cm)
Introduced: 1952
Withdrawn: 1955

HN 2093 Georgiana
Designer: Margaret Davies
Size: 8½ in (21.5 cm)
Introduced: 1952
Withdrawn: 1955

HN 2094 Uncle Ned
Designer: H. Fenton
Size: 6¾ in (17.1 cm)
Introduced: 1952
Withdrawn: 1965
For illustration, see page 310
Made as a pair to HN 1974, *Forty Winks*

HN 2095 Ibrahim
See page 245

HN 2096 The Fat Boy (third version)
Designer: L. Harradine
Size: 7¼ in (18.4 cm)
Introduced: 1952
Withdrawn: 1967

HN 2097 Mr Micawber (third version)
Designer: L. Harradine
Size: 7½ in (19.0 cm)
Introduced: 1952
Withdrawn: 1967

HN 2098 Pecksniff (third version)
Designer: L. Harradine
Size: 7¼ in (18.4 cm)
Introduced: 1952
Withdrawn: 1967

HN 2099 Mr Pickwick (third verison)
Designer: L. Harradine
Size: 7½ in (19.0 cm)
Introduced: 1952
Withdrawn: 1967

HN 2100 Sairey Gamp (third version)
Designer: L. Harradine
Size: 7¼ in (18.4 cm)
Introduced: 1952
Withdrawn: 1967

HN 2101 Uriah Heep (third version)
Designer: L. Harradine
Size: 7¼ in (18.4 cm)
Introduced: 1952
Withdrawn: 1967

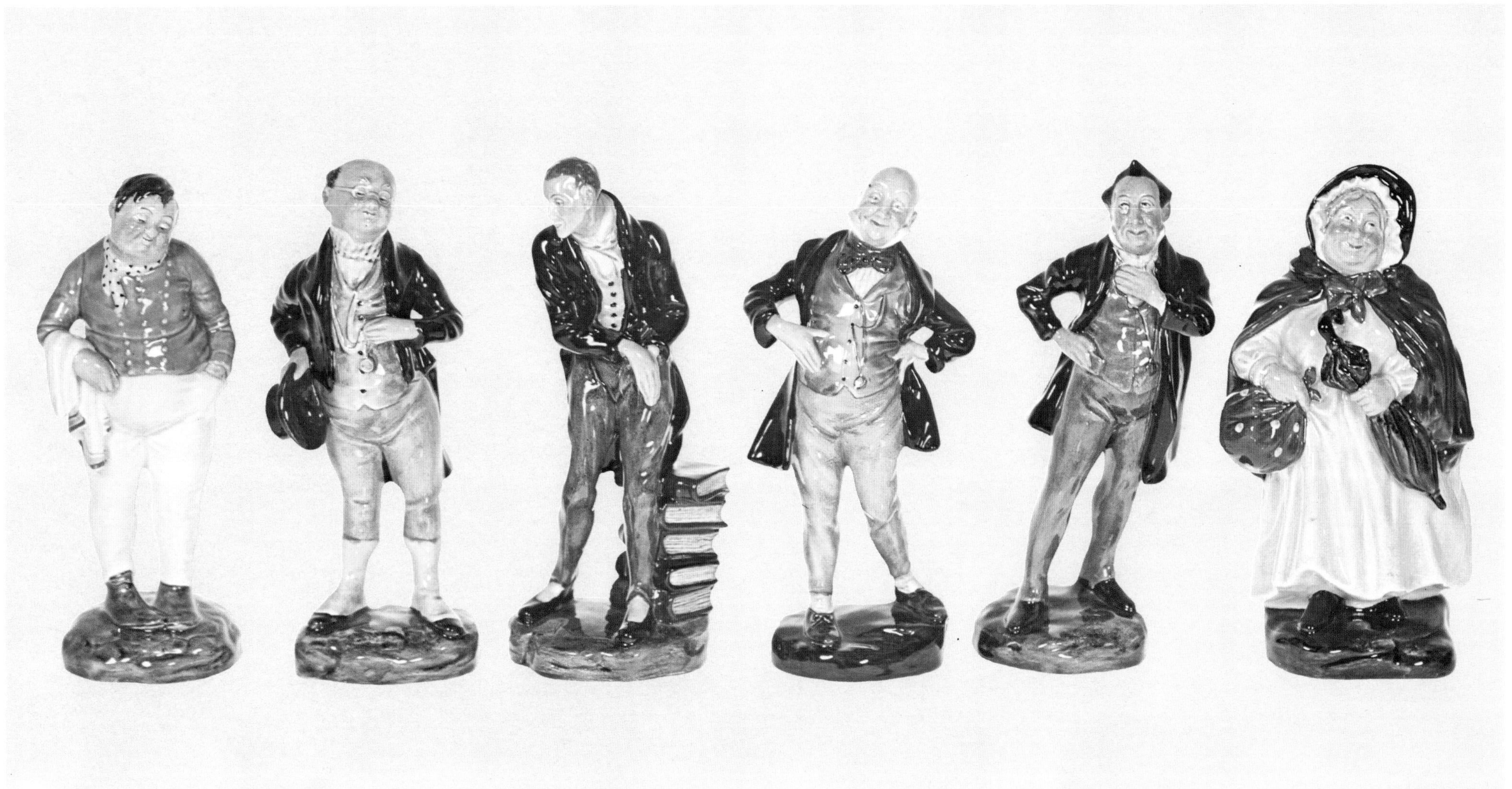

Dickens Figures (third version): HN 2096 Fat Boy, HN 2099 Mr Pickwick, HN 2101 Uriah Heep, HN 2097 Mr Micawber, HN 2098 Pecksniff, HN 2100 Sairey Gamp (illustration not in scale)

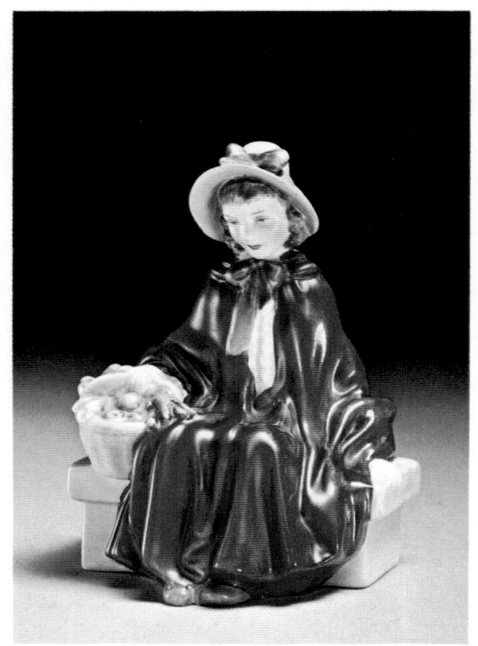

HN 2106 Linda

HN 2107 Valerie

HN 2108 Baby Bunting

HN 2109 Wendy

HN 2106 Linda
Designer: L. Harradine
Size: $4\frac{3}{4}$ in (12.0 cm)
Introduced: 1953
Withdrawn: 1976

HN 2107 Valerie
Designer: Margaret Davies
Size: 5 in (12.7 cm)
Introduced: 1953
Still in production

HN 2108 Baby Bunting
Designer: Margaret Davies
Size: $5\frac{1}{4}$ in (13.3 cm)
Introduced: 1953
Withdrawn: 1959

HN 2110 Christmas Time

HN 2102 Pied Piper
See page 171

HN 2103 Mask Seller
See page 199

HN 2104 Abdullah
See page 208

HN 2105 Bluebeard (second version, model 745)
See page 234

HN 2111 Betsy

HN 2112 Carolyn

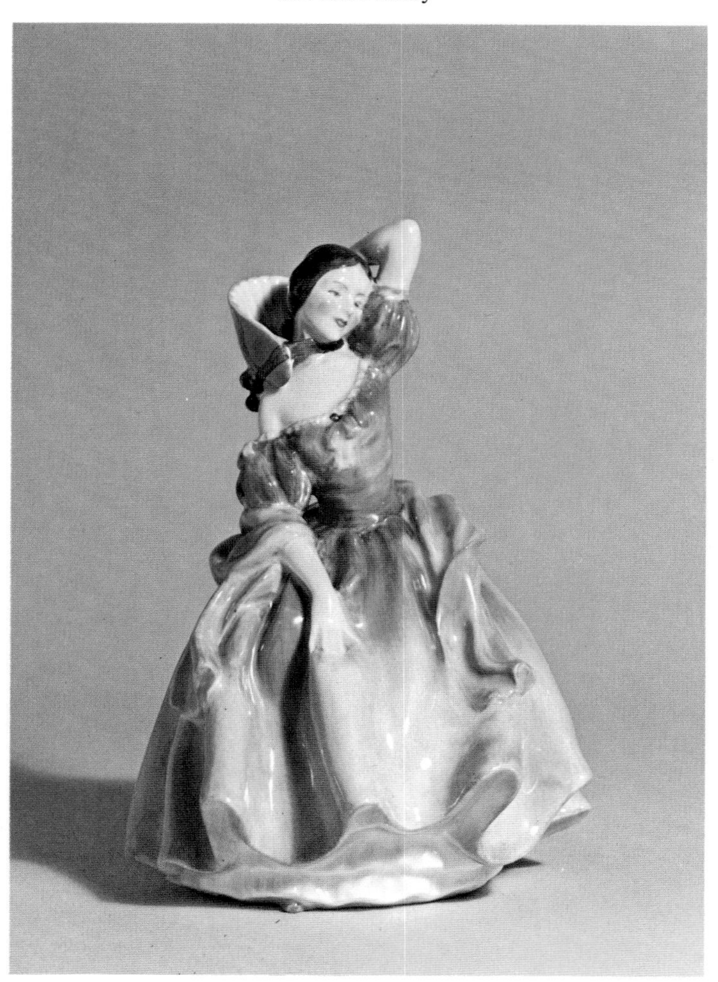

HN 2113 Maytime

HN 2109 Wendy
Designer: L. Harradine
Size: $4\frac{3}{4}$ in (12.0 cm)
Introduced: 1953
Still in production

HN 2110 Christmas Time
Designer: Margaret Davies
Size: 7 in (17.7 cm)
Introduced: 1953
Withdrawn: 1967

HN 2111 Betsy
Designer: L. Harradine
Size: 7 in (17.7 cm)
Introduced: 1953
Withdrawn: 1959

HN 2112 Carolyn
Designer: L. Harradine
Size: 7 in (17.7 cm)
Introduced: 1953
Withdrawn: 1965

HN 2113 Maytime
Designer: L. Harradine
Size: $6\frac{3}{4}$ in (17.1 cm)
Introduced: 1953
Withdrawn: 1967

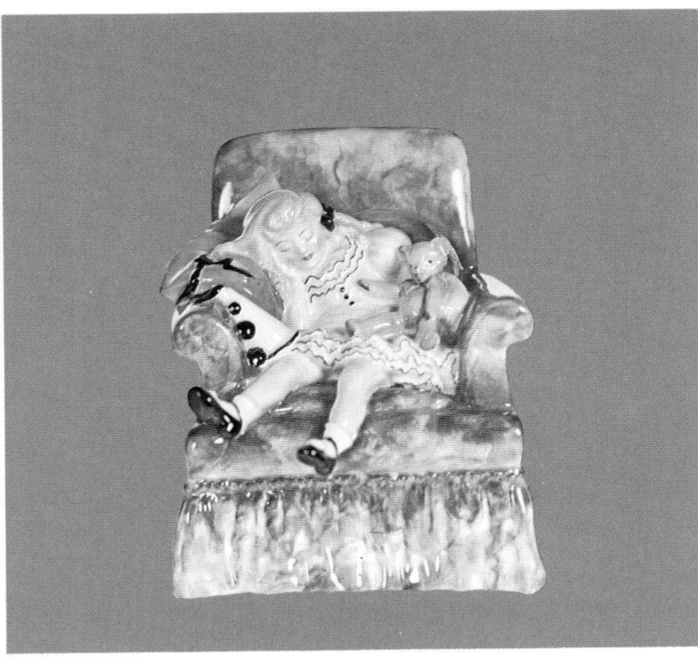

HN 2114 Sleepyhead

HN 2114 Sleepyhead
Designer: Margaret Davies
Size: $4\frac{3}{4}$ in (12.0 cm)
Introduced: 1953
Withdrawn: 1955

HN 2115 Coppelia
Designer: Margaret Davies
Size: $7\frac{1}{4}$ in (18.4 cm)
Introduced: 1953
Withdrawn: 1959
The first of a series of ballet figures, this model was inspired by the mechanical doll in Delibes' ballet, first performed in Paris in 1870. Created by Dr Coppelius, the doll is so life-like that his son Franz falls in love with it. To win Franz back, his jilted fiancé, Swanhilda, has to disguise herself as the doll, and destroy Dr Coppelius's magic books which contain the secrets of the doll.

HN 2116 Ballerina
Designer: Margaret Davies
Size: $7\frac{1}{2}$ in (19.0 cm)
Introduced: 1953
Withdrawn: 1973
This figure shows a ballerina in 'romantic' costume. Her red shoes and red hair suggest that the model may have been inspired by the part created in the film *The Red Shoes* by Moira Shearer.

HN 2117 The Skater
Designer: Margaret Davies
Size: 7 in (17.7 cm)
Introduced: 1953
Withdrawn: 1971

HN 2115 Coppelia

HN 2116 Ballerina

HN 2117 The Skater

HN 2118 Good King Wenceslas
Designer: Margaret Davies
Size: 9¼ in (23.4 cm)
Introduced: 1953
Withdrawn: 1976
The figure is based on the traditional Christmas Carol about King Wenceslas and the poor man.

HN 2119 Town Crier
Designer: Margaret Davies
Size: 8½ in (21.5 cm)
Introduced: 1953
Withdrawn: 1976

HN 2120-2121 Not issued

HN 2122 Yeoman of the Guard
See page 156

HN 2123–2127 Not issued

HN 2118 Good King Wenceslas

HN 2119 Town Crier

HN 2128 River Boy
Designer: Margaret Davies
Size: 4 in (10.1 cm)
Introduced: 1962
Withdrawn: 1975
The figure is based on Mark Twain's character, Huckleberry Finn.

HN 2128 River Boy

HN 2132 The Suitor

HN 2133 Faraway

HN 2129–2131 Not issued

HN 2132 The Suitor
Designer: Margaret Davies
Size: $7\frac{1}{4}$ in (18.4 cm)
Introduced: 1962
Withdrawn: 1971

HN 2133 Faraway
Designer: Margaret Davies
Size: $2\frac{1}{2}$ in (6.3 cm)
Introduced: 1958
Withdrawn: 1962
This model is the first of a small group of figures whose simplified styles, subdued colouring and easy grace are very expressive of the 1950s

The group of eight untypical and quite distinctive figures produced during the late 1950s

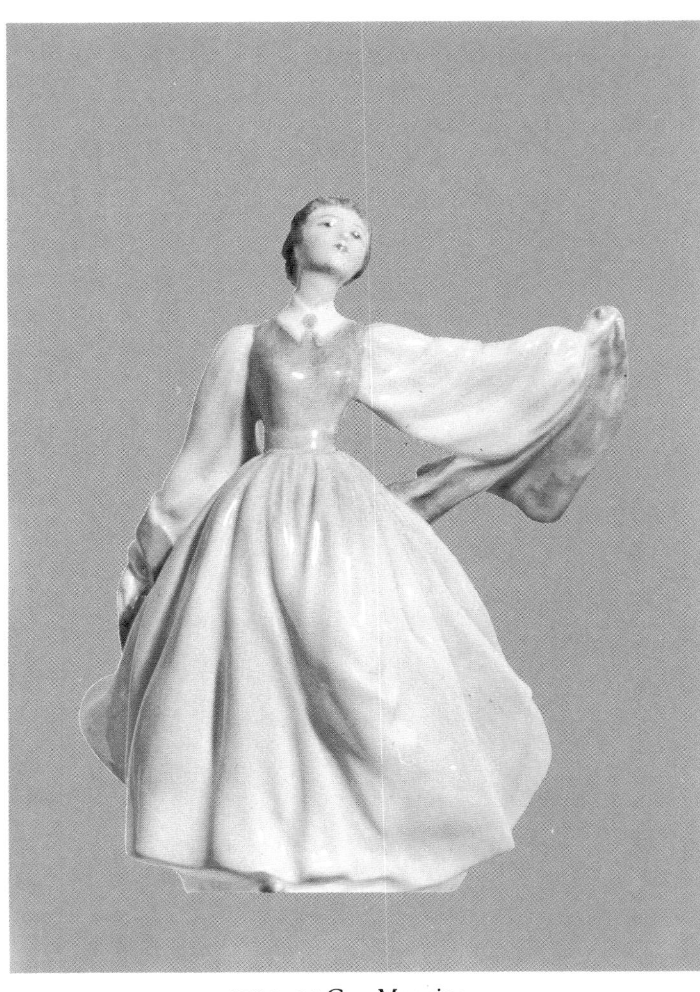

HN 2135 Gay Morning

HN 2134 An Old King
See page 111

HN 2135 Gay Morning
Designer: Margaret Davies
Size: 7 in (17.7 cm)
Introduced: 1954
Withdrawn: 1967

HN 2136 Delphine
Designer: Margaret Davies
Size: $7\frac{1}{4}$ in (18.4 cm)
Introduced: 1954
Withdrawn: 1967

HN 2137 Lilac Time
Designer: Margaret Davies
Size: $7\frac{1}{2}$ in (19.0 cm)
Introduced: 1954
Withdrawn: 1969

HN 2136 Delphine

HN 2137 Lilac Time

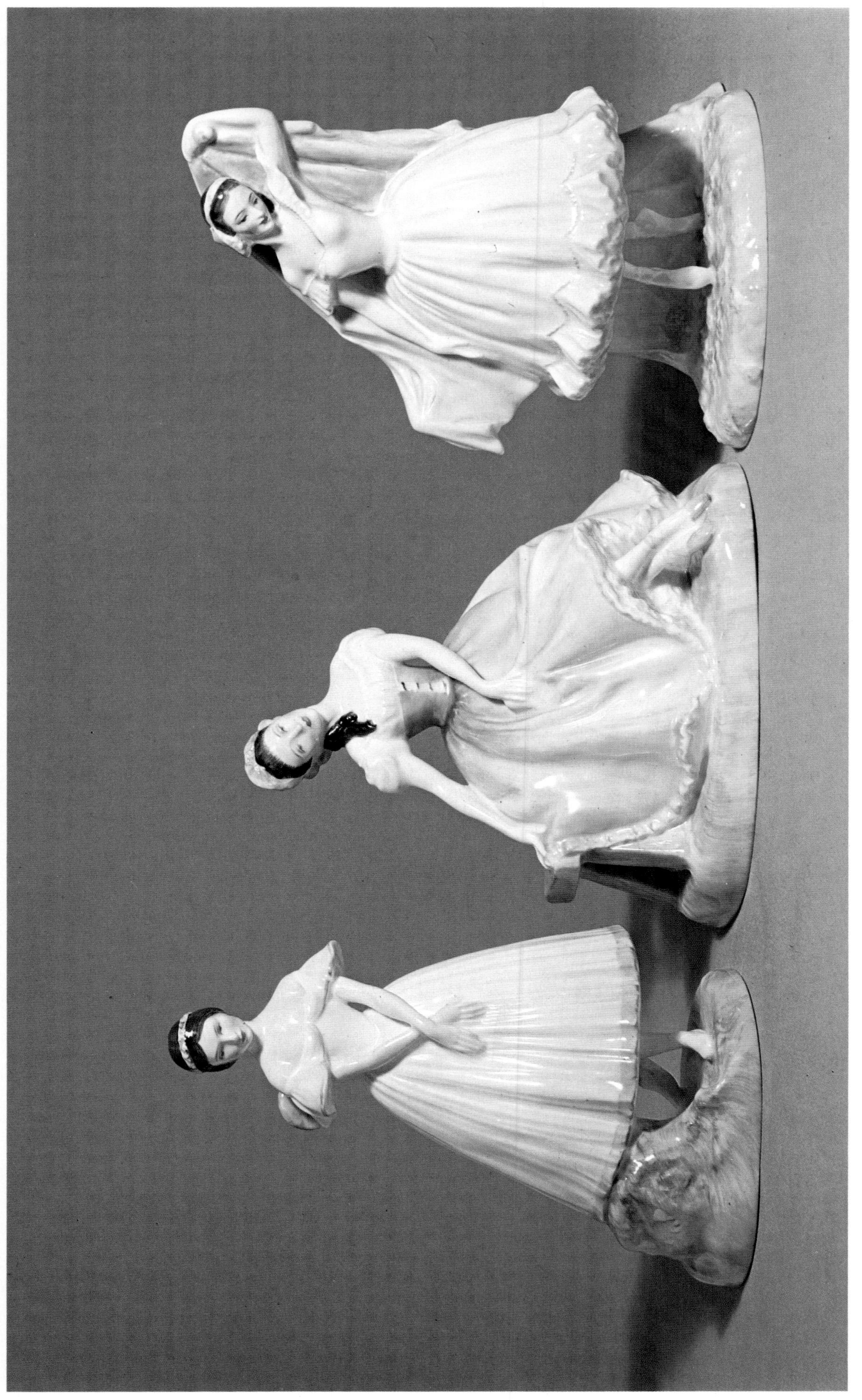

HN 2138 La Sylphide

HN 2139 Giselle

HN 2140 Giselle, The Forest Glade

HN 2141 Choir Boy HN 2142 Rag Doll

HN 2138 La Sylphide
Designer: Margaret Davies
Size: $7\frac{1}{4}$ in (18.4 cm)
Introduced: 1956
Withdrawn: 1965
This figure is from the popular and regularly performed ballet, *Les Sylphides*, a series of dances with music by Chopin.

HN 2139 Giselle
Designer: Margaret Davies
Size: $6\frac{1}{4}$ in (15.8 cm)
Introduced: 1954
Withdrawn: 1969
Giselle, a two-act ballet by Gautier, was first performed in 1841. It is based on the legend of the Wilis, maidens who have died before their wedding day, and who leave their graves at night to dance until dawn in bridal dress. The first figure represents Giselle, a village girl, in love and shortly to be married. She is betrayed and, driven mad, kills herself. The second figure shows her as a Wilis, dancing in her wedding veil.

HN 2140 Giselle, Forest Glade
Designer: Margaret Davies
Size: $7\frac{1}{4}$ in (18.4 cm)
Introduced: 1954
Withdrawn: 1965

HN 2141 Choir Boy
Designer: Margaret Davies
Size: 5 in (12.7 cm)
Introduced: 1954
Withdrawn: 1975

HN 2142 Rag Doll
Designer: Margaret Davies
Size: $4\frac{3}{4}$ in (12.0 cm)
Introduced: 1954
Still in production

HN 2143 Friar Tuck

HN 2144 The Jovial Monk

HN 2145 Wardrobe Mistress

HN 2146 The Tinsmith

HN 2143 Friar Tuck
Designer: Margaret Davies
Size: 8 in (20.3 cm)
Introduced: 1954
Withdrawn: 1965
Friar Tuck was the fat, jolly, pugnacious father confessor of Robin Hood and his robber band in Sherwood Forest, as willing to grab a sword as a tankard or a joint of beef.

HN 2144 The Jovial Monk
Designer: Margaret Davies
Size: 7¾ in (19.6 cm)
Introduced: 1954
Withdrawn: 1976

HN 2145 Wardrobe Mistress
Designer: Margaret Davies
Size: 5¾ in (14.6 cm)
Introduced: 1954
Withdrawn: 1967

HN 2146 The Tinsmith
Designer: M. Nicoll
Size: 6½ in (16.5 cm)
Introduced: 1962
Withdrawn: 1967

HN 2147 Autumn Breezes
See page 301

HN 2148 The Bridesmaid (second version, model 1481)
Designer: Margaret Davies
Size: 5½ in (13.9 cm)
Introduced: 1955
Withdrawn: 1959

HN 2149 Love Letter
Designer: Margaret Davies
Size: 5 in (12.7 cm)
Introduced: 1958
Withdrawn: 1976

HN 2150 Willy Won't He
See page 238

HN 2148 The Bridesmaid (second version)

HN 2149 Love Letter

HN 2151 Mother's Help

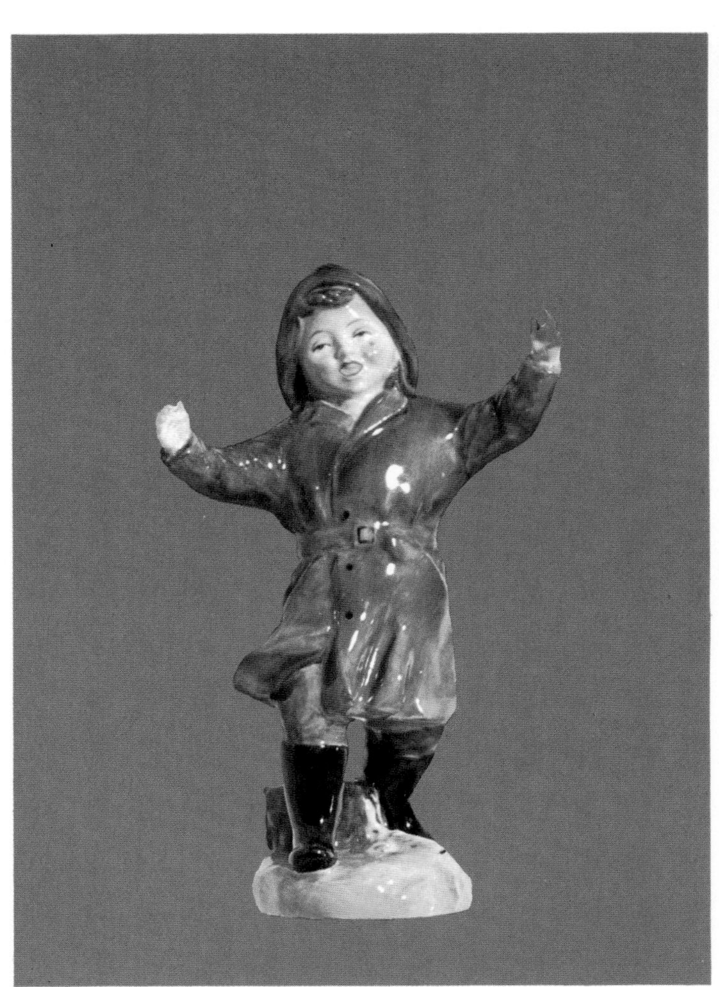

HN 2153 The One that Got Away

HN 2152 & HN 2304 Adrienne

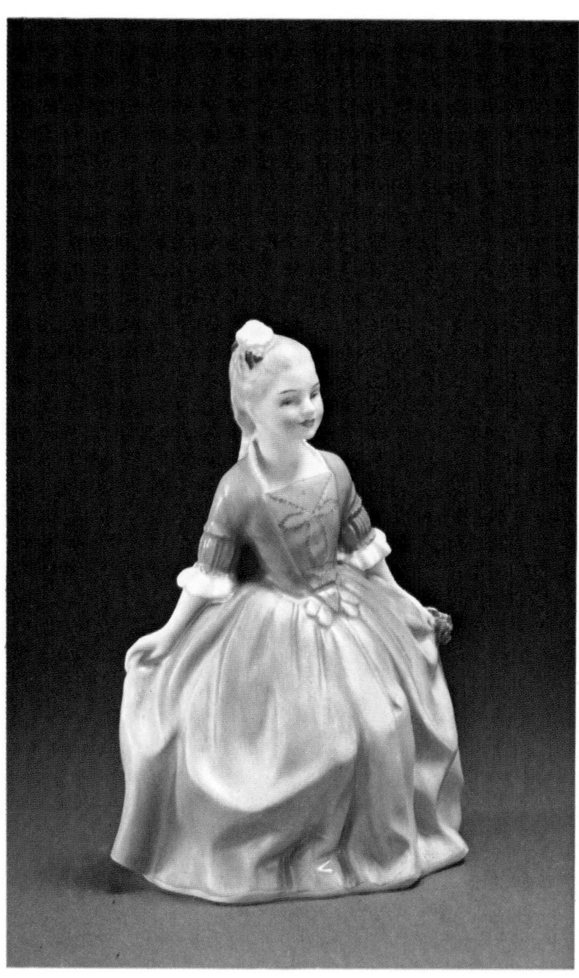

HN 2154 A Child from Williamsburg

HN 2151 Mother's Help
Designer: Margaret Davies
Size: 5 in (12.7 cm)
Introduced: 1962
Withdrawn: 1969

HN 2152 Adrienne
Designer: Margaret Davies
Size: 8 in (20.3 cm)
Introduced: 1964
Withdrawn: 1976

HN 2304 Adrienne
Introduced: 1964
Still in production

HN 2153 The One That Got Away
Designer: Margaret Davies
Size: 6½ in (16.5 cm)
Introduced: 1955
Withdrawn: 1959
The fisherman's tale of the one that got away is always the largest of all.

HN 2154 A Child from Williamsburg
Designer: Margaret Davies
Size: 5¾ in (14.6 cm)
Introduced: 1964
Still in production
Named in honour of King William III, eighteenth-century Williamsburg was the capital of Virginia, oldest of the British colonies in America. With a conception of planning and layout that was far-sighted, Williamsburg became the political, social, and cultural centre of the colony. When it ceased to be the seat of government in 1780, Williamsburg lost its position of eminence and fell into decay. Some years ago the decision was taken that this shrine of American character and tradition should be restored; that each of its buildings should be reconstructed and refurnished exactly in detail to the pleasing dignity of its eighteenth-century appearance.
Side by side with the physical restoration is the re-creation of the spirit of old Williamsburg; costumed craftsmen ply the trades of two hundred years ago in the manner of their worthy forebears. Today the Foundation includes 211 exhibition rooms, 36 craft shops, 3 hotels and 7 restaurants, staffed by over 600, all in colonial costume.
It was with pride that Royal Doulton introduced these eighteenth-century personalities as "Figures of Williamsburg", as a tribute to American history and culture. Their authenticity is vouched for in the approval given by The Colonial Williamsburg Foundation.

HN 2155 Not issued

HN 2156 The Polka

HN 2156 The Polka
Designer: Margaret Davies
Size: 7½ in (19.0 cm)
Introduced: 1955
Withdrawn: 1969
Originally a Bohemian dance, the polka spread across Europe during the 19th century, achieving extraordinary popularity. It featured frequently in ballets of the period.

HN 2157 A Gypsy Dance (first version, model 1492)
Designer: Margaret Davies
Size: 7 in (17.7 cm)
Introduced: 1955
Withdrawn: 1957
This figure, expressing the wild dancing of gypsy girls, was probably inspired by the film *The Barefoot Contessa*, which starred Ava Gardner and was first shown in 1953.

HN 2230 A Gypsy Dance (second version)

HN 2157 A Gypsy Dance (first version)

HN 2158 Alice

HN 2158 Alice
Designer: Margaret Davies
Size: 5 in (12.7 cm)
Introduced: 1960
Still in production

HN 2159 Fortune Teller
Designer: L. Harradine
Size: 6½ in (16.5 cm)
Introduced: 1955
Withdrawn: 1967

HN 2160 The Apple Maid
Designer: L. Harradine
Size: 6½ in (16.5 cm)
Introduced: 1957
Withdrawn: 1962

HN 2159 Fortune Teller

HN 2160 The Apple Maid

HN 2161 The Hornpipe

HN 2162 The Foaming Quart

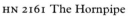

HN 2163 In the Stocks (second version)

HN 2166 The Bride (second version)

HN 2161 The Hornpipe
Designer: M. Nicoll
Size: 9¼ in (23.4 cm)
Introduced: 1955
Withdrawn: 1962

HN 2162 The Foaming Quart
Designer: Margaret Davies
Size: 6¼ in (15.8 cm)
Introduced: 1955
Still in production

HN 2163 In the Stocks (second version, model 1502)
Designer: M. Nicoll
Size: 6 in (15.2 cm)
Introduced: 1955
Withdrawn: 1959

HN 2164 Not issued

HN 2165 Janice
See page

HN 2166 The Bride (second version, model 1553)
Designer: Margaret Davies
Size: 8¼ in (20.9 cm)
Introduced: 1956
Withdrawn: 1976

HN 2167 Home Again
Designer: Margaret Davies
Size: 3½ in (8.9 cm)
Introduced: 1956
Still in production

HN 2168 Esmeralda
Designer: Margaret Davies
Size: 5¾ in (14.6 cm)
Introduced: 1956
Withdrawn: 1959

HN 2169 Dimity
Designer: L. Harradine
Size: 5¾ in (14.6 cm)
Introduced: 1956
Withdrawn: 1959

HN 2167 Home Again

HN 2169 Dimity HN 2168 Esmeralda

HN 2170 Invitation

HN 2171 The Fiddler

HN 2172 Jolly Sailor

HN 2173 The Organ Grinder

HN 2174 The Tailor

HN 2175 The Beggar (second version)

HN 2170 Invitation
Designer: Margaret Davies
Size: 5½ in (13.9 cm)
Introduced: 1956
Withdrawn: 1975

HN 2171 The Fiddler
Designer: M. Nicoll
Size: 8½ in (21.5 cm)
Introduced: 1956
Withdrawn: 1962

HN 2172 Jolly Sailor
Designer: M. Nicoll
Size: 6½ in (16.5 cm)
Introduced: 1956
Withdrawn: 1965

HN 2173 The Organ Grinder
Designer: M. Nicoll
Size: 8¾ in (22.2 cm)
Introduced: 1956
Withdrawn: 1965

HN 2174 The Tailor
Designer: M. Nicoll
Size: 4 in (10.1 cm)
Introduced: 1956
Withdrawn: 1959

HN 2175 The Beggar (second version, model 1574)
Designer: L. Harradine
Size: 7 in (17.7 cm)
Introduced: 1956
Withdrawn: 1962
This figure is an adapted version of HN 526, one of *The Beggar's Opera* characters.

HN 2176 Not issued

HN 2177 My Teddy
Designer: Margaret Davies
Size: 3¼ in (8.3 cm)
Introduced: 1962
Withdrawn: 1967
The teddy bear first appeared in 1903, inspired by a cartoon of President 'Teddy' Roosevelt, and rapidly achieved great popularity.
Bears have featured in many books and songs, including *Winnie the Pooh* and *The Teddy Bears' Picnic.*

HN 2177 My Teddy

HN 2178 Enchantment
Designer: Margaret Davies
Size: 8 in (20.3 cm)
Introduced: 1957
Still in production

HN 2179 Noelle
Designer: Margaret Davies
Size: 6¾ in (17.1 cm)
Introduced: 1957
Withdrawn: 1967

HN 2180 Not issued

HN 2181 Summer's Day
Designer: Margaret Davies
Size: 6 in (15.2 cm)
Introduced: 1957
Withdrawn: 1962
Probably inspired by Shakespeare's sonnet, 'Shall I compare thee to a summer's day? Thou art more lovely and more temperate . . .'

HN 2182 Not issued

HN 2183 Boy from Williamsburg
Designer: Margaret Davies
Size: 5½ in (13.9 cm)
Introduced: 1969
Still in production

HN 2184 Sunday Morning
Designer: Margaret Davies
Size: 7½ in (19.0 cm)
Introduced: 1963
Withdrawn: 1969

HN 2178 Enchantment

HN 2179 Noelle

HN 2181 Summer's Day

HN 2183 Boy from Williamsburg

HN 2184 Sunday Morning

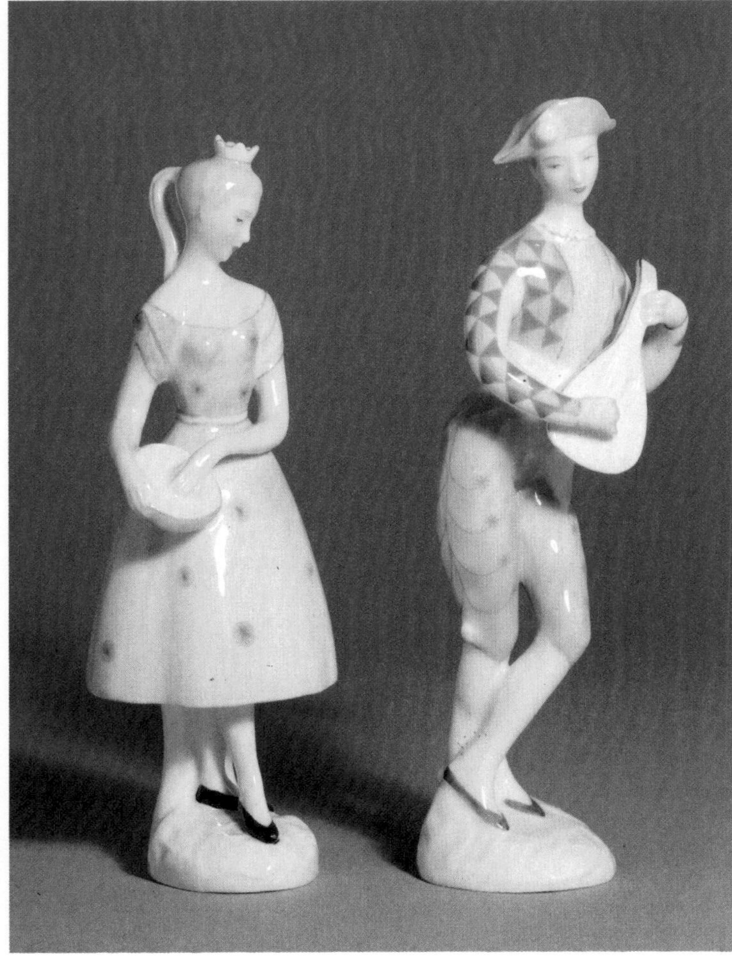

HN 2185 Columbine & HN 2186 Harlequin

HN 2185 Columbine (second version, model 1589)
Designer: Margaret Davies
Size: $7\frac{1}{4}$ in (18.4 cm)
Introduced: 1957
Withdrawn: 1969

HN 2186 Harlequin
Designer: Margaret Davies
Size: $7\frac{1}{2}$ in (19.0 cm)
Introduced: 1957
Withdrawn: 1969

HN 2187–2190 Not issued

HN 2191 Sea Sprite (second version, model 1595)
Designer: Margaret Davies
Size: $7\frac{1}{4}$ in (18.4 cm)
Introduced: 1958
Withdrawn: 1962

HN 2192 Wood Nymph
Designer: Margaret Davies
Size: $7\frac{1}{2}$ in (19.0 cm)
Introduced: 1958
Withdrawn: 1962

HN 2191 Sea Sprite & HN 2192 Wood Nymph

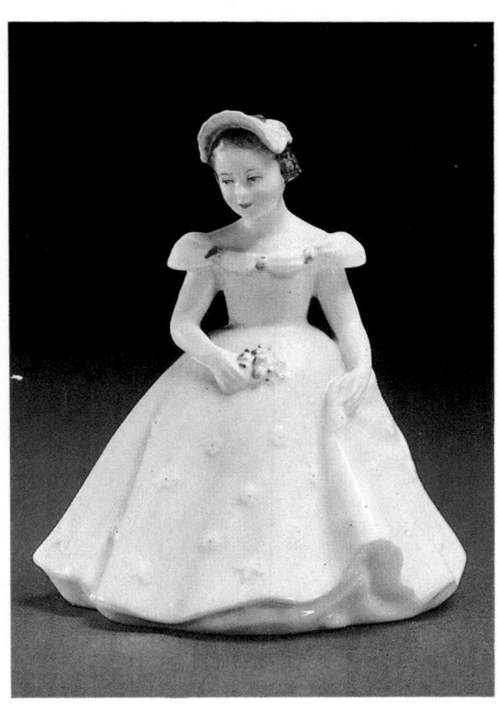

HN 2196 The Bridesmaid (second version)

HN 2193 Fair Lady

HN 2832 Fair Lady

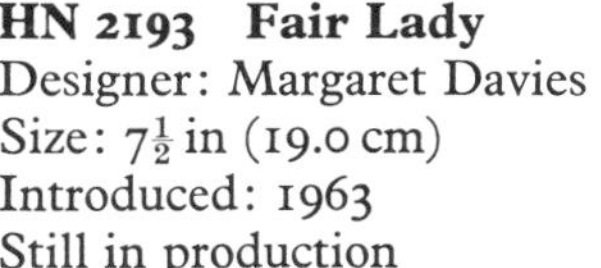

HN 2193 Fair Lady
Designer: Margaret Davies
Size: 7½ in (19.0 cm)
Introduced: 1963
Still in production
Perhaps inspired by the musical *My Fair Lady*, based on G. B. Shaw's *Pygmalion*, which opened in London in 1959, starring Julie Andrews. The film version was first shown in 1964.

HN 2832 Fair Lady
Introduced: 1977
Still in production

HN 2835 Fair Lady
Introduced: 1977
Still in production

HN 2194–2195 Not issued

HN 2196 The Bridesmaid (third version, model 1681)
Designer: Margaret Davies
Size: 5 in (12.7 cm)
Introduced: 1960
Withdrawn: 1976

HN 2197–2201 Not issued

HN 2835 Fair Lady

HN 2202 Melody

HN 2203 Teenager

HN 2204 Long John Silver

HN 2205 Master Sweep

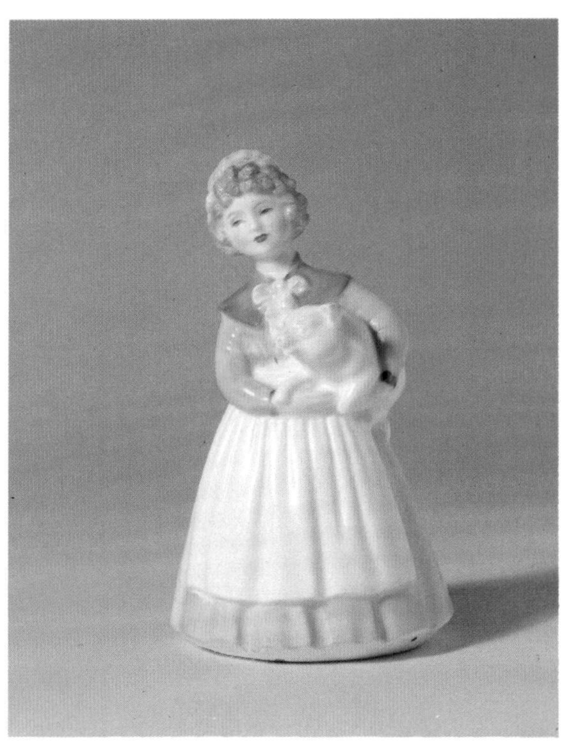

HN 2207 Stayed at Home

HN 2208 Silversmith of Williamsburg

HN 2202 Melody
Designer: Margaret Davies
Size: $6\frac{1}{4}$ in (15.8 cm)
Introduced: 1957
Withdrawn: 1962

HN 2203 Teenager
Designer: Margaret Davies
Size: $7\frac{1}{4}$ in (18.4 cm)
Introduced: 1957
Withdrawn: 1962

HN 2204 Long John Silver
Designer: M. Nicoll
Size: 9 in (22.8 cm)
Introduced: 1957
Withdrawn: 1965
Long John Silver, with his wooden leg and his parrot, Capt. Flint, is the romantic pirate in R. L. Stevenson's *Treasure Island.*

HN 2205 Master Sweep
Designer: M. Nicoll
Size: $8\frac{1}{2}$ in (21.5 cm)
Introduced: 1957
Withdrawn: 1962
Probably inspired by the boy sweeps in Charles Kingsley's *The Water Babies*, who, driven on by their master Mr Grimes, spent their lives climbing up the twisted, blackened chimneys to sweep them clean.

HN 2206 Not issued

HN 2207 Stayed at Home
Designer: Margaret Davies
Size: 5 in (12.7 cm)
Introduced: 1958
Withdrawn: 1969

HN 2208 Silversmith of Williamsburg
Designer: Margaret Davies
Size: $6\frac{1}{4}$ in (15.8 cm)
Introduced: 1960
Still in production

HN 2209 Hostess of Williamsburg

HN 2212 Rendezvous

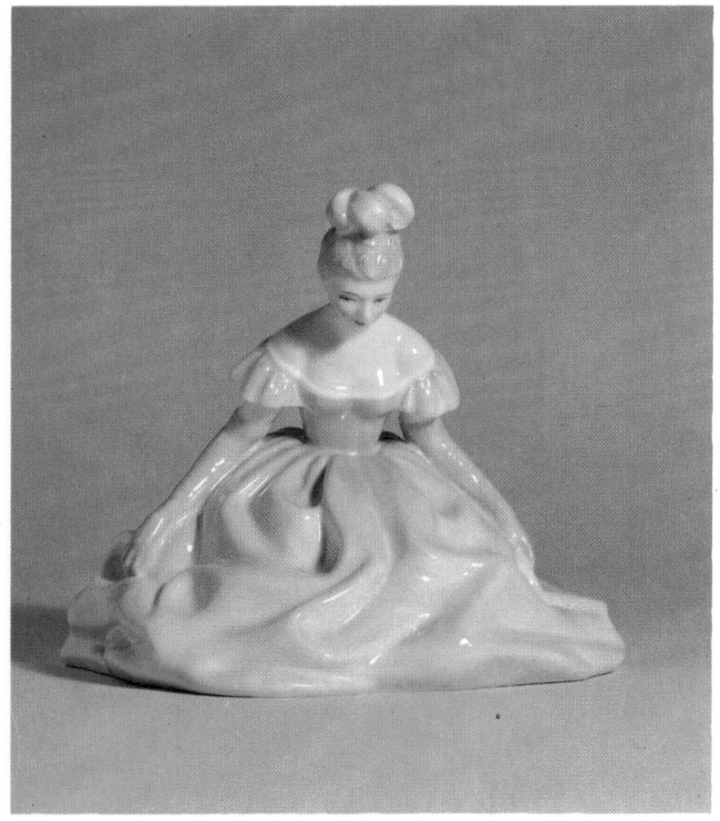

HN 2210 Debutante

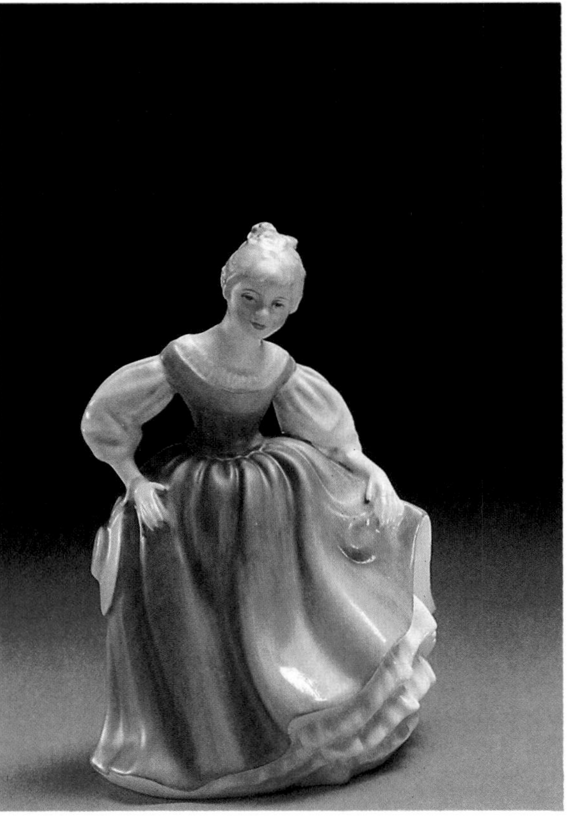

HN 2211 Fair Maiden

HN 2214 Bunny

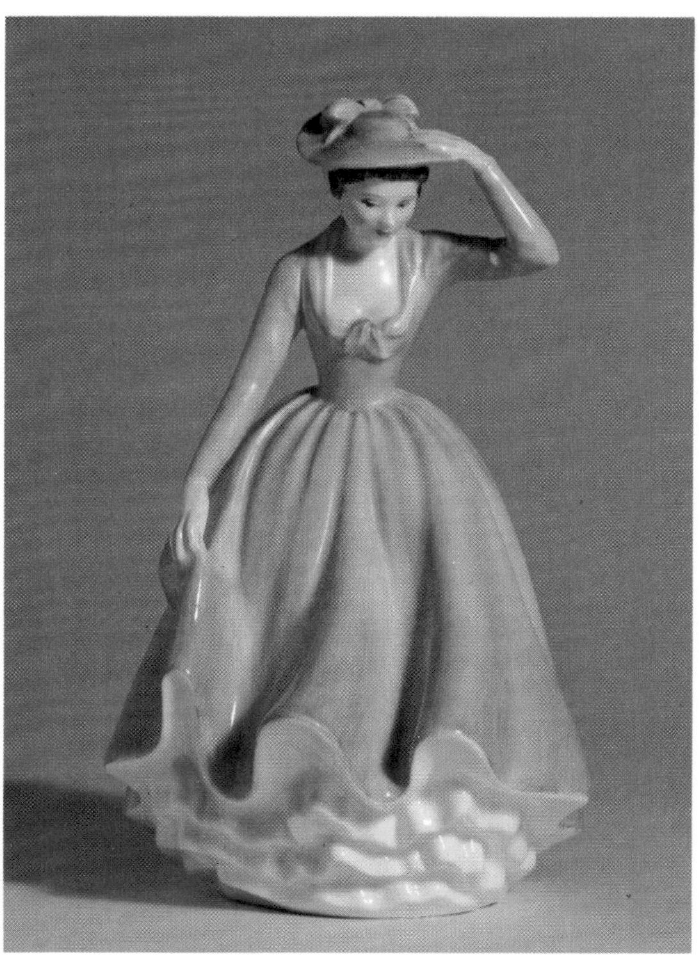

HN 2215 Sweet April

HN 2209 Hostess of Williamsburg
Designer: Margaret Davies
Size: 7¼ in (18.4 cm)
Introduced: 1960
Still in production

HN 2210 Debutante
Designer: Margaret Davies
Size: 5 in (12.7 cm)
Introduced: 1963
Withdrawn: 1967
The debutante is the traditional title for a girl appearing for the first time in Society, usually launched by her parents during the Season. At one time debutantes were presented to the Queen each year, but this custom has recently been given up.

HN 2211 Fair Maiden
Designer: Margaret Davies
Size: 5¼ in (13.3 cm)
Introduced: 1967
Still in production

HN 2212 Rendezvous
Designer: Margaret Davies
Size: 7¼ in (18.4 cm)
Introduced: 1962
Withdrawn: 1971

HN 2213 Not issued

HN 2214 Bunny
Designer: Margaret Davies
Size: 5 in (12.7 cm)
Introduced: 1960
Withdrawn: 1975

HN 2215 Sweet April
Designer: Margaret Davies
Size: 7½ in (19.0 cm)
Introduced: 1965
Withdrawn: 1967

HN 2216 Pirouette

HN 2217 Old King Cole

HN 2218 Cookie

HN 2220 Winsome

HN 2216 Pirouette
Designer: Margaret Davies
Size: 5¾ in (14.6 cm)
Introduced: 1959
Withdrawn: 1967

HN 2217 Old King Cole
Designer: Margaret Davies
Size: 6¾ in (17.1 cm)
Introduced: 1963
Withdrawn: 1967
Named after the traditional nursery rhyme about Old King Cole, who called for his pipe, his bowl and his fiddlers three.

HN 2218 Cookie
Designer: Margaret Davies
Size: 4¾ in (12.0 cm)
Introduced: 1958
Withdrawn: 1975

HN 2219 Not issued

HN 2220 Winsome
Designer: Margaret Davies
Size: 8 in (20.3 cm)
Introduced: 1960
Still in production

HN 2221 Nanny
Designer: Margaret Davies
Size: 6¼ in (15.8 cm)
Introduced: 1958
Still in production

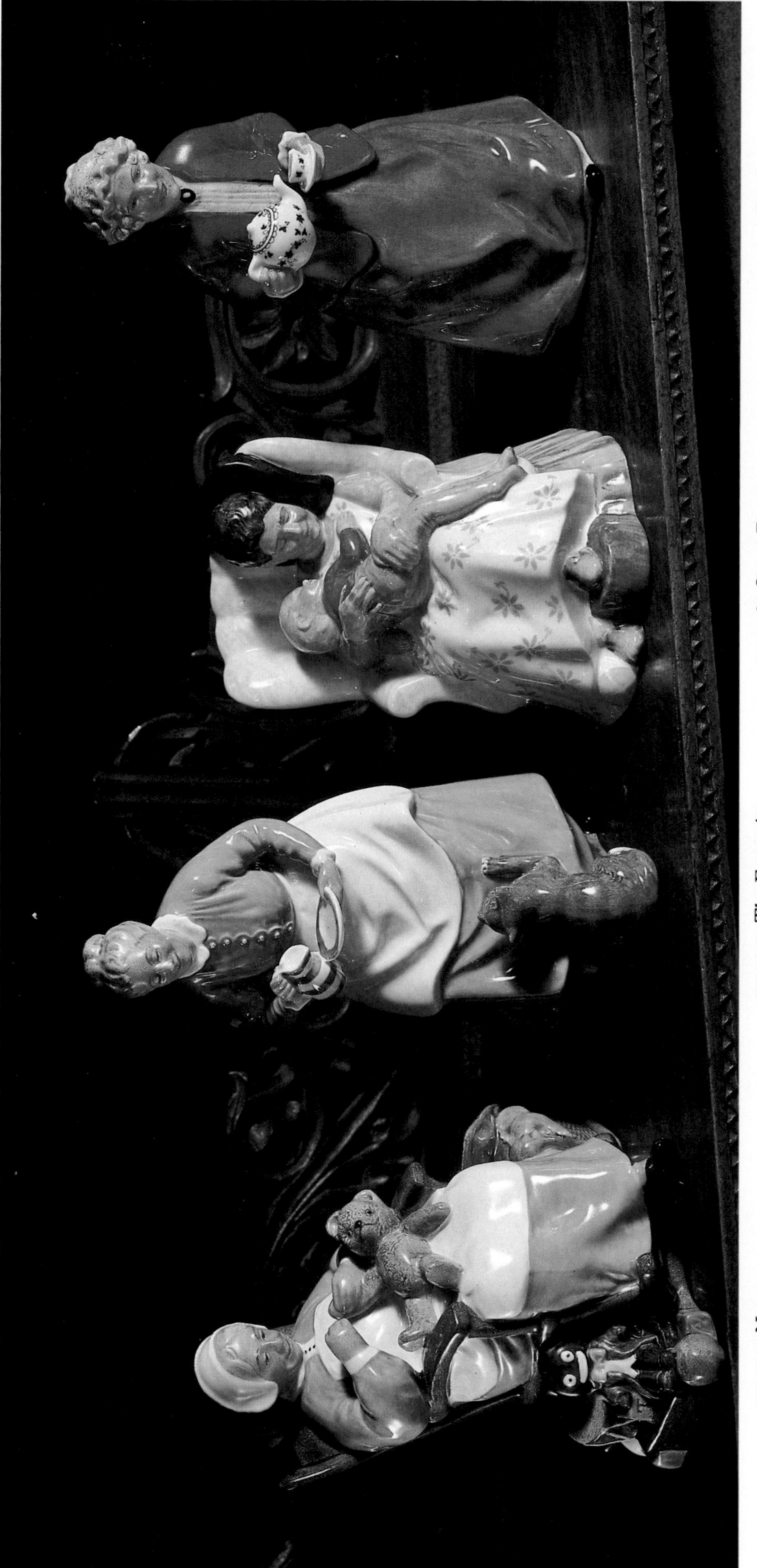

HN 2221 Nanny HN 2249 The Favourite HN 2380 Sweet Dreams HN 2255 Teatime

HN 2222 Camellia

HN 2223 Schoolmarm

HN 2225 Make Believe

HN 2226 The Cellist

HN 2222 Camellia
Designer: Margaret Davies
Size: 7¾ in (19.6 cm)
Introduced: 1960
Withdrawn: 1971

HN 2223 Schoolmarm
Designer: Margaret Davies
Size: 7 in (17.7 cm)
Introduced: 1958
Still in production

HN 2224 Not issued

HN 2225 Make Believe
Designer: M. Nicoll
Size: 5¾ in (14.6 cm)
Introduced: 1962
Still in production

HN 2226 The Cellist
Designer: Margaret Davies
Size: 8¼ in (20.9 cm)
Introduced: 1960
Withdrawn: 1967

HN 2227 Gentleman from Williamsburg
Designer: Margaret Davies
Size: 6¼ in (15.8 cm)
Introduced: 1960
Still in production

HN 2228 Lady from Williamsburg
Designer: Margaret Davies
Size: 6 in (15.5 cm)
Introduced: 1960
Still in production

HN 2229 Southern Belle
Designer: Margaret Davies
Size: 7½ in (19.0 cm)
Introduced: 1958
Still in production

HN 2230 A Gypsy Dance (second version, model 1671)
Designer: Margaret Davies
Size: 7 in (17.7 cm)
Introduced: 1959
Withdrawn: 1971
For illustration, see page 352

HN 2227 Gentleman from Williamsburg

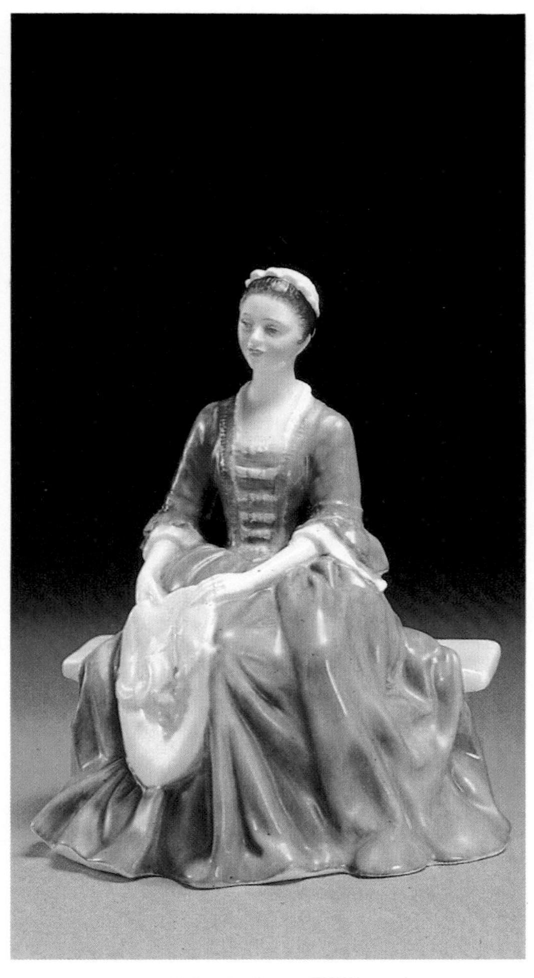
HN 2228 Lady from Williamsburg

HN 2229 Southern Belle

HN 2231 Sweet Sixteen

HN 2233 Royal Governor's Cook

HN 2234 Michelle

HN 2235 Dancing Years

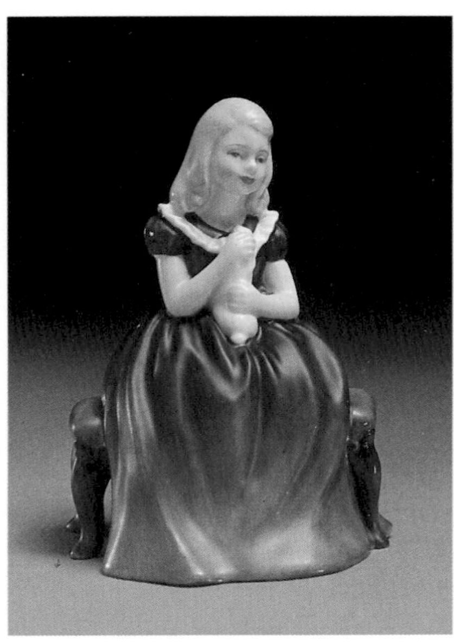

HN 2236 Affection

HN 2231 Sweet Sixteen
Designer: Margaret Davies
Size: 7¼ in (18.4 cm)
Introduced: 1958
Withdrawn: 1965
Sweet Sixteen has been the title of many songs, films and musicals, but is best known in the phrase, 'sweet sixteen and never been kissed.'

HN 2232 Not issued

HN 2233 Royal Governor's Cook
Designer: Margaret Davies
Size: 6 in (15.2 cm)
Introduced: 1960
Still in production

HN 2234 Michelle
Designer: Margaret Davies
Size: 6¾ in (17.1 cm)
Introduced: 1967
Still in production
This figure probably takes its name from the popular song *Michelle*, recorded by the Beatles in 1967

HN 2235 Dancing Years
Designer: Margaret Davies
Size: 7 in (17.7 cm)
Introduced: 1965
Withdrawn: 1971
Dancing Years, a musical comedy by Ivor Novello, was first performed in 1939. Set in the carefree Vienna of the 1930s, the play was a popular escapist success during the Second World War

HN 2237 Celeste

HN 2236 Affection
Designer: Margaret Davies
Size: 4½ in (11.4 cm)
Introduced: 1962
Still in production

HN 2237 Celeste
Designer: Margaret Davies
Size: 7 in (17.7 cm)
Introduced: 1959
Withdrawn: 1971

HN 2238 My Pet
Designer: Margaret Davies
Size: 3 in (7.6 cm)
Introduced: 1962
Withdrawn: 1975

HN 2238 My Pet

HN 2239 Wigmaker of Williamsburg

HN 2240 Blacksmith of Williamsburg

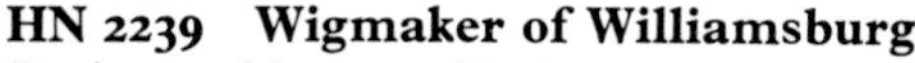

HN 2239 Wigmaker of Williamsburg
Designer: Margaret Davies
Size: $7\frac{1}{2}$ in (19.0 cm)
Introduced: 1960
Still in production

HN 2240 Blacksmith of Williamsburg
Designer: Margaret Davies
Size: 7 in (17.7 cm)
Introduced: 1960
Still in production

HN 2241 Not issued

HN 2242 First Steps
Designer: Margaret Davies
Size: $6\frac{3}{4}$ in (17.1 cm)
Introduced: 1959
Withdrawn: 1965

HN 2243 Treasure Island
Designer: Margaret Davies
Size: 5 in (12.7 cm)
Introduced: 1962
Withdrawn: 1975
Treasure Island, the pirate romance by R. L. Stevenson, was first published in 1883. Since then it has remained a firm favourite, and has frequently been adapted for screen and stage.

HN 2242 First Steps

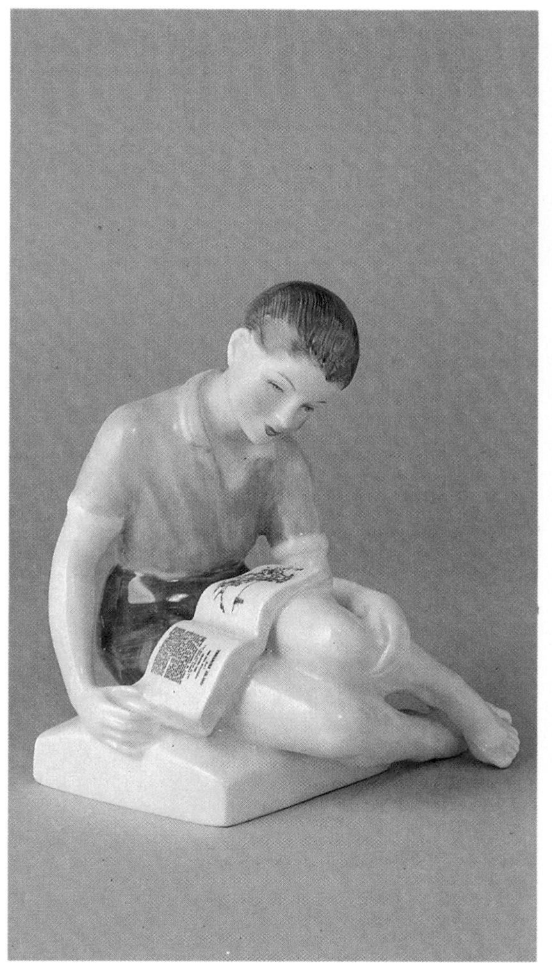

HN 2243 Treasure Island

HN 2244 Newsboy

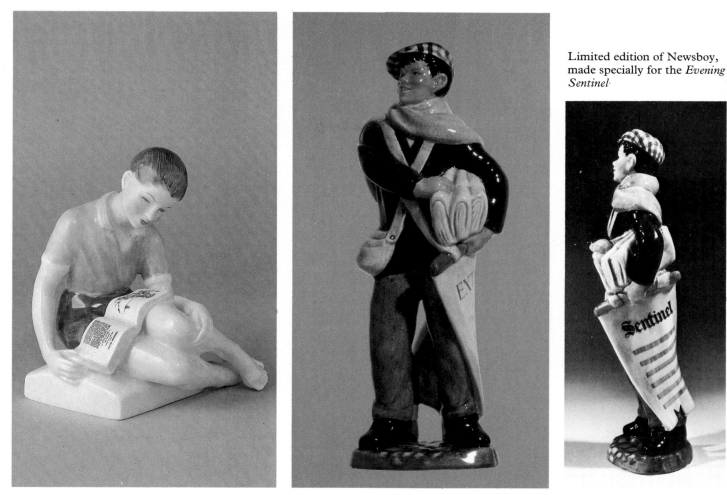

Limited edition of Newsboy, made specially for the *Evening Sentinel*

HN 2245 The Basket Weaver

HN 2246 Cradle Song

HN 2244 Newsboy
Designer: Margaret Davies
Size: $8\frac{1}{2}$ in (21.5 cm)
Introduced: 1959
Withdrawn: 1965
A limited edition of 250 was also produced for Stoke-on-Trent's local paper, *The Evening Sentinel;* these figures had the word *Sentinel* printed on the newsboy's placard.

HN 2245 The Basket Weaver
Designer: M. Nicoll
Size: $6\frac{1}{4}$ in (15.8 cm)
Introduced: 1959
Withdrawn: 1962

HN 2246 Cradle Song
Designer: Margaret Davies
Size: $5\frac{1}{2}$ in (13.9 cm)
Introduced: 1959
Withdrawn: 1962

HN 2247 Omar Khayyam (second version)

HN 2248 Tall Story

HN 2250 The Toymaker

HN 2253 The Puppetmaker

HN 2251 & HN 2259 Masquerade (second version)

HN 2247 Omar Khayyam (second version, model 1870)
Designer: M. Nicoll
Size: 6½ in (16.5 cm)
Introduced: 1965
Still in production

HN 2248 Tall Story
Designer: M. Nicoll
Size: 6¼ in (15.8 cm)
Introduced: 1968
Withdrawn: 1975
This figure is the first of a series of distinctive sea subjects, modelled by Mary Nicoll, which represented a new theme for Doulton figures. Many of the later models are still in production.

HN 2249 The Favourite
Designer: M. Nicoll
Size: 7¾ in (19.6 cm)
Introduced: 1960
Still in production
For illustration, see page 367

HN 2250 The Toymaker
Designer: M. Nicoll
Size: 6 in (15.2 cm)
Introduced: 1959
Withdrawn: 1973

HN 2251 Masquerade (second version, model 1690)
Designer: Margaret Davies
Size: 8½ in (21.5 cm)
Introduced: 1960
Withdrawn: 1965

HN 2259 Masquerade (second version, model 1690)
Introduced: 1960
Withdrawn: 1965

HN 2252 Not issued

HN 2253 The Puppetmaker
Designer: M. Nicoll
Size: 8¼ in (20.9 cm)
Introduced: 1962
Withdrawn: 1973

HN 2254 Shore Leave
Designer: M. Nicoll
Size: 8¼ in (20.9 cm)
Introduced: 1965
Still in production
For illustration, see next page

HN 2255 Teatime
Designer: M. Nicoll
Size: 7½ in (19.0 cm)
Introduced: 1972
Still in production
For illustration, see page 367

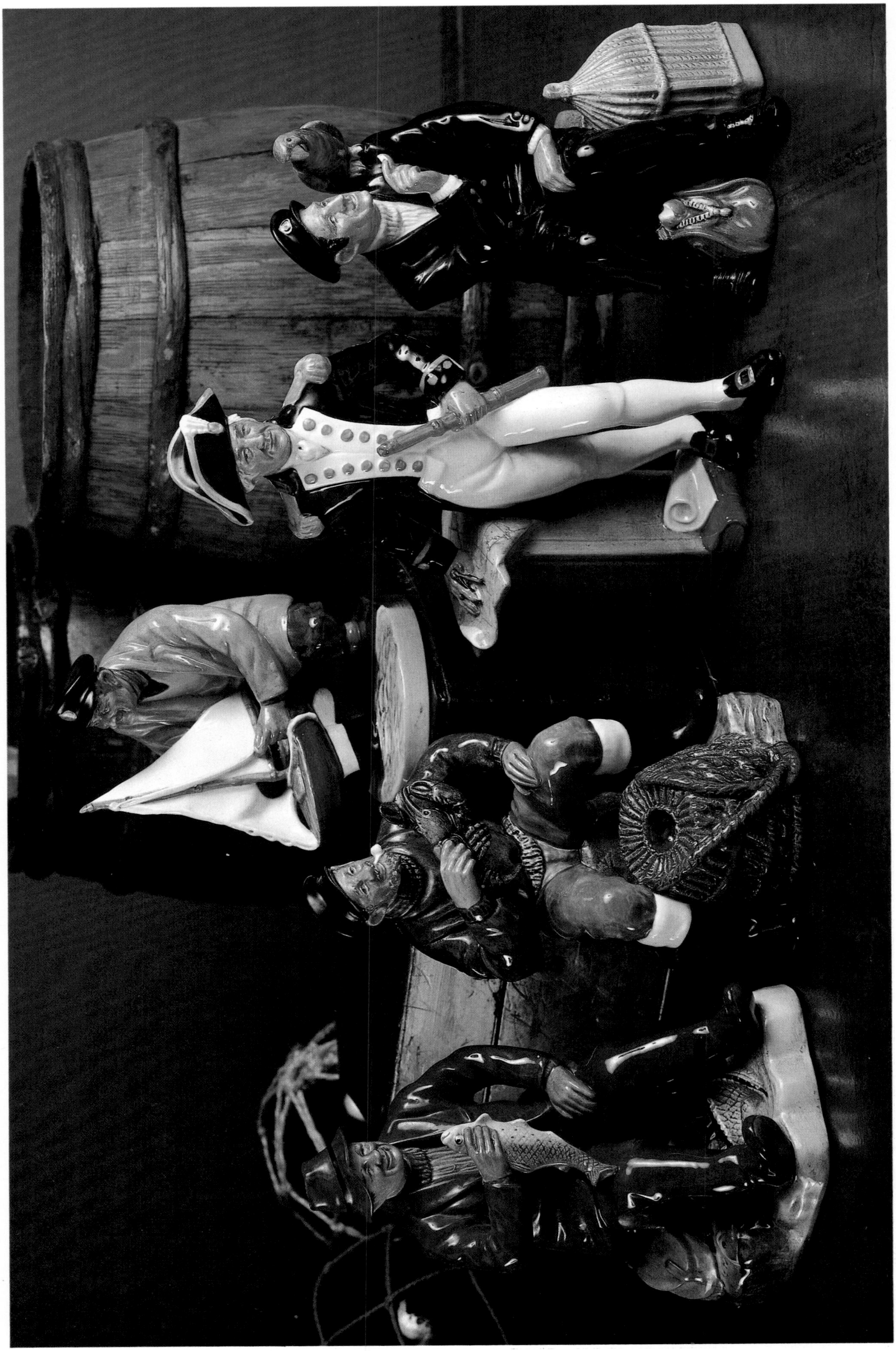

HN 2258 A Good Catch HN 2317 The Lobster Man HN 2442 Sailor's Holiday HN 2260 The Captain (second version) HN 2254 Shore Leave

HN 2256 Twilight

HN 2257 Sea Harvest

HN 2256 Twilight
Designer: M. Nicoll
Size: 5 in (12.7 cm)
Introduced: 1971
Withdrawn: 1976

HN 2257 Sea Harvest
Designer: M. Nicoll
Size: $7\frac{3}{4}$ in (19.6 cm)
Introduced: 1969
Withdrawn: 1976

HN 2258 A Good Catch
Designer: M. Nicoll
Size: $7\frac{1}{4}$ in (18.4 cm)
Introduced: 1966
Still in production

HN 2259 Masquerade (second version, model 1690)
See page 375

HN 2260 The Captain (second version, model 1887)
Designer: M. Nicoll
Size: $9\frac{1}{2}$ in (24.1 cm)
Introduced: 1965
Still in production
From the uniform, this figure would appear to date from the 18th century, the period of British naval dominance of the high seas; however, it does not seem to represent any actual character

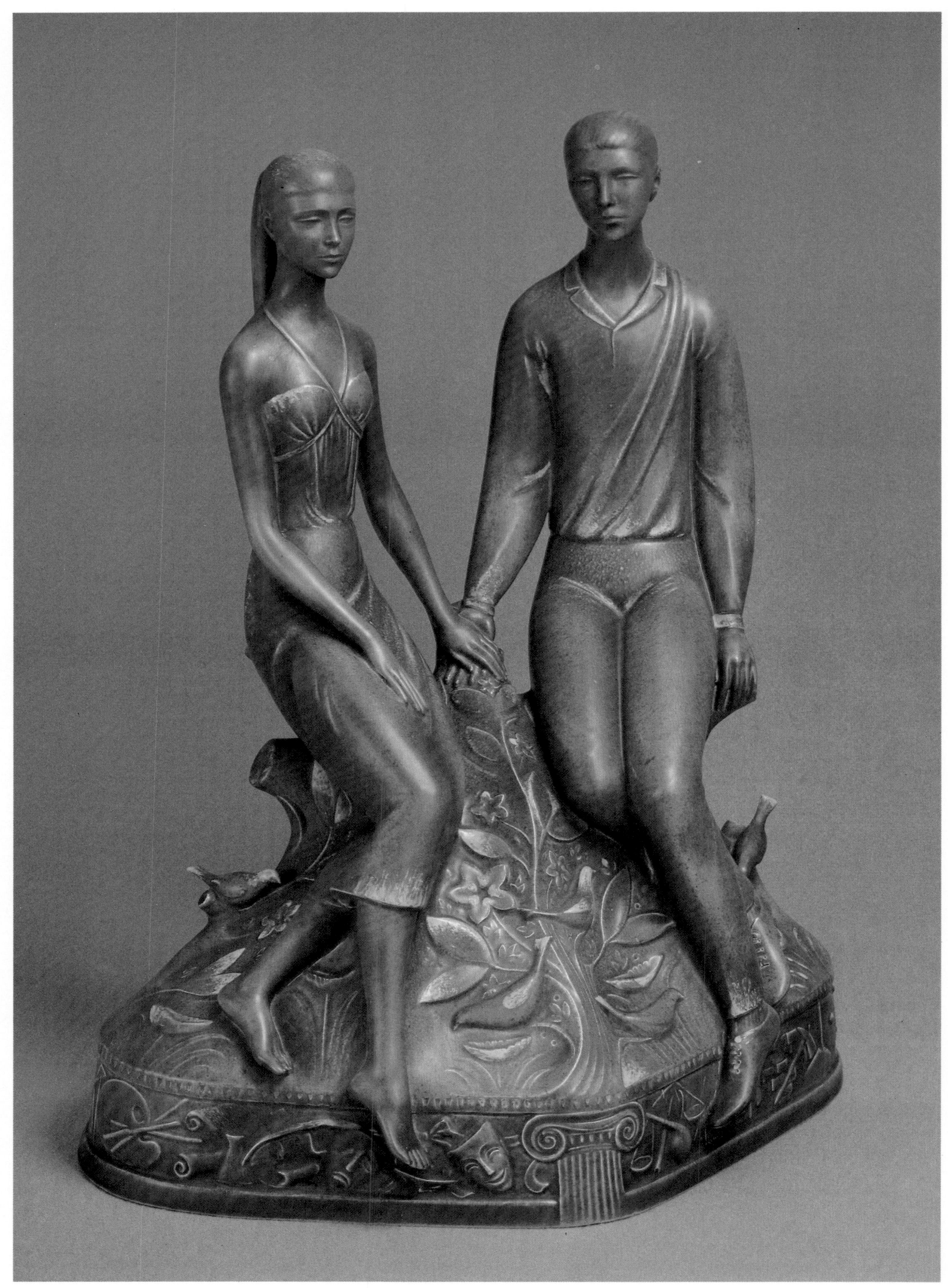

HN 2261 Marriage of Art and Industry

HN 2262 Lights Out & HN 2270 Pillow Fight

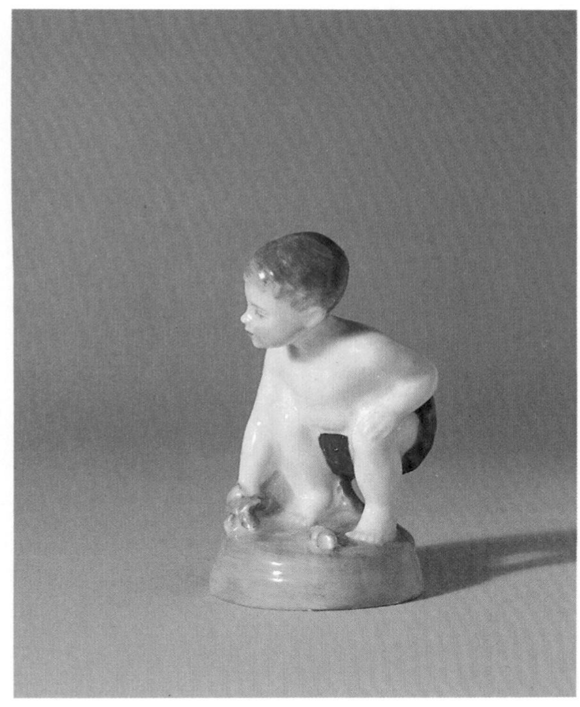

HN 2263 Seashore

HN 2261 Marriage of Art and Industry
Designer: Margaret Davies
Size: 18 in (45.7 cm)
Limited edition of 12, introduced 1958
This figure, specially made for the Brussels International Exhibition of 1958, at which Royal Doulton were awarded the *Grand Prix*, was never put on sale. When visiting the Doulton stand at the Exhibition, HRH the Duke of Edinburgh is reported to have nicknamed this model, 'Young Love in Brussels.'

HN 2262 Lights Out
Designer: Margaret Davies
Size: 5 in (12.7 cm)
Introduced: 1965
Withdrawn: 1969
Made as a pair to HN 2270, *Pillow Fight*

HN 2263 Seashore
Designer: Margaret Davies
Size: 3½ in (8.9 cm)
Introduced: 1961
Withdrawn: 1965

HN 2264 Elegance
Designer: Margaret Davies
Size: 7½ in (19.0 cm)
Introduced: 1961
Still in production

HN 2265 Not issued

HN 2264 Elegance

HN 2266 Ballad Seller

HN 2267 Rhapsody

HN 2266 Ballad Seller
Designer: Margaret Davies
Size: 7¾ in (19.6 cm)
Introduced: 1968
Withdrawn: 1973
A ballad, traditionally a narrative poem describing events historical, heroic, marvellous and sentimental, was commonly sold in the streets by itinerant ballad sellers until the 19th century. This figure may have been inspired by the ballad seller included in Francis Wheatley's engravings of London Cries.

HN 2267 Rhapsody
Designer: Margaret Davies
Size: 7¼ in (18.4 cm)
Introduced: 1961
Withdrawn: 1973

HN 2268 Daphne
Designer: Margaret Davies
Size: 8½ in (21.5 cm)
Introduced: 1963
Withdrawn: 1975

HN 2269 Leading Lady
Designer: Margaret Davies
Size: 7¾ in (19.6 cm)
Introduced: 1965
Withdrawn: 1976

HN 2270 Pillow Fight
Designer: Margaret Davies
Size: 5¼ in (13.3 cm)
Introduced: 1965
Withdrawn: 1969
Made as a pair to HN 2262, *Lights Out*
For illustration, see page 379

HN 2271 Melanie
Designer: Margaret Davies
Size: 8 in (20.3 cm)
Introduced: 1965
Still in production
For illustration, see page 382

HN 2272 Repose
Designer: Margaret Davies
Size: 5¼ in (13.3 cm)
Introduced: 1972
Still in production

HN 2273 Denise
Designer: Margaret Davies
Size: 7¼ in (18.4 cm)
Introduced: 1964
Withdrawn: 1971
Not to be confused with the miniature figures of the same name, M34 and M35, made between 1933 and 1945. See list of miniature figures.

HN 2268 Daphne

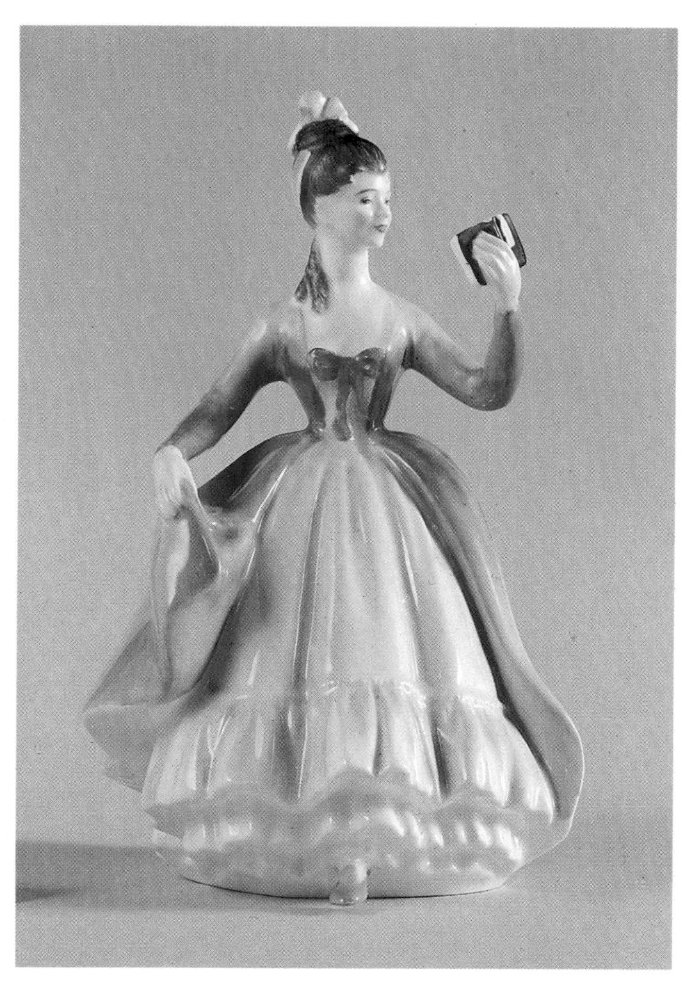

HN 2269 Leading Lady

HN 2272 Repose

HN 2273 Denise

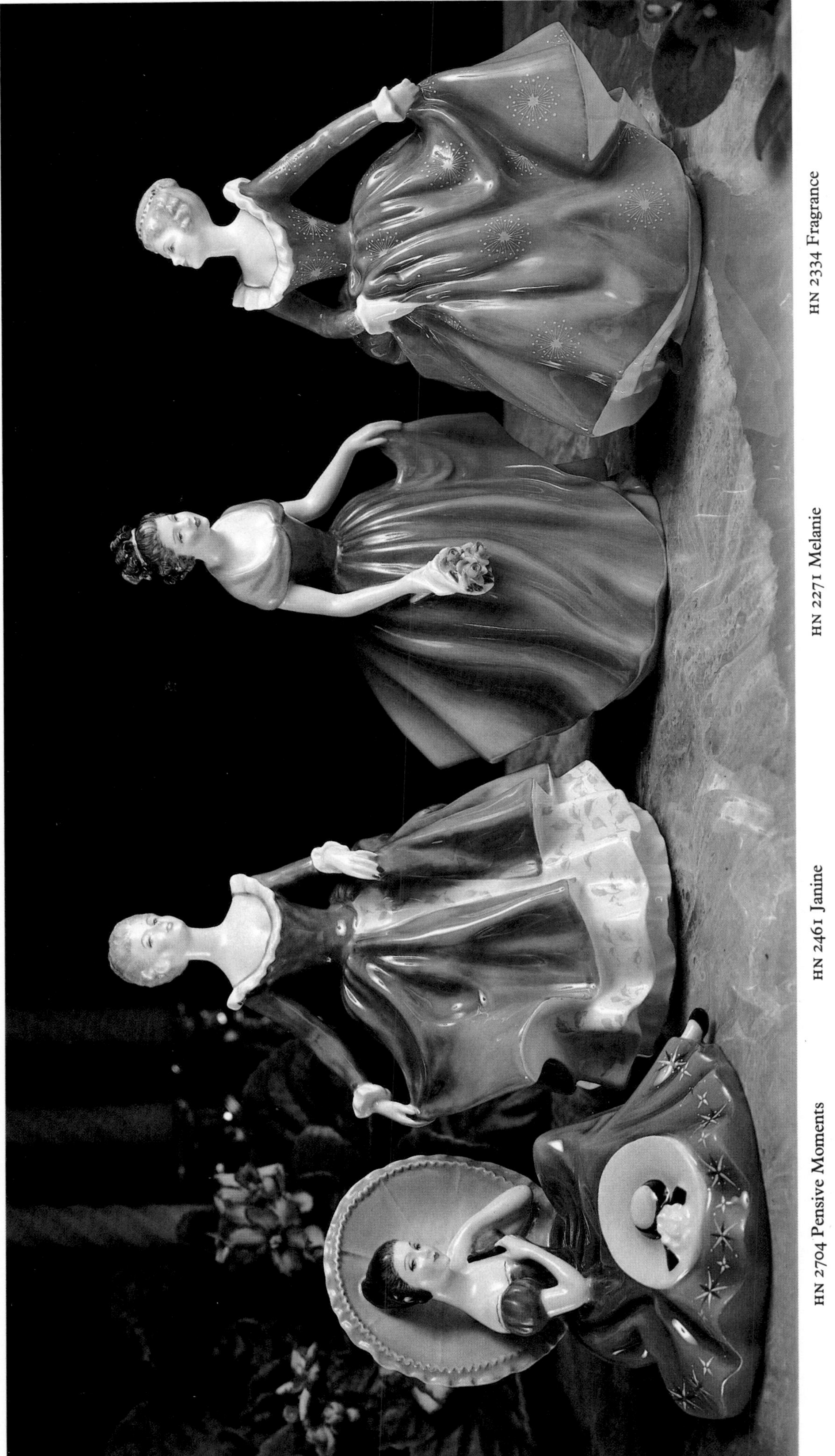

HN 2704 Pensive Moments HN 2461 Janine HN 2271 Melanie HN 2334 Fragrance

HN 2274 Golden Days

HN 2274 Golden Days
Designer: Margaret Davies
Size: 4 in (10.1 cm)
Introduced: 1964
Withdrawn: 1973

HN 2275 Sandra
Designer: Margaret Davies
Size: 8 in (20.3 cm)
Introduced: 1969
Still in production

HN 2275 Sandra

HN 2315 Last Waltz

HN 2276 Heart to Heart

HN 2279 The Clockmaker

HN 2280 The Mayor

HN 2281 The Professor

HN 2282 The Coachman

HN 2276 Heart to Heart
Designer: Margaret Davies
Size: 5½ in (13.9 cm)
Introduced: 1961
Withdrawn: 1971

HN 2277–2278 Not issued

HN 2279 The Clockmaker
Designer: M. Nicoll
Size: 7¼ in (18.4 cm)
Introduced: 1961
Withdrawn: 1975

HN 2280 The Mayor
Designer: M. Nicoll
Size: 8¼ in (20.9 cm)
Introduced: 1963
Withdrawn: 1971

HN 2281 The Professor
Designer: M. Nicoll
Size: 7¾ in (19.6 cm)
Introduced: 1965
Still in production
Perhaps inspired by the film, *The Absent-Minded Professor*, which starred Fred MacMurray.

HN 2282 The Coachman
Designer: M. Nicoll
Size: 6¾ in (17.1 cm)
Introduced: 1963
Withdrawn: 1971

HN 2283 Dreamweaver
Designer: M. Nicoll
Size: 8¾ in (22.2 cm)
Introduced: 1972
Withdrawn: 1976
This figure has a matt finish

HN 2283 Dreamweaver

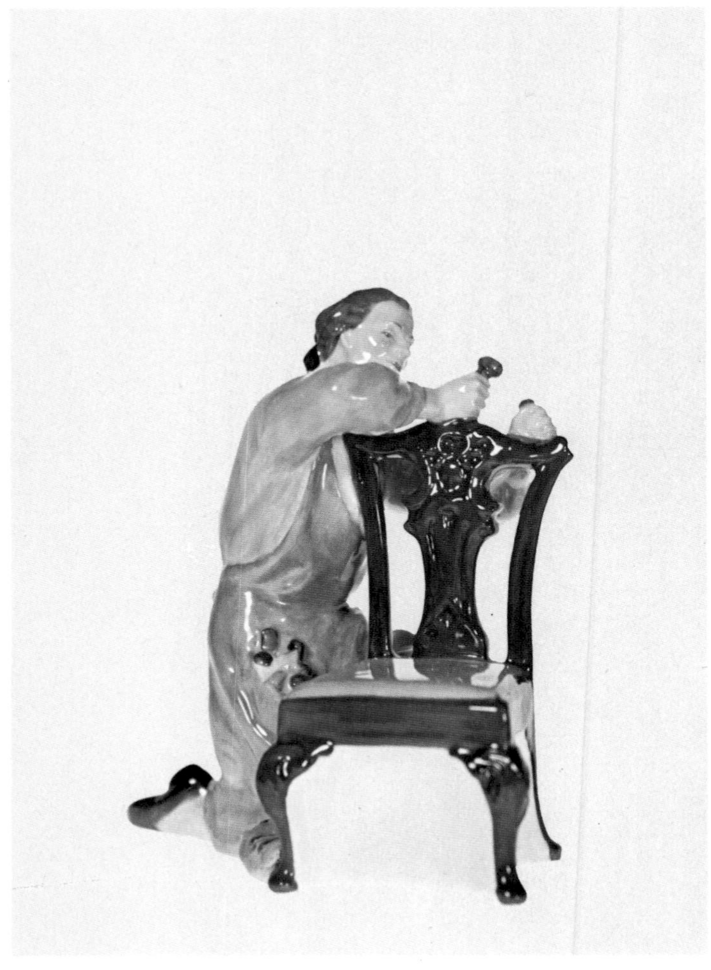

HN 2284 The Craftsman

HN 2287 Symphony

HN 2306 Reverie

HN 2308 Picnic

HN 2284 The Craftsman
Designer: M. Nicoll
Size: 6 in (15.2 cm)
Introduced: 1961
Withdrawn: 1965
This figure of an 18th century cabinet-maker would seem to be based on a well-known painting of Thomas Chippendale at work, dated 1779. Certainly the style of the chair under construction is typical of Chippendale's work.

HN 2285–2286 Not issued

HN 2287 Symphony
Designer: D. B. Lovegrove
Size: 5½ in (13.9 cm)
Introduced: 1961
Withdrawn: 1965

HN 2288–2303 Not issued

HN 2304 Adrienne
See page 350

HN 2305 Not issued

HN 2306 Reverie
Designer: Margaret Davies
Size: 7 in (17.7 cm)
Introduced: 1964
Still in production

HN 2307 Coralie
Designer: Margaret Davies
Size: 8 in (20.3 cm)
Introduced: 1964
Still in production

HN 2308 Picnic
Designer: Margaret Davies
Size: 3¾ in (9.5 cm)
Introduced: 1965
Still in production

HN 2309 Buttercup
Designer: Margaret Davies
Size: 7½ in (19.0 cm)
Introduced: 1964
Still in production

HN 2307 Coralie

HN 2309 Buttercup

HN 2310 Lisa

HN 2311 Lorna

HN 2310 Lisa
Designer: Margaret Davies
Size: 7½ in (19.0 cm)
Introduced: 1969
Still in production
This figure has a matt finish

HN 2311 Lorna
Designer: Margaret Davies
Size: 8¼ in (20.9 cm)
Introduced: 1965
Still in production

HN 2312 Soirée
Designer: Margaret Davies
Size: 7½ in (19.0 cm)
Introduced: 1967
Still in production

HN 2313 Not issued

HN 2314 Old Mother Hubbard
Designer: M. Nicoll
Size: 8¼ in (20.9 cm)
Introduced: 1964
Withdrawn: 1975
The title is taken from the traditional nursery rhyme about Old Mother Hubbard, whose dog went without its bone because the cupboard was bare.

HN 2315 Last Waltz
Designer: Margaret Davies
Size: 7¾ in (19.6 cm)
Introduced: 1967
Still in production
Traditionally the final dance of the evening, the last waltz was always popular as its slow tempo allowed the couples to dance close together; also the last partner was generally expected to escort the lady home.
The waltz was introduced in the late 18th century, when it was strongly opposed as a wholly improper dance.
For illustration, see page 383

HN 2316 Not issued

HN 2317 The Lobster Man
Designer: M. Nicoll
Size: 7½ in (19.0 cm)
Introduced: 1964
Still in production
For illustration, see page 376

HN 2318 Grace
Designer: M. Nicoll
Size: 7½ in (19.0 cm)
Introduced: 1966
Still in production

HN 2319 The Bachelor
Designer: M. Nicoll
Size: 6¾ in (17.1 cm)
Introduced: 1964
Withdrawn: 1975

HN 2312 Soirée

HN 2314 Old Mother Hubbard

HN 2318 Grace

HN 2319 The Bachelor

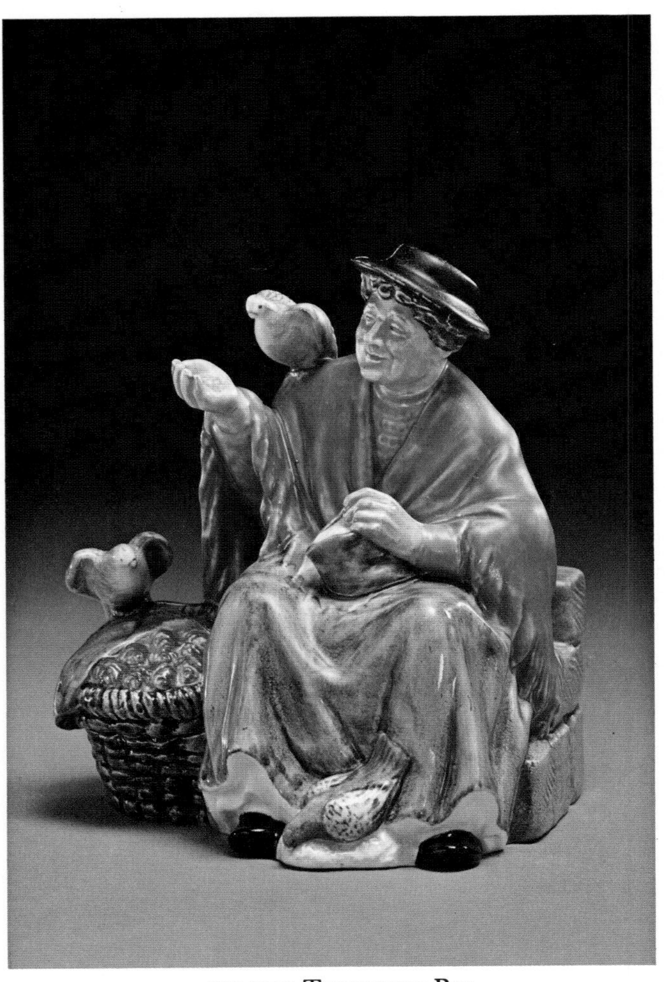

HN 2320 Tuppence a Bag

HN 2321 Family Album

HN 2322 The Cup of Tea

HN 2320 Tuppence a Bag
Designer: M. Nicoll
Size: 6 in (16.5 cm)
Introduced: 1968
Still in production
This addition to the street seller figures was probably inspired by the ladies in London's Trafalgar Square who sell bags of corn for feeding to the pigeons.

HN 2321 Family Album
Designer: M. Nicoll
Size: 6¼ in (15.8 cm)
Introduced: 1966
Withdrawn: 1973

HN 2322 The Cup of Tea
Designer: M. Nicoll
Size: 7½ in (19.0 cm)
Introduced: 1964
Still in production
Despite its great popularity today, tea drinking is a relatively recent habit. In his diary for 28 September, 1666, Samuel Pepys wrote: 'I did send for a cup of tea (a China drink) of which I never had drank before.'

HN 2323 Not issued

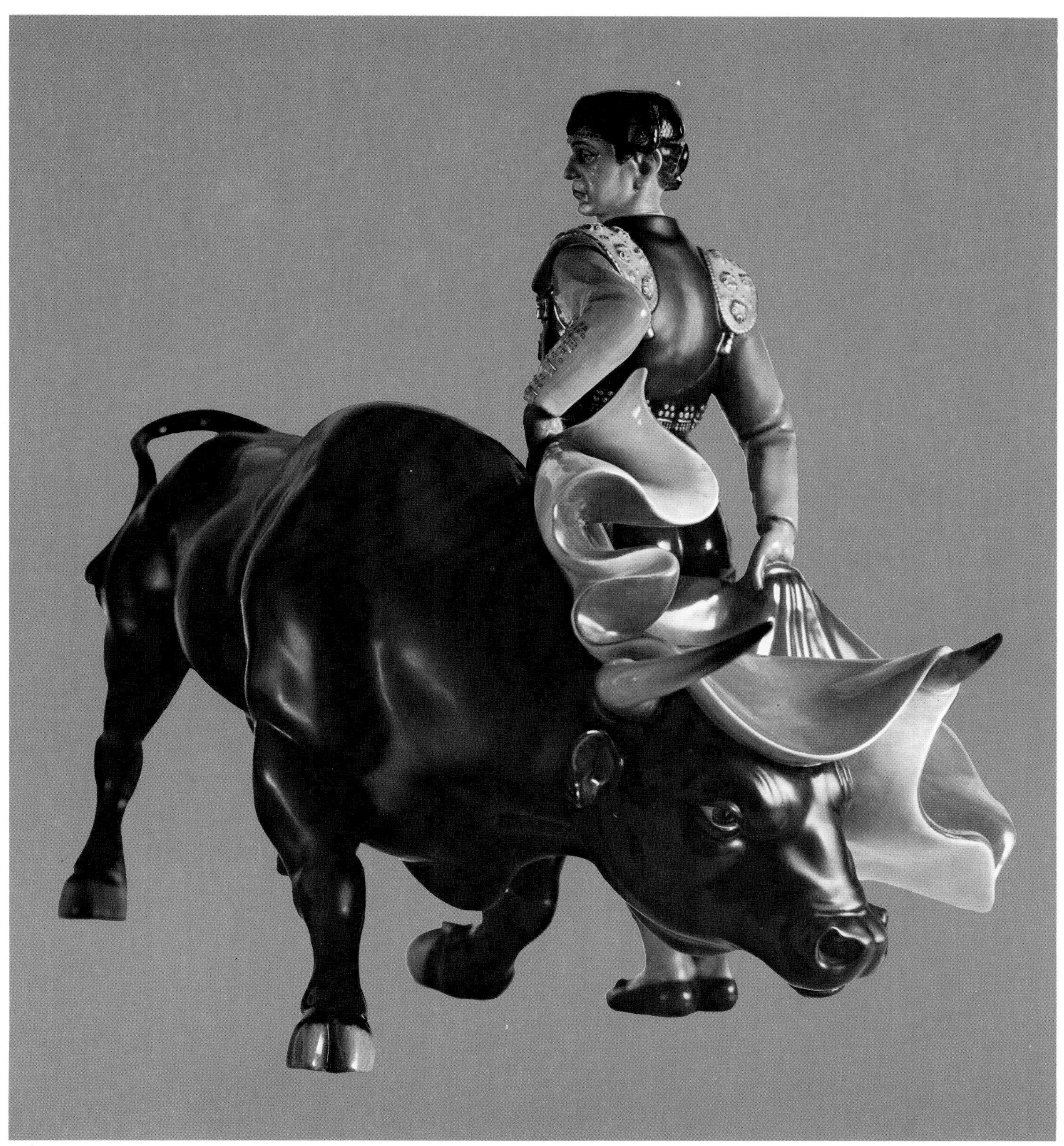

HN 2324 Matador and Bull

HN 2324 Matador and Bull
Designer: Margaret Davies
Size: 16 in (40.6 cm)
Introduced: 1964
Still in production
For this prestige figure, inspired partly by traditional Spanish bull-fight posters, Margaret Davies made extensive first-hand studies of bulls in local agricultural research establishments; she also visited local abattoirs to study in detail their anatomy.

HN 2325 The Master

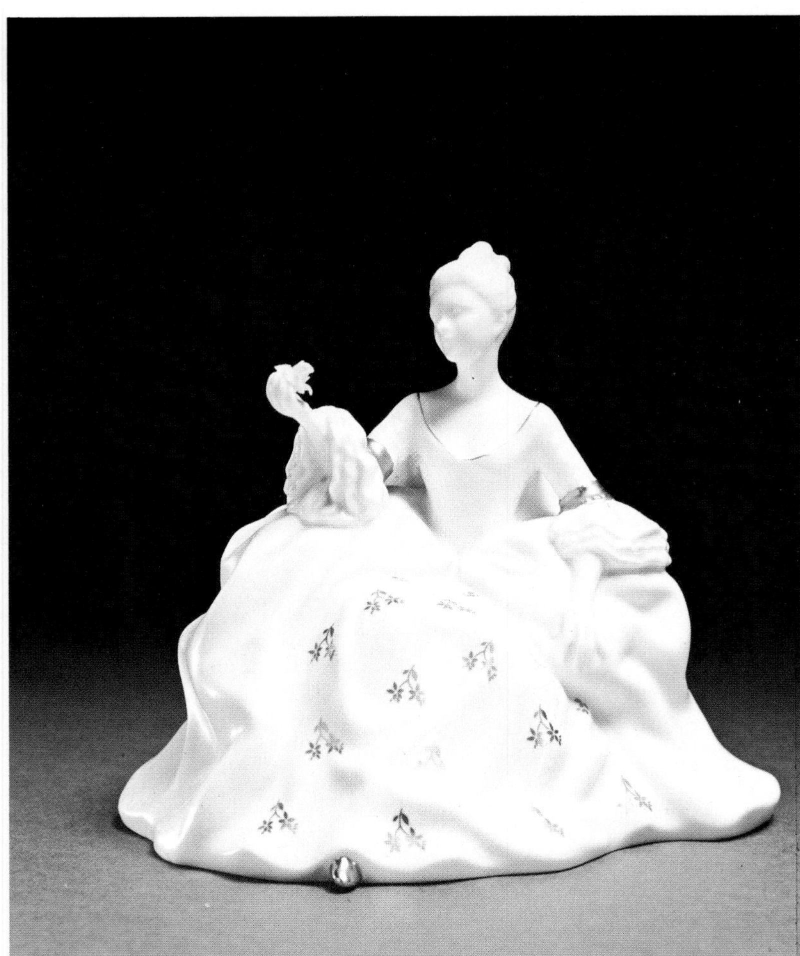

HN 2326 Antoinette (second version)

HN 2327 Katrina

HN 2329 Lynne

HN 2325 The Master
Designer: Margaret Davies
Size: 6½ in (16.5 cm)
Introduced: 1967
Still in production

HN 2326 Antoinette (second version, model 1904)
Designer: Margaret Davies
Size: 6¼ in (15.8 cm)
Introduced: 1967
Still in production

HN 2327 Katrina
Designer: Margaret Davies
Size: 7¾ in (19.6 cm)
Introduced: 1965
Withdrawn: 1969

HN 2328 Not issued

HN 2329 Lynne
Designer: Margaret Davies
Size: 7 in (17.7 cm)
Introduced: 1971
Still in production

HN 2330 Meditation
Designer: Margaret Davies
Size: 5¾ in (14.6 cm)
Introduced: 1971
Still in production

HN 2330 Meditation

HN 2331 Cello (Lady Musicians series)
Designer: Margaret Davies
Size: 6¼ in (15.8 cm)
Limited edition of 750, introduced 1970, now sold out. The twelve figures in the Lady Musicians series, Cello, Virginals, Lute, Violin, Harp, Flute, Cymbals, Chitarrone, French Horn, Hurdy Gurdy, Viola d'Amore and Dulcimer were introduced progressively from 1970, all in limited editions of 750. The series was characterised by its graceful and elegant reflection of the styles of 18th century music, although some of the models were inspired by painters as diverse as Vermeer and Augustus John. The Musicians were the first Doulton figures to carry the designer's name on every model since the 1930s, and so represented a major break with tradition.
For illustration, see next page

HN 2332–2333 Not issued

HN 2334 Fragrance
Designer: Margaret Davies
Size: 7½ in (19.0 cm)
Introduced: 1966
Still in production
For illustration, see page 382

HN 2335 Hilary
Designer: Margaret Davies
Size: 7¼ in (18.4 cm)
Introduced: 1967
Still in production

HN 2335 Hilary

Lady Musicians: *top* HN 2795, HN 2432, HN 2331
centre HN 2483, HN 2699, HN 2482, HN 2797
bottom HN 2700, HN 2798, HN 2796, HN 2427, HN 2431

HN 2336 Alison

HN 2337 Loretta

HN 2338 Penny

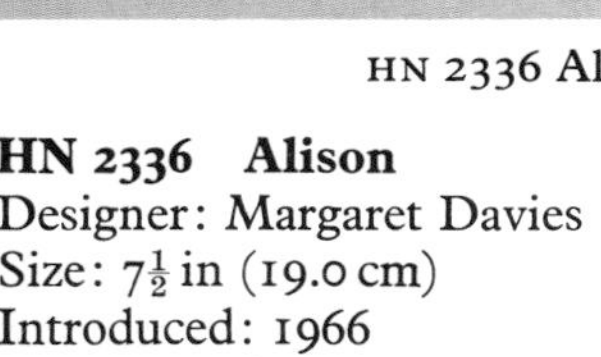

HN 2336 Alison
Designer: Margaret Davies
Size: 7$\frac{1}{2}$ in (19.0 cm)
Introduced: 1966
Still in production

HN 2337 Loretta
Designer: Margaret Davies
Size: 7$\frac{3}{4}$ in (19.6 cm)
Introduced: 1966
Still in production

HN 2338 Penny
Designer: Margaret Davies
Size: 4$\frac{3}{4}$ in (12.0 cm)
Introduced: 1968
Still in production

HN 2339 My Love
Designer: Margaret Davies
Size: 6$\frac{1}{4}$ in (15. 8cm)
Introduced: 1969
Still in production
This figure is an alternative version of HN 2326, *Antoinette*, with additional colouring

HN 2339 My Love

HN 2340 Belle & HN 2341 Chérie

HN 2340 Belle (second version, model 2038)
Designer: Margaret Davies
Size: $4\frac{3}{4}$ in (12.0 cm)
Introduced: 1968
Still in production

HN 2341 Chérie
Designer: Margaret Davies
Size: $5\frac{1}{4}$ in (13.3 cm)
Introduced: 1966
Still in production

HN 2342 Not issued

HN 2343 Première
Designer: Margaret Davies
Size: $7\frac{3}{4}$ in (19.6 cm)
Introduced: 1969
Still in production

HN 2343 Première

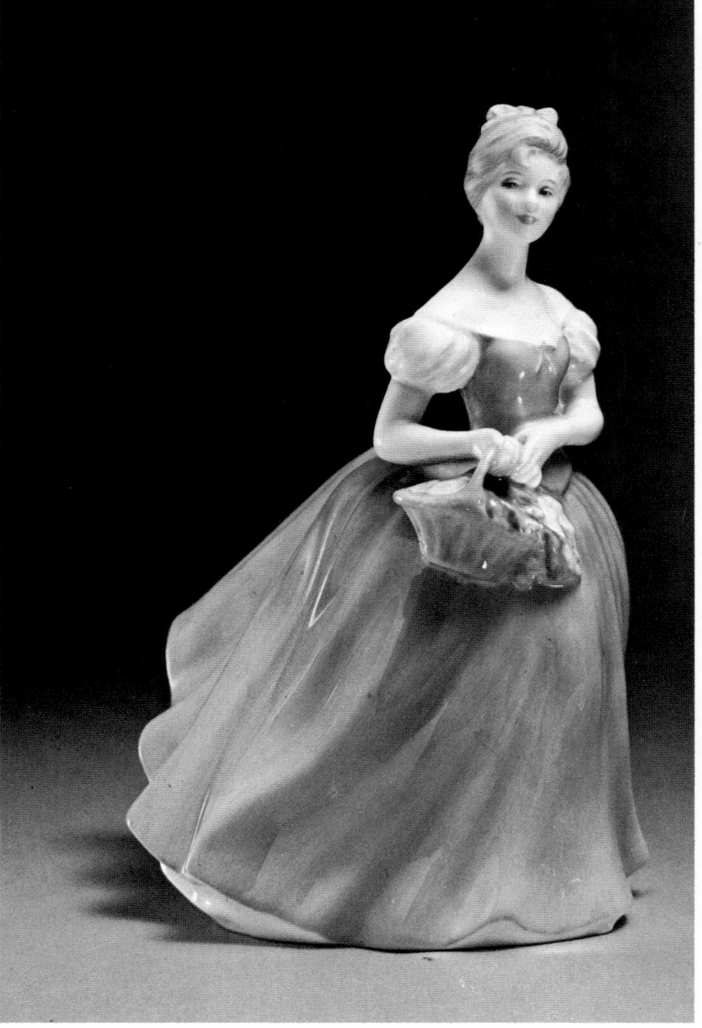

HN 2345 Clarissa (second version)

HN 2344 Not issued

HN 2345 Clarissa (second version, model 2001)
Designer: Margaret Davies
Size: 8 in (20.3 cm)
Introduced: 1968
Still in production

HN 2347 Nina

HN 2348 Geraldine

HN 2346 Not issued

HN 2347 Nina
Designer: Margaret Davies
Size: $7\frac{3}{4}$ in (19.6 cm)
Introduced: 1969
Withdrawn: 1976
This figure has a matt finish

HN 2348 Geraldine
Designer: Margaret Davies
Size: $7\frac{1}{2}$ in (19.0 cm)
Introduced: 1972
Withdrawn: 1976
This figure has a matt finish
Although now in popular use, the name Geraldine was in fact invented by the poet Henry Howard during the reign of Henry VIII as a romantic term of endearment for his lover, Lady Elizabeth Fitzgerald. It only came into use as a Christian name after 1800.

HN 2349 Flora
Designer: M. Nicoll
Size: $7\frac{3}{4}$ in (19.6 cm)
Introduced: 1966
Withdrawn: 1973

HN 2350–2351 Not issued

HN 2349 Flora

HN 2352 A Stitch in Time

HN 2356 Ascot

HN 2359 The Detective

HN 2361 The Laird

HN 2352 A Stitch in Time
Designer: M. Nicoll
Size: 6 in (15.2 cm)
Introduced: 1966
Still in production
The title is taken from the well-known proverb, 'A stitch in time saves nine.'

HN 2353–2355 Not issued

HN 2356 Ascot
Designer: Margaret Davies
Size: 6 in (15.2 cm)
Introduced: 1968
Still in production
Ascot is pre-eminently *the* Royal and fashionable race meeting. The course was laid out in 1711 by order of Queen Anne, and the traditional Royal procession was instituted by George IV in 1820. Although this figure represents the Edwardian period, perhaps the heyday of Royal Ascot, the meeting is still most famous for its fashion parade.

HN 2357–2358 Not issued

HN 2359 The Detective
Designer: E. J. Griffiths
Size: $9\frac{1}{4}$ in (23.4 cm)
Introduced: 1977
Still in production
This figure is clearly inspired by Sherlock Holmes, the famous Victorian private detective, created by Sir Arthur Conan Doyle. Holmes, with his magnifying glass, his brilliant powers of deduction and his amiable colleague Dr. Watson, is one of the great detectives of fiction.

HN 2360 Not issued

HN 2361 The Laird
Designer: M. Nicoll
Size: $8\frac{1}{4}$ in (20.9 cm)
Introduced: 1969
Still in production
The laird is the traditional Scottish landowner. This figure shows him wearing correct Highland dress for everyday use, including the kilt, tweed jacket, knitted hose, sporran and 'Glengarry' bonnet

HN 2362 The Wayfarer
Designer: M. Nicoll
Size: $5\frac{1}{2}$ in (13.9 cm)
Introduced: 1970
Withdrawn: 1976

HN 2363–2367 Not issued

HN 2362 The Wayfarer

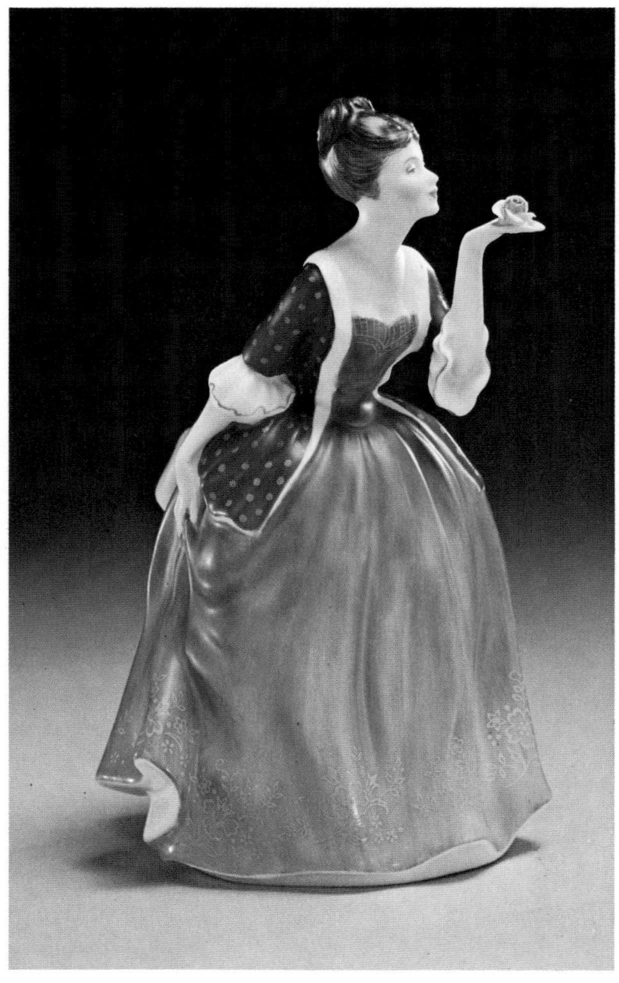

HN 2368 Fleur

HN 2368 Fleur
Designer: J. Bromley
Size: $7\frac{3}{4}$ in (19.6 cm)
Introduced: 1968
Still in production
Perhaps inspired by Fleur, the daughter of Soames Forsyte in Galsworthy's *Forsyte Saga*, which achieved world-wide acclaim as a BBC television serial during the 1960s

HN 2375 The Viking

HN 2369–2374 Not issued

HN 2375 The Viking
Designer: J. Bromley
Size: $8\frac{3}{4}$ in (22.2 cm)
Introduced: 1973
Withdrawn: 1976
This figure has a matt finish.
This figure represents the Viking Warriors, the pagan Norsemen who swept across Britain during the 9th century, whose reputation for violence, cruelty and skill in battle was without equal.

HN 2376 Indian Brave
Designer: Margaret Davies
Size: $15\frac{1}{2}$ in (39.3 cm)
Limited edition of 500, introduced in 1967, now sold out
This limited edition prestige model of a North American Indian warrior, mounted on his pony, represented on its introduction a new height of realism and accuracy of modelling for Royal Doulton figures.

HN 2377 Not issued

HN 2378 Simone
Designer: Margaret Davies
Size: $7\frac{1}{2}$ in (19.0 cm)
Introduced: 1971
Still in production

Left
HN 2381 Kirsty

Right
HN 2378 Simone

HN 2376 Indian Brave (illustration not in scale)

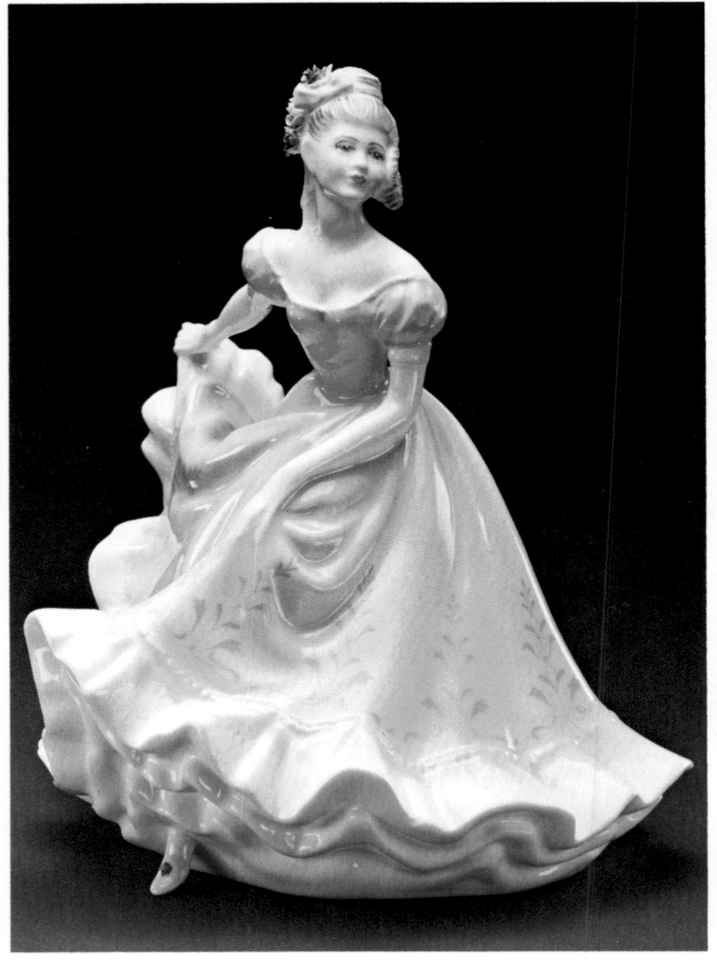

HN 2379 Ninette

HN 2382 Secret Thoughts

HN 2379 Ninette
Designer: Margaret Davies
Size: 8 in (20.3 cm)
Introduced: 1971
Still in production
This dancing figure was perhaps named after Ninette de Valois, the ballet dancer and choreographer who, after training with the Russian Ballet, formed her own company which revitalised ballet in Britain.

HN 2380 Sweet Dreams
Designer: Margaret Davies
Size: 5 in (12.7 cm)
Introduced: 1971
Still in production
For illustration, see page 367

HN 2381 Kirsty
Designer: Margaret Davies
Size: 7¾ in (19.6 cm)
Introduced: 1971
Still in production
For illustration, see page 400

HN 2382 Secret Thoughts
Designer: Margaret Davies
Size: 6½ in (16.5 cm)
Introduction: 1971
Still in production

HN 2383–2384 Not issued

HN 2385 Debbie
Designer: Margaret Davies
Size: 6 in (15.2 cm)
Introduced: 1969
Still in production

HN 2386–2392 Not issued

HN 2393 Rosalind
Designer: Margaret Davies
Size: 5½ in (13.9 cm)
Introduced: 1970
Withdrawn: 1975

HN 2394–2397 Not issued

HN 2398 Alexandra
Designer: Margaret Davies
Size: 7¾ in (19.6 cm)
Introduced: 1970
Withdrawn: 1976

HN 2399–2416 Not issued

HN 2385 Debbie

HN 2393 Rosalind

HN 2398 Alexandra

HN 2417 The Boatman

HN 2417 The Boatman
Designer: M. Nicoll
Size: 6½ in (16.5 cm)
Introduced: 1971
Still in production
The old boatman, a common sight at seaside resorts, spends his time doing odd jobs, telling yarns to visitors about the adventures of his youth and running the local trip boats.

HN 2421 Charlotte

HN 2422 Francine

HN 2418–2420 Not issued

HN 2421 Charlotte
Designer: J. Bromley
Size: $6\frac{3}{4}$ in (17.1 cm)
Introduced: 1972
Still in production

HN 2422 Francine
Designer: J. Bromley
Size: $5\frac{1}{4}$ in (13.3 cm)
Introduced: 1972
Still in production

HN 2423–2426 Not issued

HN 2427 Virginals (Lady Musicians series)
Designer: Margaret Davies
Size: $6\frac{1}{2}$ in (16.5 cm)
Limited edition of 750, introduced 1971, now sold out
For illustration, see page 394

HN 2428 The Palio
Designer: Margaret Davies
Size: 18in (45.7 cm)
Limited edition of 500, introduced 1971
The Palio, held in Sienna in June and August each year, is one of the most exciting of Italy's traditional festivals. Held in the Campo in the centre of the town, the festival includes a flag tattoo, a procession of mounted warriors who represent the colourful life of the ancient republic of Sienna, and a dramatic horse race around the Campo, the winner of which is awarded the Palio, or prize.

HN 2429 Elyse
Designer: Margaret Davies
Size: $6\frac{3}{4}$ in (17.1 cm)
Introduced: 1972
Still in production

HN 2429 Elyse

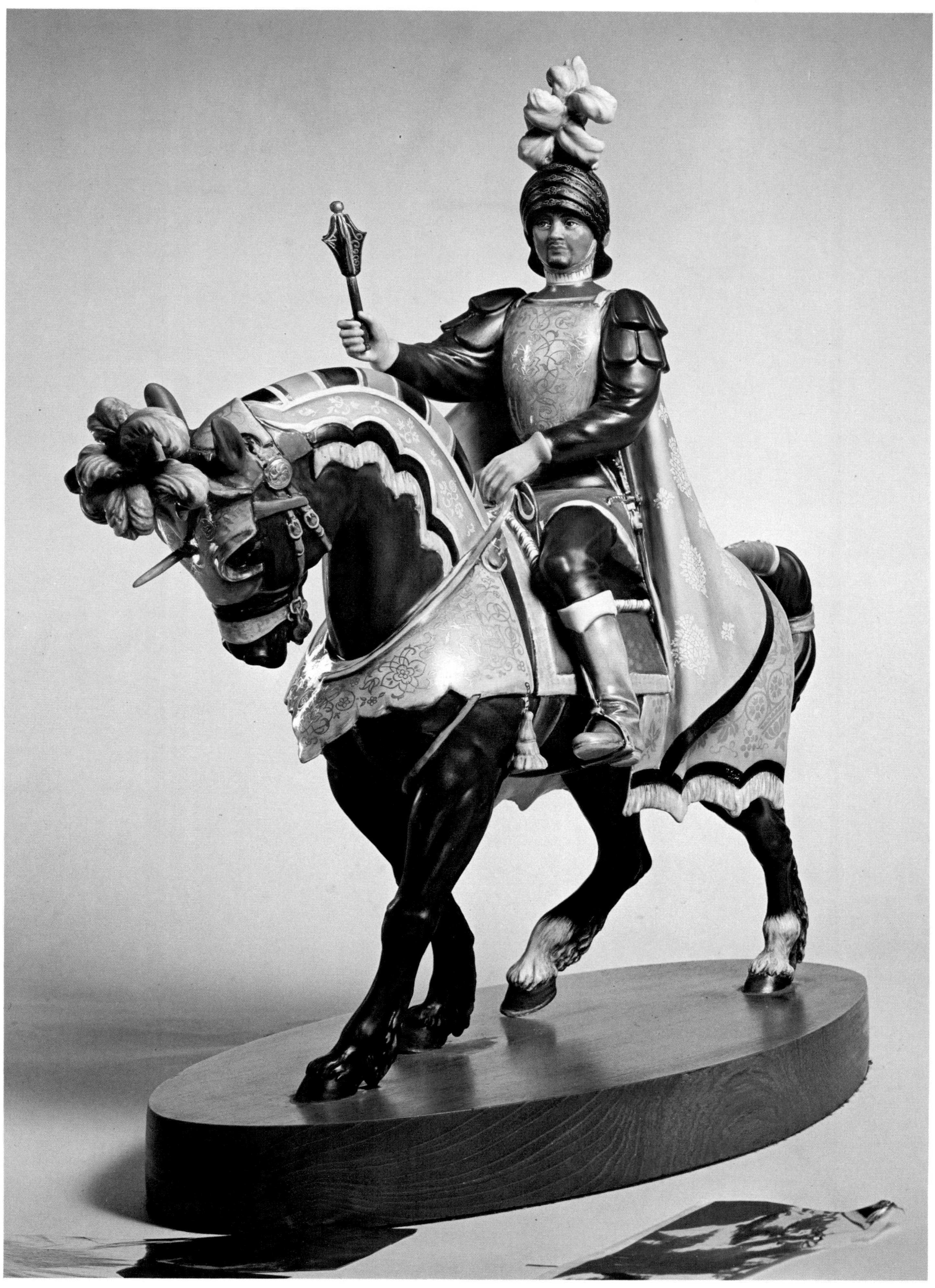

HN 2428 The Palio (illustration not in scale)

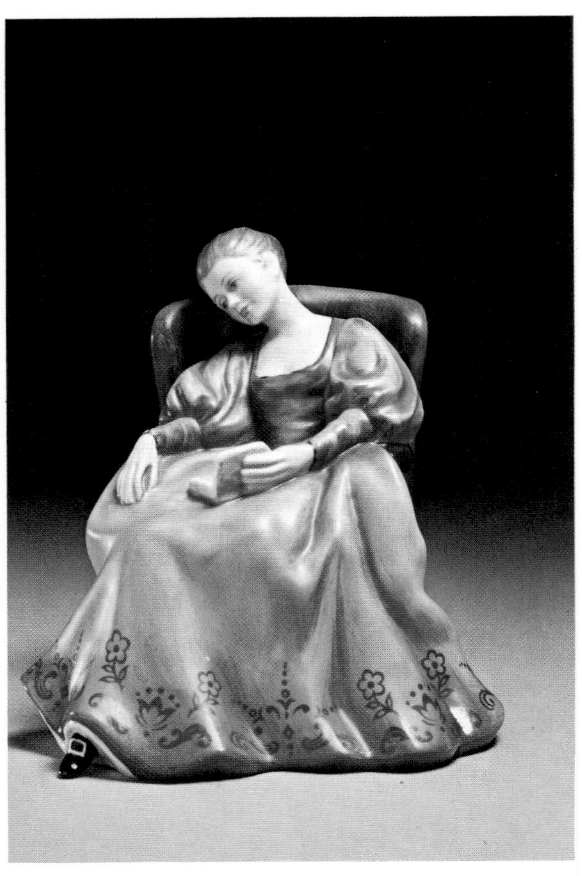

HN 2430 Romance

HN 2430 Romance
Designer: Margaret Davies
Size: $5\frac{1}{4}$ in (13.3 cm)
Introduced: 1972
Still in production

HN 2431 Lute (Lady Musicians series)
Designer: Margaret Davies
Size: $6\frac{1}{2}$ in (16.5 cm)
Limited edition of 750, introduced 1972, now sold out
For illustration, see page 394

HN 2432 Violin (Lady Musician series)
Designer: Margaret Davies
Size: $6\frac{1}{2}$ in (16.5 cm)
Limited edition of 750, introduced 1972, now sold out
For illustration, see page 394

HN 2433–2435 Not issued

HN 2436 Scottish Highland Dancer

HN 2439 Philippine Dancer

HN 2443 The Judge

HN 2444 Bon Appétit

HN 2436 Scottish Highland Dancer (Dancers of the World series)
Designer: Margaret Davies
Size: 10 in (25.4 cm)
Limited edition of 750, introduced 1978
Dancers of the World is a new series of prestige limited edition figures whose fine design, modelling and craftsmanship bring to life dance forms from many countries, some formal, some informal, some classical and some dramatic.

HN 2437–2438 Not issued

HN 2439 Philippine Dancer (Dancers of the World series)
Designer: Margaret Davies
Size: $9\frac{3}{4}$ in (24.7 cm)
Limited edition of 750, introduced 1978

HN 2440–2441 Not issued

HN 2442 Sailor's Holiday
Designer: M. Nicoll
Size: 6 in (15.2 cm)
Introduced: 1972
Still in production
For illustration, see page 376

HN 2443 The Judge
Designer: M. Nicoll
Size: $6\frac{1}{2}$ in (16.5 cm)
Introduced: 1972
Still in production
In 1976 this figure was changed from a matt to a glazed finish.

HN 2444 Bon Appétit
Designer: M. Nicoll
Size: $6\frac{1}{4}$ in (15.8 cm)
Introduced: 1972
Withdrawn: 1976
This figure has a matt finish

HN 2445 Parisian
Designer: M. Nicoll
Size: 8 in (20.3 cm)
Introduced: 1972
Withdrawn: 1975
This figure has a matt finish

HN 2445 Parisian

HN 2446 Thanksgiving

HN 2455 The Seafarer

HN 2446 Thanksgiving
Designer: M. Nicoll
Size: 8 in (20.3 cm)
Introduced: 1972
Withdrawn: 1976
This figure has a matt finish
Thanksgiving Day, held annually on November 24th in the United States, represents the continuity of a tradition established by the Plymouth settlers in 1621, in celebration of their first successful harvest. The food eaten at celebrations today, turkey and pumpkin pie, is a reminder of the settlers' original diet.

HN 2447–2454 Not issued

HN 2455 The Seafarer
Designer: M. Nicoll
Size: 8½ in (21.5 cm)
Introduced: 1972
Withdrawn: 1976
This figure has a matt finish

HN 2456–2460 Not issued

HN 2461 Janine
Designer: J. Bromley
Size: 8 in (20.3 cm)
Introduced: 1971
Still in production
For illustration, see page 382

HN 2462 Not issued

HN 2463 Olga
Designer: J. Bromley
Size: 8¼ in (20.9 cm)
Introduced: 1972
Withdrawn: 1975

HN 2464–2470 Not issued

HN 2471 Victoria
Designer: Margaret Davies
Size: 6½ in (16.5 cm)
Introduced: 1973
Still in production

HN 2472 Not issued

HN 2463 Olga

HN 2471 Victoria

HN 2473 At Ease

HN 2473 At Ease
Designer: Margaret Davies
Size: 6 in (15.2 cm)
Introduced: 1973
Still in production

HN 2474 Not issued

HN 2475 Vanity
Designer: Margaret Davies
Size: $5\frac{1}{4}$ in (13.3 cm)
Introduced: 1973
Still in production

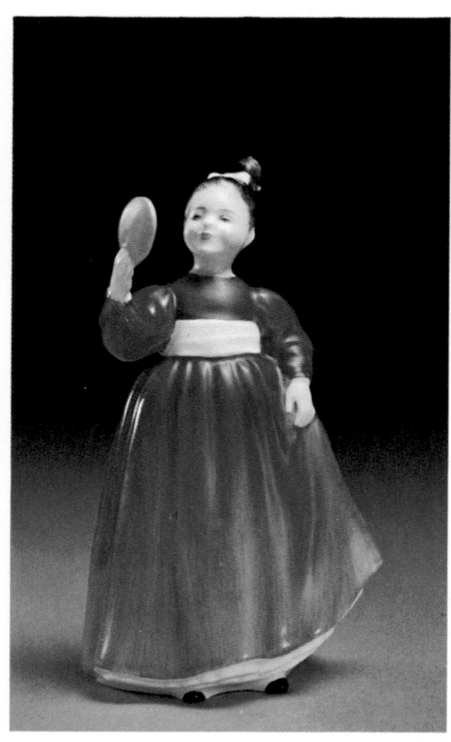

HN 2475 Vanity

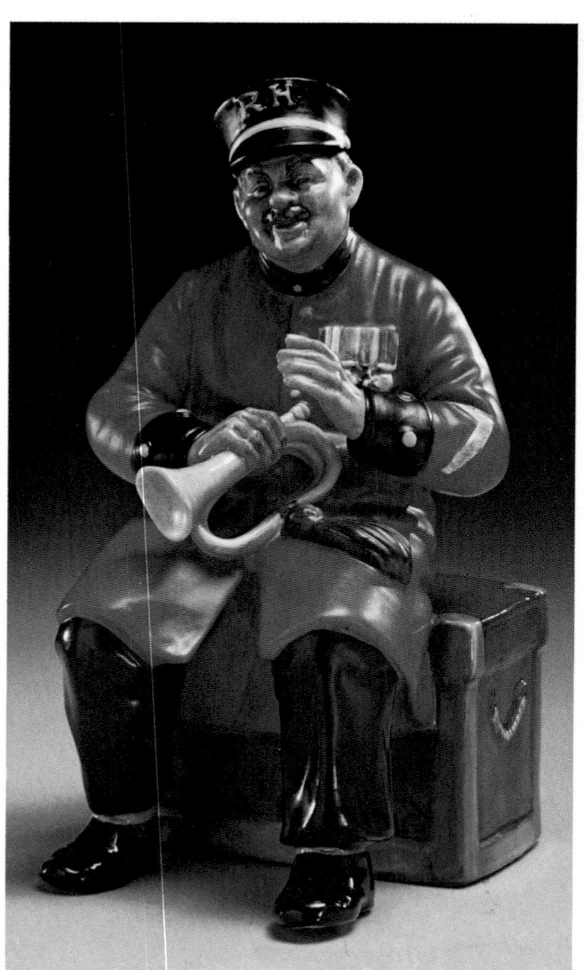

HN 2484 Past Glory

HN 2485 Lunchtime

HN 2487 Beachcomber

HN 2476–2481 Not issued

HN 2482 Harp (Lady Musicians series)
Designer: Margaret Davies
Size: 9 in (22.8 cm)
Limited edition of 750, introduced 1973, now sold out
For illustration, see page 394

HN 2483 Flute (Lady Musicians series)
Designers: Margaret Davies
Size: 6¼ in (15.8 cm)
Limited edition of 750, introduced 1973, now sold out
For illustration, see page 394

HN 2484 Past Glory
Designer: M. Nicoll
Size: 7½ in (19.0 cm)
Introduced: 1973
Still in production
This figure, with his bugle, medals and traditional uniform represents one of the old soldiers living in retirement in the Royal Hospital, Chelsea, popularly known as Chelsea Pensioners.

HN 2485 Lunchtime
Designer: M. Nicoll
Size: 8 in (20.3 cm)
Introduced: 1973
Still in production

HN 2486 Not issued

HN 2487 Beachcomber
Designer: M. Nicoll
Size: 6½ in (16.5 cm)
Introduced: 1973
Withdrawn: 1976
This figure has a matt finish

HN 2488–2491 Not issued

HN 2492 The Huntsman (third version, model 2277)
Designer: M. Nicoll
Size: 8 in (20.3 cm)
Introduced: 1974
Still in production

HN 2493 Not issued

HN 2494 Old Meg
Designer: M. Nicoll
Size: 8 in (20.3 cm)
Introduced: 1974
Withdrawn: 1976

HN 2495–2498 Not issued

HN 2492 The Huntsman (third version)

HN 2494 Old Meg

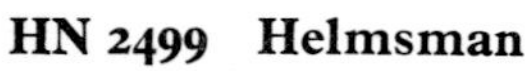

HN 2499 Helmsman

HN 2502 Queen Elizabeth II

HN 2520 The Farmer's Boy

HN 2542 Boudoir

HN 2499 Helmsman
Designer: M. Nicoll
Size: 8½ in (21.5 cm)
Introduced: 1974
Still in production

HN 2500–2501 Animal models

HN 2502 Queen Elizabeth II
Designer: Margaret Davies
Size: 7¾ in (19.6 cm)
Limited edition of 750, introduced 1973, now sold out
This figure was made to commemorate the twentieth anniversary of the Queen's coronation, in 1953.

HN 2503–2519 Animal models

HN 2520 The Farmer's Boy
Designer: W. M. Chance
Size: 8¾ in (22.2 cm)
Introduced: 1938
Withdrawn: 1960

HN 2521–2541 Animal models

HN 2542 Boudoir (Haute Ensemble series)
Designer: E. J. Griffiths
Size: 12¼ in (31.0 cm)
Introduced: 1974
Still in production
The Haute Ensemble range represents a new dimension of tall, slender elegance that blends with a subtle realism and femininity. Their size and sensuality are reminiscent of some of the earliest Doulton female figures. In style and character they are a mixture of fact and fantasy – Carmen from Bizet's opera, Eliza the flower girl heroine of *My Fair Lady*.

HN 2543 Eliza

HN 2544 A la Mode

HN 2545 Carmen (second version)

HN 2546 Buddies

HN 2543 Eliza (Haute Ensemble series)
Designer: E. J. Griffiths
Size: 11¾ in (29.8 cm)
Introduced: 1974
Still in production

HN 2544 A la Mode (Haute Ensemble series)
Designer: E. J. Griffiths
Size: 12½ in (31.7 cm)
Introduced: 1974
Still in production

HN 2545 Carmen (second version, model 2198, Haute Ensemble series)
Designer: E. J. Griffiths
Size: 11½ in (29.2 cm)
Introduced: 1974
Still in production

HN 2546 Buddies
Designer: E. J. Griffiths
Size: 6¼ in (15.8 cm)
Introduced: 1973
Withdrawn: 1976
This figure has a matt finish

HN 2554 Masque

HN 2671 Good Morning

HN 2677 Taking Things Easy

HN 2547–2553 Bird models

HN 2554 Masque
Designer: D. V. Tootle
Size: 9 in (22.8 cm)
Introduced: 1973
Still in production

HN 2555–2670 Animal and Bird models

HN 2671 Good Morning
Designer: M. Nicoll
Size: 8 in (20.3 cm)
Introduced: 1974
Withdrawn: 1976
This figure has a matt finish

HN 2672–2676 Not issued

HN 2677 Taking Things Easy
Designer: M. Nicoll
Size: 7 in (17.7 cm)
Introduced: 1975
Still in production

HN 2679 Drummer Boy

HN 2678 Not issued

HN 2679 Drummer Boy
Designer: M. Nicoll
Size: 8½ in (21.5 cm)
Introduced: 1976
Still in production
Dressed in the uniform of the period of the Battle of Waterloo (1815), the figure represents one of the drummer boys whose side drums gave the marching armies their pace and rhythm and urged them on with rousing marches.

HN 2680–2682 Not issued

HN 2683 Stop Press

HN 2694 Fiona (second version)

HN 2705 Julia

HN 2683 Stop Press
Designer: M. Nicoll
Size: 7½ in (19.0 cm)
Introduced: 1977
Still in production

HN 2684–2693 Not issued

HN 2694 Fiona (second version, model 2230)
Designer: Margaret Davies
Size: 7½ in (19.0 cm)
Introduced: 1974
Still in production

HN 2695–2698 Not issued

HN 2699 Cymbals (Lady Musicians series)
Designer: Margaret Davies
Size: 7½ in (19 cm)
Limited edition of 750, introduced 1974, now sold out
For illustration, see page 394

HN 2700 Chitarrone (Lady Musicians series)
Designer: Margaret Davies
Size: 8 in (20.3 cm)
Limited edition of 750, introduced 1974, now sold out
For illustration, see page 394

HN 2701–2703 Not issued

HN 2704 Pensive Moments
Designer: Margaret Davies
Size: 5 in (12.7 cm)
Introduced: 1975
Still in production
For illustration, see page 382

HN 2705 Julia
Designer: Margaret Davies
Size: 7½ in (19.0 cm)
Introduced: 1975
Still in production

HN 2706–2708 Not issued

HN 2709 Regal Lady
Designer: Margaret Davies
Size: 7½ in (19.0 cm)
Introduced: 1975
Still in production

HN 2710–2711 Not issued

HN 2712 Mantilla (Haute Ensemble series)
Designer: E. J. Griffiths
Size: 11¾ in (29.8 cm)
Introduced: 1974
Still in production

HN 2713–2715 Not issued

HN 2716 Cavalier (second version, model 2199)
Designer: E. J. Griffiths
Size: 10 in (25.4 cm)
Introduced: 1976
Still in production

HN 2709 Regal Lady

HN 2712 Mantilla

HN 2716 Cavalier

HN 2717 Private, 2nd South Carolina Regiment, 1781 (Soldiers of the Revolution series)
Designer: E. J. Griffiths
Size: $11\frac{1}{2}$ in (29.2 cm)
Limited edition of 350, introduced 1975
The magnificently detailed collection of thirteen military sculptures that make up the Soldiers of the Revolution series was produced to celebrate the bicentenary of the United States. Made in limited editions of 350 of each figure, and available only in North America, the series was designed by Royal Doulton in close association with the Colonial Williamsburg Foundation. Six years of research have ensured that each figure is historically correct down to the smallest details of uniform and equipment. The thirteen soldiers, which represent the regiments of the original thirteen states, have justly been described as, 'a masterpiece of historical accuracy sculpted in porcelain'.
For illustration, see next page

HN 2718 Lady Pamela

HN 2718 Lady Pamela
Designer: D. V. Tootle
Size: 8 in (20.3 cm)
Introduced: 1974
Still in production

HN 2719 Laurianne
Designer: D. V. Tootle
Size: $6\frac{1}{2}$ in (16.5 cm)
Introduced: 1974
Still in production

HN 2720–2721 Not issued

HN 2722 Veneta
Designer: W. K. Harper
Size: $7\frac{3}{4}$ in (19.6 cm)
Introduced: 1974
Still in production

HN 2719 Laurianne

HN 2722 Veneta

HN 2717, HN 2779, HN 2752 & HN 2780

HN 2815, HN 2755 & HN 2754

HN 2845

The Thirteen Limited Edition Soldiers of the Revolution Figures

HN 2846

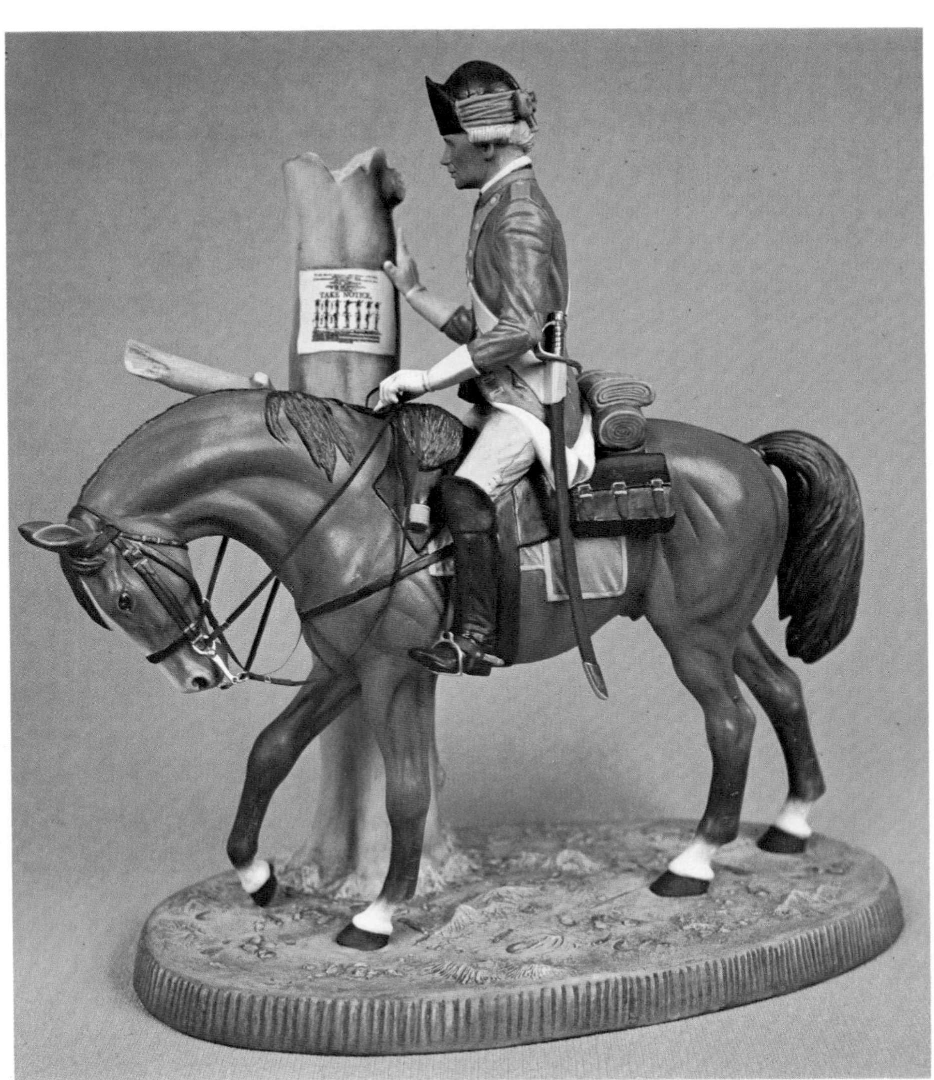

HN 2844

HN 2759, HN 2760 & HN 2761

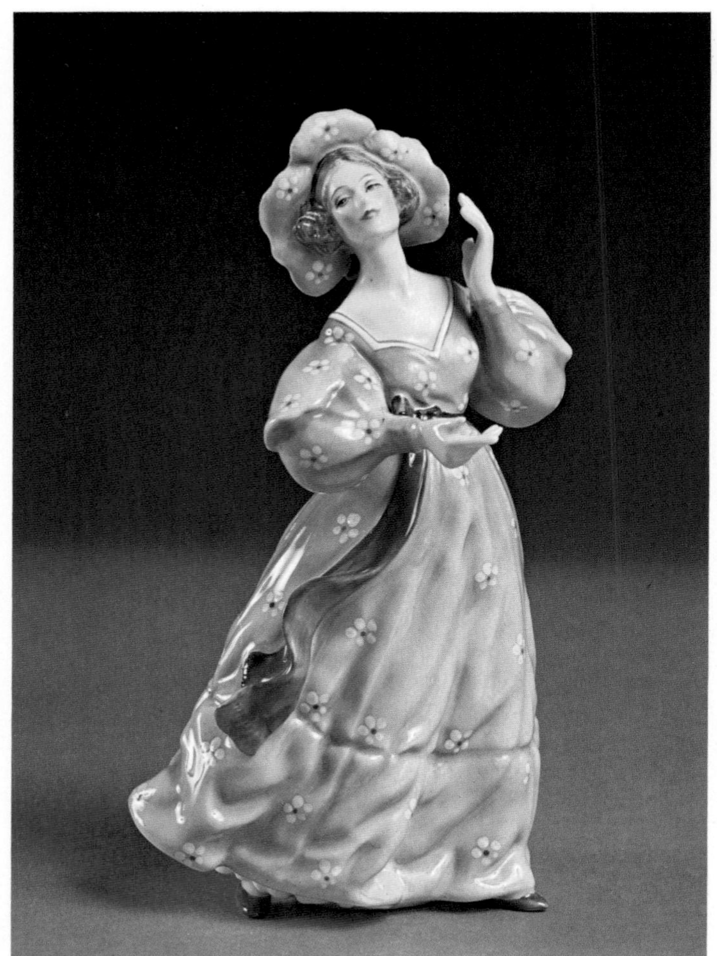

HN 2723 Grand Manner

HN 2724 Clarinda

HN 2731 Thanks Doc

HN 2734 Sweet Seventeen

HN 2723 Grand Manner
Designer: W. K. Harper
Size: 7¾ in (19.6 cm)
Introduced: 1975
Still in production

HN 2724 Clarinda
Designer: W. K. Harper
Size: 8½ in (21.5 cm)
Introduced: 1975
Still in production

HN 2725–2730 Not issued

HN 2731 Thanks Doc
Designer: W. K. Harper
Size: 8¾ in (22.2 cm)
Introduced: 1975
Still in production

HN 2732–2733 Not issued

HN 2734 Sweet Seventeen
Designer: D. V. Tootle
Size: 7½ in (19.0 cm)
Introduced: 1975
Still in production

HN 2735 Young Love
Designer: D. V. Tootle
Size: 10 in (25.4 cm)
Introduced: 1975
Still in production

HN 2736–2751 Not issued

HN 2752 Major, 3rd New Jersey Regiment, 1776
(Soldiers of the Revolution series)
Designer: E. J. Griffiths
Size: 10 in (25.4 cm)
Limited edition of 350, introduced 1975
For illustration, see page 418

HN 2753 Not issued

HN 2754 Private, 3rd North Carolina Regiment, 1778 (Soldiers of the Revolution series)
Designer: E. J. Griffiths
Size: 11 in (27.9 cm)
Limited edition of 350, introduced 1976
For illustration, see page 418

HN 2755 Captain, 2nd New York Regiment, 1775
(Soldiers of the Revolution series)
Designer: E. J. Griffiths
Size: 10¼ in (26 cm)
Limited edition of 350, introduced 1976
For illustration, see page 418

HN 2735 Young Love

HN 2756–2758 Not issued

HN 2759 Private, Rhode Island Regiment, 1781
(Soldiers of the Revolution series)
Designer: E. J. Griffiths
Size: 11¾ in (29.8 cm)
Limited edition of 350, introduced 1977
For illustration, see page 419

HN 2760 Private, Massachusetts Regiment, 1778
(Soldiers of the Revolution series)
Designer: E. J. Griffiths
Size: 12½ in (31.7 cm)
Limited edition of 350, introduced 1977
For illustration, see page 419

HN 2761 Private, Delaware Regiment, 1776 (Soldiers of the Revolution series)
Designer: E. J. Griffiths
Size: 12½ in (31.7 cm)
Limited edition of 350, introduced 1977
For illustration, see page 419

HN 2762–2778 Not issued

HN 2789 Kate

HN 2792 Christine (second version)

HN 2779 Private, 1st Georgia Regiment, 1777
(Soldiers of the Revolution series)
Designer: E. J. Griffiths
Size: $11\frac{1}{4}$ in (28.5 cm)
Limited edition of 350, introduced 1975
For illustration, see page 418

HN 2780 Corporal, 1st New Hampshire Regiment, 1778 (Soldiers of the Revolution series)
Designer: E. J. Griffiths
Size: $13\frac{1}{4}$ in (33.6 cm)
Limited edition of 350, introduced 1975
For illustration, see page 418

HN 2781–2788 Not issued

HN 2789 Kate
Designer: Margaret Davies
Size: $7\frac{1}{2}$ in (19 cm)
Introduced: 1978
Still in production

HN 2790–2791 Not issued

HN 2792 Christine (second version, model 2380)
Designer: Margaret Davies
Size: $7\frac{3}{4}$ in (19.6 cm)
Introduced: 1978
Still in production

HN 2793–2794 Not issued

HN 2795 French Horn (Lady Musicians series)
Designer: Margaret Davies
Size: 6 in (15.2 cm)
Limited edition of 750, introduced 1976, now sold out
For illustration, see page 394

HN 2796 Hurdy Gurdy (Lady Musicians series)
Designer: Margaret Davies
Size: 6 in (15.2 cm)
Limited edition of 750, introduced 1975, now sold out
For illustration, see page 394

HN 2797 Viola d'Amore (Lady Musicians series)
Designer: Margaret Davies
Size: 6 in (15.2 cm)
Limited edition of 750, introduced 1976, now sold out
For illustration, see page 394

HN 2798 Dulcimer (Lady Musicians series)
Designer: Margaret Davies
Size: $6\frac{1}{2}$ in (16.5 cm)
Limited edition of 750, introduced 1975, now sold out
For illustration, see page 394

HN 2802 Anna, HN 2799 Ruth, HN 2801 Lori & HN 2800 Carrie

HN 2799 Ruth (Kate Greenaway series)
Designer: Margaret Davies
Size: 6¼ in (15.8 cm)
Introduced: 1976
Still in production
Kate Greenaway (1846–1901), the English artist and book illustrator, revolutionised both children's books and children's clothes at the end of the 19th century. Vast quantities of books, such as *Under the Window*, *Little Ann* and *The Birthday Book* were sold throughout the world, while the fashion styles she created, the simple, high-waisted and ruffled dresses, the flower prints, the mob caps and poke bonnets, are still popular today. The figures in this series express these styles and reflect the simple elegance of the charming illustrations

HN 2800 Carrie (Kate Greenaway series)
Designer: Margaret Davies
Size: 6¼ in (15.8 cm)
Introduced: 1976
Still in production

HN 2801 Lori (Kate Greenaway series)
Designer: Margaret Davies
Size: 6 in (15.2 cm)
Introduced: 1976
Still in production

HN 2802 Anna (Kate Greenaway series)
Designer: Margaret Davies
Size: 6 in (15.2 cm)
Introduced: 1976
Still in production

HN 2803 First Dance
Designer: Margaret Davies
Size: 7¼ in (18.4 cm)
Introduced: 1977
Still in production

HN 2804–2806 Not issued

HN 2803 First Dance

HN 2807 Stephanie

HN 2810 Solitude

HN 2814 Eventide

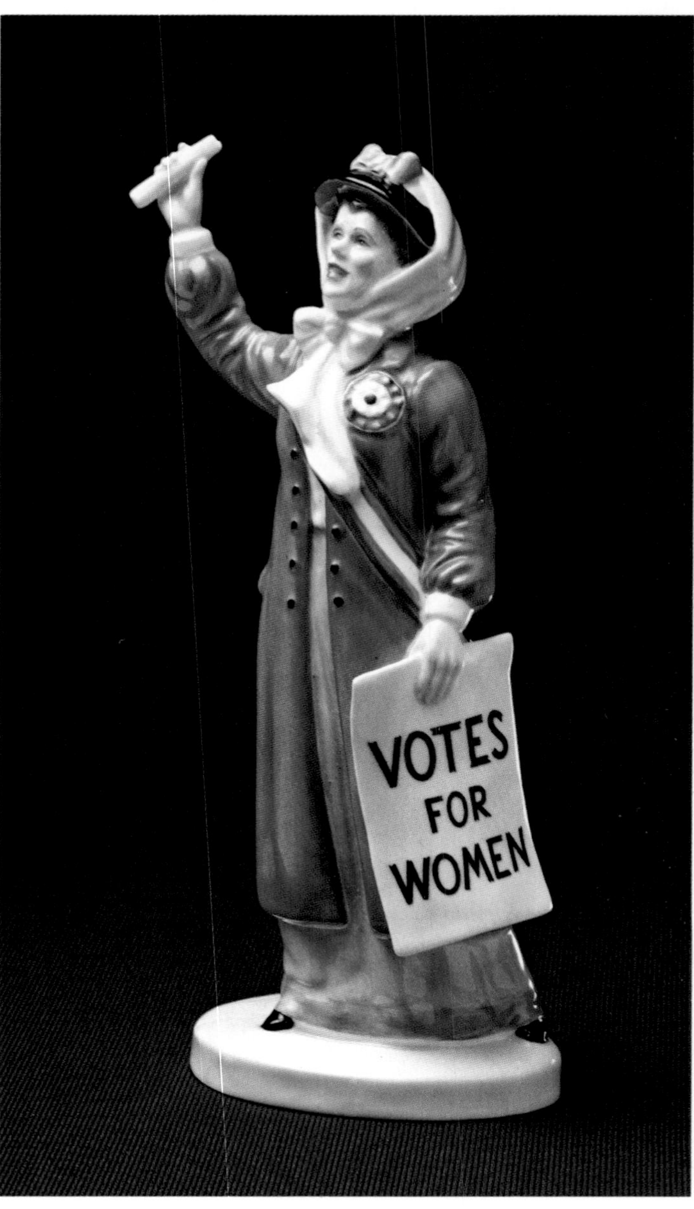

HN 2816 Votes for Women

HN 2824 Harmony

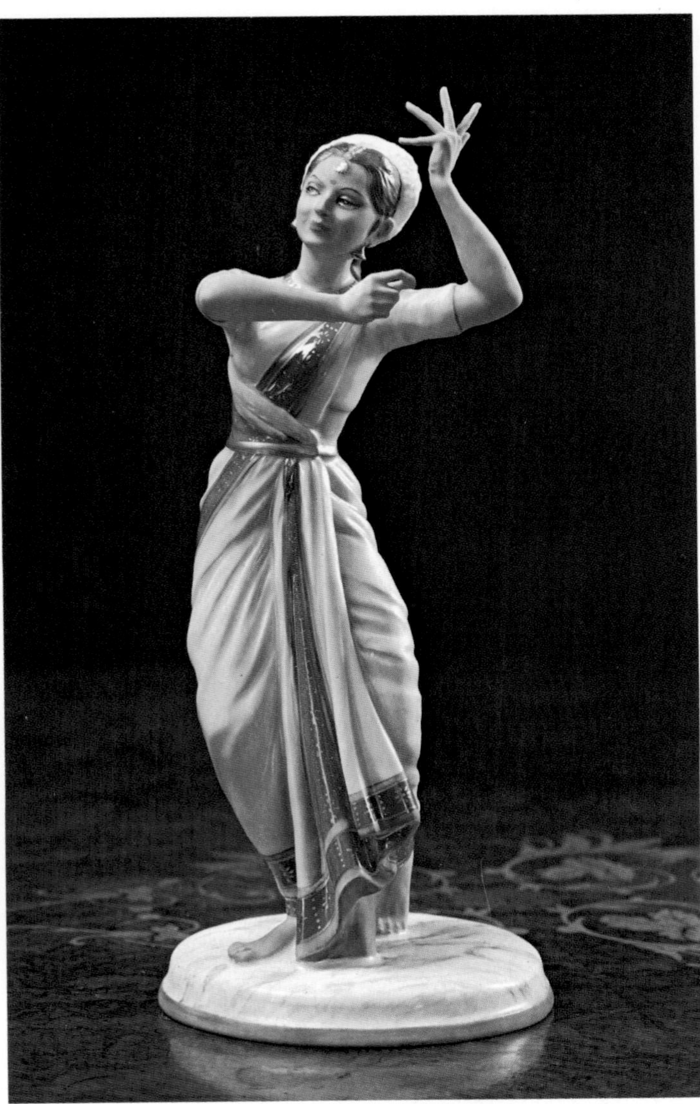
HN 2830 Indian Temple Dancer

HN 2807 Stephanie
Designer: Margaret Davies
Size: 7½ in (19.0 cm)
Introduced: 1977
Still in production

HN 2808–2809 Not issued

HN 2810 Solitude
Designer: Margaret Davies
Size: 5½ in (13.9 cm)
Introduced: 1977
Still in production

HN 2811–2813 Not issued

HN 2814 Eventide
Designer: W. K. Harper
Size: 7½ in (19.0 cm)
Introduced: 1977
Still in production

HN 2815 Sergeant, 6th Maryland Regiment, 1777
(Soldiers of the Revolution series)
Designer: E. J. Griffiths
Size: 13¾ in (34.9 cm)
Limited edition of 350, introduced 1976
For illustration, see page 418

HN 2816 Votes for Women
Designer: W. K. Harper
Size: 9¾ in (24.7 cm)
Introduced: 1978
Still in production
This figure represents one of the Suffragettes, a society whose members campaigned vigorously, and sometimes violently for female equality during the early years of this century. Their main success was the achievement of equal voting rights for women in Britain.

HN 2817–2823 Not issued

HN 2824 Harmony
Designer: R. Jefferson
Size: 8 in (20.3 cm)
Introduced: 1978
Still in production

HN 2825–2829 Not issued

HN 2830 Indian Temple Dancer (Dancers of the World series)
Designer: Margaret Davies
Size: 9½ in (24.1 cm)
Limited edition of 750, introduced 1977

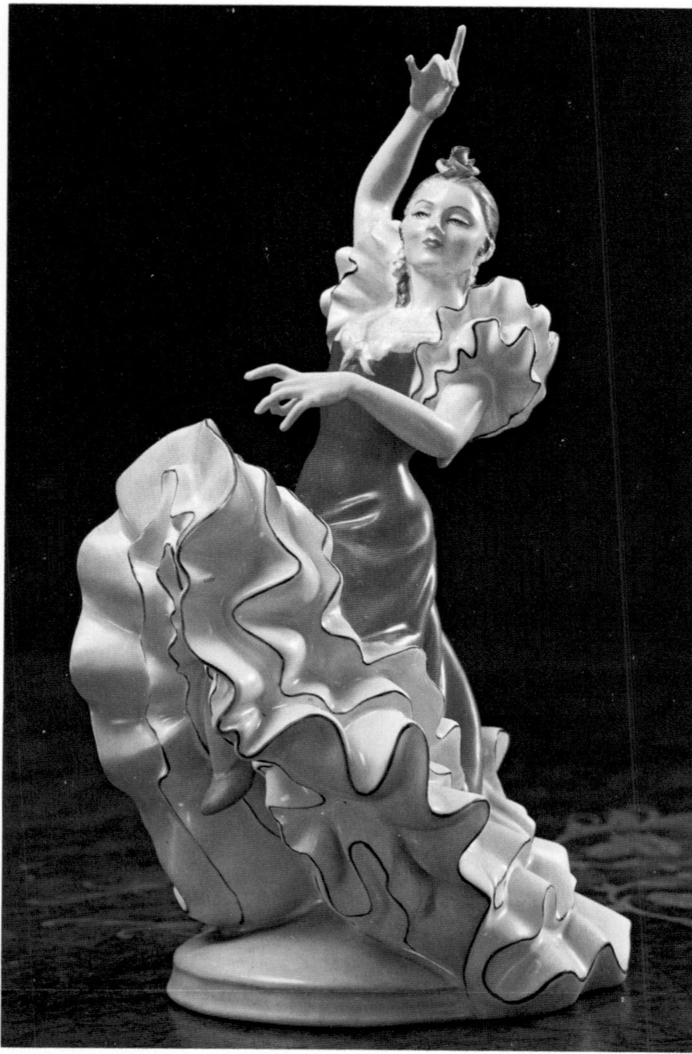

HN 2831 Spanish Flamenco Dancer

HN 2831 Spanish Flamenco Dancer (Dancers of the World series)
Designer: Margaret Davies
Size: $9\frac{1}{2}$ in (24.1 cm)
Limited edition of 750, introduced 1977

HN 2832 Fair Lady
See page 361

HN 2833 Sophie (Kate Greenaway series)
Designer: Margaret Davies
Size: $6\frac{1}{4}$ in (15.8 cm)
Introduced: 1977
Still in production

HN 2834 Emma (Kate Greenaway series)
Designer: Margaret Davies
Size: 6 in (15.2 cm)
Introduced: 1977
Still in production

HN 2835 Fair Lady
See page 361

HN 2836–2838 Not issued

HN 2839 Nicola
Designer: Margaret Davies
Size: 7 in (17.7 cm)
Introduced: 1978
Still in production

HN 2840–2843 Not issued

HN 2844 Sergeant, Virginia 1st Regiment Continental Light Dragoons, 1777 (Soldiers of the Revolution series)
Designer: E. J. Griffiths
Size: $14\frac{1}{4}$ in (36.1 cm)
Limited edition of 350, introduced 1978
For illustration, see page 419

HN 2833 Sophie

HN 2834 Emma

HN 2865 Tess & HN 2864 Tom

HN 2851 Christmas Parcels

HN 2845 Private, Connecticut Regiment, 1777
(Soldiers of the Revolution series)
Designer: E. J. Griffiths
Size: 11¾ in (29.8 cm)
Limited edition of 350, introduced 1978
For illustration, see page 418

HN 2846 Private, Pennsylvania Rifle Battalion, 1776 (Soldiers of the Revolution series)
Designer: E. J. Griffiths
Size: 8½ in (21.5 cm)
Limited edition of 350, introduced 1978
For illustration, see page 419

HN 2847–2850 Not issued

HN 2851 Christmas Parcels
Designer: W. K. Harper
Size: 8¾ in (22.2 cm)
Introduced: 1978
Still in production

HN 2861 George Washington at Prayer (illustration not in scale)

HN 2852–2855 Not issued

HN 2856 St George
(third version, model 2565)
Designer: W. K. Harper
Size: 16½ in (42 cm)
Introduced: 1978
Still in production
For illustration, see page 8

HN 2857–2860 Not issued

HN 2861 George Washington at Prayer (Winter at Valley Forge 1777–78)
Designer: Laszlo Ispanky
Size: 12½ in (31.7 cm)
Introduced: 1977, limited edition of 750
This figure was specially made by Royal Doulton for the members of the Limited Editions Collectors Society, from an original model by the sculptor Laszlo Ispanky. Adopted as the official bicentenary commemorative of The Freedom Foundation at Valley Forge, the figure was available only to members of the Collectors Society.

HN 2839 Nicola

HN 2862–2863 Not issued

HN 2864 Tom (Kate Greenaway series)
Designer: Margaret Davies
Size: 5¾ in (15 cm)
Introduced: 1978
Still in production

HN 2865 Tess (Kate Greenaway series)
Designer: Margaret Davies
Size: 5¾ in (15 cm)
Introduced: 1978
Still in production

Miniature figures: *top* M31, M16, M15, M84, M85
centre M23, M2, M1, M25
bottom M21, HN 698, HN 699

Miniature figures: *top* M65, M71, M68, M37
centre M73, M67, M34, M64
bottom M19, Pierrette, M40

Miniature figures: *top* M5, M6, M27, M33, M32
centre M69, M75, M30, M12
bottom M9, M10, M29

Miniature figures: *top* M7, M8, M28, M3, M4, M26
centre M24, M14, M13
bottom M39, M38, M72

The M Series of Miniature Figures

Introduced in 1932, the models in the M series were generally scaled down versions of figures already included in the HN series. However, a few were made only as miniatures, including *Denise* (M34 and M35), *Norma* (M36 and M37), *Robin* (M38 and M39) and *Erminie* (M40). Equally, a number of miniatures already included in the HN series, such as *Pierrette* (HN 795), and *Tête-à-Tête* (HN 1236), were never transferred to the M series.

The original small-size Dickens figures were given HN numbers in the design book and were transferred to the M series in 1932. Further Dickens models were added in 1939 and 1949, bringing the collection to the twenty-four Dickens figures still in production. The Dickens figures are all approximately 4½ in (11.4 cm) high, and so are comparatively larger than the other M series models. Unlike the other miniature figures, the Dickens models do not appear to have carried their M numbers on their bases as well as their names. Although all the M series figures were withdrawn by 1949, the Dickens set has remained in production, but without any number identification. There are minor colour differences between early models and those in production today. In addition, some recent models have been made in a slightly larger size. Early models were marked simply DOULTON or DOULTON ENGLAND, and frequently carried impressed shape numbers. Later models carry the usual Doulton backstamp.

In addition to the models recorded in the M series, a number of other miniature figures were produced which do not appear to be mentioned in either HN or M design books. Where examples have been found, such as *Robert Burns*, they have been illustrated with the full-size models. Also, some versions of M series figures, particularly *Polly Peachum* were produced with colour schemes not recorded in the design books.

Page from an old Doulton catalogue, *c* 1933

M1 Victorian Lady
Size: 4 in (10.1 cm)
Introduced: 1932
Withdrawn: 1945

M2 Victorian Lady
Introduced: 1932
Withdrawn: 1945

M25 Victorian Lady
Introduced: 1932
Withdrawn: 1945

M3 Paisley Shawl
Size: 4 in (10.1 cm)
Introduced: 1932
Withdrawn: 1938

M4 Paisley Shawl
Introduced: 1932
Withdrawn: 1945

M26 Paisley Shawl
Introduced: 1932
Withdrawn: 1945

M5 Sweet Anne
Size: 4 in (10.1 cm)
Introduced: 1932
Withdrawn: 1945

M6 Sweet Anne
Introduced: 1932
Withdrawn: 1945

M27 Sweet Anne
Introduced: 1932
Withdrawn: 1945

M7 Patricia
Size: 4 in (10.1 cm)
Introduced: 1932
Withdrawn: 1945

M8 Patricia
Introduced: 1932
Withdrawn: 1938

M28 Patricia
Introduced: 1932
Withdrawn: 1945

M9 Chloe
Size: 3 in (7.6 cm)
Introduced: 1932
Withdrawn: 1945

M10 Chloe
Introduced: 1932
Withdrawn: 1945

M29 Chloe
Introduced: 1932
Withdrawn: 1945

M11 Bridesmaid
Size: 4 in (10.1 cm)
Introduced: 1932
Withdrawn: 1938
As M12, but pink and lilac dress

M12 Bridesmaid
Introduced: 1932
Withdrawn: 1945

M30 Bridesmaid
Introduced: 1932
Withdrawn: 1945

M13 Priscilla
Size: 4 in (10.1 cm)
Introduced: 1932
Withdrawn: 1938

M14 Priscilla
Introduced: 1932
Withdrawn: 1945

M24 Priscilla
Introduced: 1932
Withdrawn: 1945

M15 Pantalettes
Size: 4 in (10.1 cm)
Introduced: 1932
Withdrawn: 1945

M16 Pantalettes
Introduced: 1932
Withdrawn: 1945

M31 Pantalettes
Introduced: 1932
Withdrawn: 1945

M17 Shepherd
Size: 3¾ in (9.5 cm)
Introduced: 1932
Withdrawn: 1938

M18 Shepherdess
Size: 3¾ in (9.5 cm)
Introduced: 1932
Withdrawn: 1938
Green bodice, pink overskirt

M19 Shepherd
Introduced: 1932
Withdrawn: 1938

M20 Shepherdess
Introduced: 1932
Withdrawn: 1938
Yellow bodice, flowered dress

M21 Polly Peachum
Size: 2¼ in (5.7 cm)
Introduced: 1932
Withdrawn: 1945

M22 Polly Peachum
Introduced: 1932
Withdrawn: 1938
As M21, but spotted blue skirt

M23 Polly Peachum
Introduced: 1932
Withdrawn: 1938

M24 Priscilla
See M13

M25 Victorian Lady
See M1

M26 Paisley Shawl
See M3

M27 Sweet Anne
See M5

M28 Patricia
See M7

M29 Chloe
See M9

M30 Bridesmaid
See M11

M31 Pantalettes
See M15

M32 Rosamund
Size: 4¼ in (10.7 cm)
Introduced: 1932
Withdrawn: 1945

M33 Rosamund
Introduced: 1932
Withdrawn: 1945

M34 Denise
Size: 4½ in (11.4 cm)
Introduced: 1933
Withdrawn: 1945

M35 Denise
Introduced: 1933
Withdrawn: 1945

M36 Norma
Size: 4¼ in (10.7 cm)
Introduced: 1933
Withdrawn: 1945
As M37, but plain pink dress

M37 Norma
Introduced: 1933
Withdrawn: 1945

M38 Robin
Size: 2½ in (6.3 cm)
Introduced: 1933
Withdrawn: 1945

M39 Robin
Introduced: 1933
Withdrawn: 1945

M40 Erminie
Size: 4 in (10.1 cm)
Introduced: 1933
Withdrawn: 1945

M41 Mr Pickwick
Introduced: 1932
Still in production

M42 Mr Micawber
Introduced: 1932
Still in production

M43 Mr Pecksniff
Introduced: 1932
Still in production

M44 Fat Boy
Introduced: 1932
Still in production

M45 Uriah Heep
Introduced: 1932
Still in production

M46 Sairey Gamp
Introduced: 1932
Still in production

M47 Tony Weller
Introduced: 1932
Still in production

M48 Sam Weller
Introduced: 1932
Still in production

M49 Fagin
Introduced: 1932
Still in production

M50 Stiggins
Introduced: 1932
Still in production

M51 Little Nell
Introduced: 1932
Still in production

M52 Alfred Jingle
Introduced: 1932
Still in production

M53 Buz Fuz
Introduced: 1932
Still in production

M54 Bill Sykes
Introduced: 1932
Still in production

M55 Artful Dodger
Introduced: 1932
Still in production

M56 Tiny Tim
Introduced: 1932
Still in production

M57–M62 Dickens Napkin Rings.
Other details not recorded

M63 Not issued

M64 Veronica
Size: 4¼ in (10.7 cm)
Introduced: 1934
Withdrawn: 1949

M70 Veronica
Introduced: 1936
Withdrawn: 1949
As M64, but green dress

M65 June
Size: 4¼ in (10.7 cm)
Introduced: 1935
Withdrawn: 1949

M71 June
Introduced: 1936
Withdrawn: 1949

M66 Monica
Size: 3 in (7.6 cm)
Introduced: 1935
Withdrawn: 1949

M72 Monica
Introduced: 1936
Withdrawn: 1949

M35 Denise

M78 Windflower

M22 Polly Peachum

M66 Monica M17 Shepherd

M81 Goody Two Shoes M83 Bo-Peep

M67 Dainty May
Size: 4 in (10.1 cm)
Introduced: 1935
Withdrawn: 1949

M73 Dainty May
Introduced: 1936
Withdrawn: 1949

M68 Mirabel
Size: 4 in (10.1 cm)
Introduced: 1936
Withdrawn: 1949

M74 Mirabel
Introduced: 1936
Withdrawn: 1949
As M68, but green dress

M69 Janet
Size: $4\frac{1}{4}$ in (10.7 cm)
Introduced: 1936
Withdrawn: 1949

M75 Janet
Introduced: 1936
Withdrawn: 1949

M70 Veronica
See M64

M71 June
See M65

M72 Monica
See M66

M73 Dainty May
See M67

M74 Mirabel
See M68

M75 Janet
See M69

M76 Bumble
Introduced: 1939
Still in production

M77 Captain Cuttle
Introduced: 1939
Still in production

M78 Windflower
Size: 4 in (10.1 cm)
Introduced: 1939
Withdrawn: 1949

M79 Windflower
Introduced: 1939
Withdrawn: 1949
As M78, but green skirt

M80 Goody Two Shoes
Size: 4 in (10.1 cm)
Introduced: 1939
Withdrawn: 1949
As M81, but blue skirt

M81 Goody Two Shoes
Introduced: 1939
Withdrawn: 1949

M82 Bo-Peep
Size: 4 in (10.1 cm)
Introduced: 1939
Withdrawn: 1949
As M83, but red dress

M83 Bo-Peep
Introduced: 1939
Withdrawn: 1949

M84 Maureen
Size: 4 in (10.1 cm)
Introduced: 1939
Withdrawn: 1949

M85 Maureen
Introduced: 1939
Withdrawn: 1949

M86 Mrs Bardell
Introduced: 1949
Still in production

M87 Scrooge
Introduced: 1949
Still in production

M88 David Copperfield
Introduced: 1949
Still in production

M89 Oliver Twist
Introduced: 1949
Still in production

M90 Dick Swiveller
Introduced: 1949
Still in production

M91 Trotty Veck
Introduced: 1949
Still in production

Dickens figures: *top* Sairey Gamp, Artful Dodger, Fagin, Bill Sykes, Trotty Veck, Tony Weller
centre Sam Weller, David Copperfield, Scrooge, Oliver Twist, Uriah Heep
bottom Buz Fuz, Pickwick, Bumble, Mrs Bardell, Tiny Tim

M42 Micawber

M43 Pecksniff

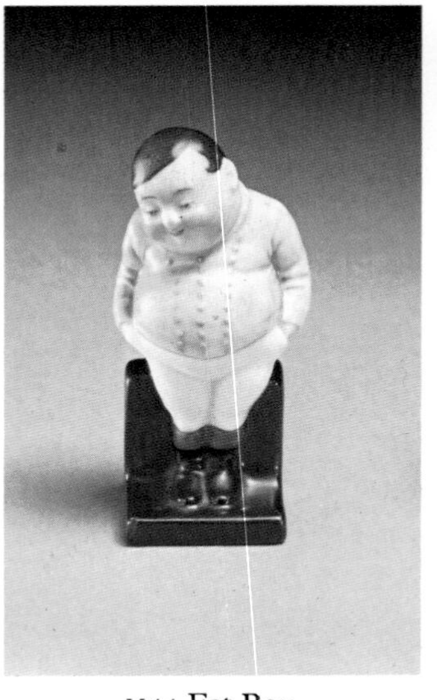

M44 Fat Boy

M50 Stiggins

M51 Little Nell

M52 Alfred Jingle

M77 Captain Cuttle

M90 Dick Swiveller

ELDREDGE PUBLIC LIBRARY
0 1780 0043232 7